this book belongs to :

2019
EDITION

The sequel to UP THE DUFF

BABIES & TODDLERS

KAZ COOKE

VIKING
an imprint of
PENGUIN BOOKS

CONTENTS

Intro 2

Part 1 YOUR BABY

how do you do?

PART 2 YOUR TODDLER

PART 3
everything else you need to know

New Parent Quiz

1 Your baby won't stop crying. First, you:

a) send it back to the hospital for a refund

b) turn it off at the wall, wait, and turn it on again

c) offer it a Kit Kat.

2 Your grooming regime is now:

a) seventeen steps, with luxury products

b) brushing your body hair in the same direction

c) checking if the face washer has baby poo on it.

3 *(Men may skip this one.)* A week after giving birth, your breasts leak visibly at the supermarket. You say to the check-out clerk:

a) 'Care for a squirt?'

b) 'Clean up on aisle me.'

c) 'Don't be frightened, young man. You should see my perineum.'

4 The Parenting Anthem is:

a) 'I Will Survive' by Gloria Gaynor

b) 'Shake it Off' by Taylor Swift

c) any karaoke with shouty swearing.

5 When a child weighs 20+ kilos, a car restraint should:

a) have a 92-point harness

b) have a 'back-arching refusal' button

c) be slightly less expensive than a submarine.

6 You've been awake three nights with a sick kid, and have banana in your ear. A friend with a dog says, 'I know exactly what it's like, I have a fur-baby'. You:

a) roll your eyes until they fall out

b) smile benignly

c) strike her lightly on the nose with a rolled-up newspaper, while saying in a firm voice, 'No! No!'

7 What's the worst thing to say at childcare?

a) 'We think of lice as our special little friends.'

b) 'Christ on a STICK, I want a vodka.'

c) 'Which one's mine?'

8 The dog and the kid have thrown up in the car, simultaneously. You:

a) pull over and say the *Serenity Prayer*

b) pull over and get emergency wipes and plastic bags from the boot

c) pull over, get out, and go to Botswana.

9 'Controlled crying' is when you:

a) cry like the guy in that *Scream* painting, but no tears come out

b) cry for 5 minutes at 5 p.m. at home each day

c) sob in the toilets at work.

10 Sex between parents of young children is:

a) totally a thing, apparently

b) subject to interruption

c) not even slightly in the vicinity of a thing.

11 Children's clothes should always be:

a) matching

b) machine washable with knives up to 40 000 degrees Celsius

c) removed from under the bed before being placed on child.

12 Dads who look after their own children are:

a) normal

b) marvellous, really quite extraordinarily marvellous

c) seahorses.

ANSWERS:

Oh, who the hell knows? We're *all* making this up as we go along.

shrug shrug

iNTRO

HeLLO THeRe.

So, you've finished reading **UP THE DUFF**: The Real Guide to Pregnancy, and now you've thrown it at the wall and you're shouting 'Yes, but what do I do now the bloody baby has arrived, you dreadful slattern?!' Hey, I get it, you're sleep deprived and need to know which end to put the nappy on. So here's the sequel, all about what to do with babies and toddlers.

Some people say we shouldn't need a book, we should just follow our 'instincts' like animals do. Piffle. Some lions eat their cubs – which I don't recommend – and squid never even meet their own children. If you want to take toilet training advice from a crocodile, you're on your own, sunshine. None of us are born with parenting skills and instincts, we develop them.

It can be scary being a new parent. The good news is, you're already a good parent, because you care enough to look at a book about it. And this is the safest time ever in history, and one of the very best places in the world to have a baby. Immunisation, medical care and good food mean your baby already has a huuuuge head start in life. What isn't so good is that lots of modern parents, especially mums, can feel more isolated and alone, and online 'information' can be dodgy, advertising, or just plain bonkers.

That's why I've made sure that all the info in this book has been checked by medical experts, is parent and kid friendly and uses evidence-based suggestions. You get to choose what ideas and solutions suit you. Lots of real parents have shared their tricks, too.

You can read **BaBieS & TODDLeRS** all the way through in order, as you probably did with **UP THE DUFF**. Or, more usefully, just read the bits you're up to, or the bits you need at the time. Look up the index to deal with problems as they arise ('poo, explosive', for example, is under P).

You won't need to know everything at once. You can start with Part 1: Your Baby, and then move in an orderly fashion to Part 2: Your Toddler. But don't forget Part 3: Everything Else You Need To Know, which contains the other sections that cover both baby and toddler stuff: safety, equipment, common health scares, immunisation, food and, yay, birthday presents.

Different versions and printings of this book, **BaBies & TODDLers**, have been around for nearly twenty years: some earlier versions were called **Kidwrangling**. Please don't sell or pass on any copies of **Kidwrangling** or **BaBies & TODDLers** or **UP THE DUFF** to somebody else, and please don't borrow or buy second-hand copies yourself. A second-hand or old book will not have the best up-to-date medical, safety and other info. Old medical information can be dangerous, especially when it comes to babies and children.

This book will be regularly reprinted with medical and other updates. Check the circle on the cover, which will show the year it was printed. To have the most up-to-date edition, the year shown should be the most recent.

I hope you'll find **BaBies & TODDLers** useful, fun and easy to read in a quiet moment or a slight panic. I hope it becomes your friend, and helps you to feel calmer and more confident about being a parent or carer. And that it gives you a laugh here and there. If not, I plan to have a complete tantrum (under T in the index).

PART 1
YOUR BABY

YOUR NEW BABY

So, you're home. Now what?

Here's this new, wee, tiny, curly-up creature in a wrapped bundle, who lies in whatever position you put 'em in and does nothing but blink, eat, poo, yell and sleep, not necessarily in any order – and who isn't all that chatty.

It's hard to get acquainted with a new friend when you're woken up seemingly every five minutes and you're possibly throwing your bosoms about at the same time. This book aims to help you to stop worrying and enjoy your baby.

good stuff to know in the first days

Here, have some new facts.

⭐ You and your baby will be learning together as you go along.

⭐ Your baby is working out how to love you.

⭐ You love your baby, even if you're feeling hormonal and gobsmacked at the moment, or blank and confused or scared.

⭐ You'll probably never be this tired or clueless again.

⭐ Being tired and clueless comes with the job, and it's like this for every new parent.

⭐ The newness and sleeplessness of everything means you're forced to go with the flow for a while.

⭐ You don't have to know everything immediately.

⭐ You're starting a new, important job for which you have no qualifications.

⭐ Treat yourself as kindly as you would a work-experience Girl Guide in space.

⭐ Your baby won't be the life of the party.

⭐ Newborn babies can cry for two to three hours a day even if you do everything right.

⭐ Newborns shouldn't even really be out of the womb – they just come out this early because otherwise they'd get too big to fit down the 'birth canal' (oh please, can we start calling it a vagina again now?). So they're not like baby giraffes, who run around an hour after the birth.

⭐ Newborn babies don't know where they are, sleep a lot, might cry a lot through no fault of theirs or yours, and need to fill their tiny tummies often (like every two to four hours – closer to four if you're lucky).

⭐ Babies like baby-talk.

⭐ A baby can't speak or fully understand, but hearing you talk to them is great for their own fun and development. If you feel weird talking to them, describe what you're doing as you go about the day, tell them things that are going to happen, or even sing silly songs. They don't care if you can't sing properly. You'll be surprised how much babies understand from your tone of voice.

⭐ Babies like close-up surprised and delighted faces and smiles as you chat (unless they're too tired, in which case they'll tell you to rack off – by crying). It's one of the ways they learn about emotion and expression.

⭐ You're pretty much it for a baby's visual entertainment. In their first few weeks newborns can only see about the same distance as from their mum's breast to her face.

Soothing your baby

Everything is new to babies: imagine landing on a planet where nothing, not even air or shapes or colours, is like anything you've experienced before. Imagine you've never felt anything on your skin or digested any food – no wonder babies cry, especially towards the end of the day. It must be so much to take in. Talk to them in a soothing, explain-y, 'Hey, it's okay' sort of way if they seem confused or uncomfortable. They're used to a muffled world inside their mum, so any sudden or loud noise will frighten them – they'll need a cuddle and some soothing words to calm down.

Your baby doesn't know why they're crying, either

At least for a while, and sometimes for months, parents have to guess why their baby is crying. They might be tired, or have a scratchy label annoying them, or feel hungry or just have something that feels wet and odd coming out of their bottom. They might be a bit affronted at the new sensation of farting. Crying for hours each day is normal. Some babies cry for unfathomable reasons. All you can do is try to be comforting and as bouncy-rocky as a womb, and share the crying baby around as much as possible so if you go mad you all go mad together. You can get so worried about solving the crying it only occurs to you months later that some of it may have been unsolvable. See Chapter 9, Crying, for lots of help.

Good things to do for a newborn baby

* Plant a tree.
* Create a 'memories' box with a newspaper or magazine from the day or month of the birth.
* Write a letter to your future grown-up child. Maybe add messages from friends and family. Keep the letter and messages safe.
* Roll some non-toxic water-based poster paint onto your baby's palms and soles, and then press them onto archival paper to make 'paw prints'. They'll only be this small for about a minute.

It's normal for very new babies to lose weight

Babies lose weight before your proper milk 'comes in' a few days after they're born, losing up to about 10 per cent of their birth weight. At about the time the milk 'comes in' you sometimes have a big, weepy hormonal crash. (Helpful, ain't it?)

Medical staff and midwives really shouldn't say anything about your baby losing weight unless it's a problem, and it so rarely is. Mentioning it just leads to thousands of parents worrying and women wondering unnecessarily if their baby is fading away and whether it's all their fault.

Premmie babies and multiple-birth babies, because they have to share the womb, are often at the lower weight end.

Most babies are back up to what they weighed at birth in a week or two. If your baby isn't gaining weight after they're 5 days old, or isn't back to their birth weight by 2 weeks, there's usually an easy fix that involves fiddling with milk supply and supplementing breastmilk with formula as needed: see your child & family health nurse (called maternal & child health nurse in Victoria) or your doctor. See Chapter 4, Breastfeeding, and Chapter 5, Bottle-feeding, for more.

Babies have personalities

Babies are born with their own characteristics. And they can have good and bad days, just like us. Midwives and other professionals who see a lot of babies know that some of them are calm and some are cranky, and some babies are dreamy and some are as alert as all get out. If your baby is clean, comfy, cuddled and well fed and still cries, it isn't a reflection on what sort of parent you are. All babies cry, whatever their personality is.

Babies grow and learn every day

Even if you never quite catch them at it. Their brain is making connections and learning important information. They do this just by observing. They don't need flashcards and lessons, just love and attention.

You make the rules for visitors

You don't have to let others hold the baby. Or you might be happy to pass your baby around. Do what feels right to you and make sure your partner backs you up.

Nobody with any illness symptoms or a cold sore or open wounds should be allowed to touch or kiss your baby, as this can cause dangerous infections. Relatives and friends should wash their hands before holding the baby, and not kiss its face. Later, your baby can fight off more germs with the help of a stronger immune system and immunisations: their first protective jabs will be at 6 weeks. All relatives and friends who visit before and after then, whether showing signs of illness or not, must be up to date with their immunisations, especially adult booster shots for whooping cough.

For the first six weeks, don't insist anyone holds your baby if they're clearly uncomfortable, or nervous about dropping them – there's a lifetime of cuddles to come. Siblings or visitors can sit on an armchair or couch and have the baby on their knee if they feel safer doing that. If somebody is holding the baby, they can't have a hot drink at the same time. As the weeks go on, you'll know which people you feel happy to let hold or even look after your baby while you escape the house or have a quiet moment for a shower.

Social media trumpetings

You may have already announced the birth on social media and be happy for the joyous news to go viral. Other parents choose private settings for their posts, and ask that relatives and friends not share pictures of the baby. Some parents only post pictures of their kids that don't show their faces, until they're 18, believing that kids should get to decide their own profile in the digital world, when they're older. Other parents have publicly posted thousands of pictures of their kids before their first day at kinder.

If you want a social media blackout on your kid, make your feelings clear. If your policy is ignored, remove that person's access to your postings. Always ask other parents if you can post pics of their kids in a group shot, for example, at a birthday party. This is one of those times when you get to practise respect for another parent's rules, even if you don't agree with them. (Also see the section on 'Social media parenting styles' in Chapter 27, Parenting Styles.)

how to pick up a new baby

As with almost everything you do with your baby, let them know what's going on. Tell them when you are going to pick them up or put them down. This is also how they start learning to anticipate and communicate. They'll get to understand and not be too startled. When you pick your baby up, slide your arm along the bub's back until your hand is supporting their head and neck and try to lift them in one steady movement (all early jerks should be accompanied by a soothing apology).

⭐ Everyone has to learn how to pick up a very new baby. Men and women can be equally good at it, with practice.

⭐ In the first weeks just make sure that when you pick up your baby you gather up the whole baby so there aren't any bits (head, arms, legs) that are dangling unsupported over the edges.

⭐ The most important part to be careful of, especially in the first two months, is the baby's neck. That oversized baby head is so heavy for the little-baby neck. Until the neck muscles develop and a baby learns to automatically hold up its own head, you'll need to help by always supporting its weight.

how to hold a new baby

Once you've picked up a baby, you can go horizontal: transfer the baby to the crook of your other arm so that the head is cradled in your elbow and the body supported along your forearm. Or you can go vertical: pick the baby up gently, continually supporting the head and neck, and hold them so that their little head is leaned against you or just peeking over your shoulder. Babies love a heartbeat – they were soothed by their mum's, inside her, for months. Being cuddled against any chest with a heart can comfortingly remind babies of those floaty times on the inside.

Keep supporting your bub's head and neck at all times until they seem to be able to hold their head up by themselves – usually about 6 weeks old. Babies love to be held close and to hear your heartbeat. Another thing you can do is sit down, put both your feet flat on the floor and lay the baby tummy up, with their head and neck supported by your knees and their feet in your lap.

Touching and massaging your baby is a great way to bond with your bub. See the 'Baby massage' box in Chapter 10, Loving Your Baby.

Wrapping a newborn baby

Most bubs like being all wrapped up, aka 'swaddled', because it reminds them of being in the womb (for 'How to', see 'More info on wrapping a baby' at the end of this section). Most little babies like to be wrapped firmly, with their arms bent up (like they probably were in the womb). But some bubs like their arms down. Legs should be flexed (bent) and able to move. Sometimes, when a baby's arms and legs are loose, you often see them give a 'startle reflex' until they're about 3 months old – they'll throw their arms and legs up because, it's thought, babies have a hard-wired fear of falling. Wrapping is thought to soothe them until this reflex fades away. Most cultures have some version of swaddling (wrapping) and carrying small babies. For most babies, it helps them be calm and fall asleep. You can use a flannelette or cotton wrap or cloth in winter and muslin in summer. You can buy fancy printed ones or just make them out of old sheets or other cotton, say about 120 cm square, as long as it's hemmed so threads don't get caught and trap little fingers.

Wrapping a new baby can be the magic trick that gets it to sleep. But by the time they are 3 or 4 months old, they tend to wriggle out, so you can wrap with the arms free. Some babies will stay happily wrapped for sleeps until they're about 6 months old. You can abandon the wrapping, either straight away or slowly, but stop wrapping as soon as the baby seems about to be able to roll over (or trying to), usually 4 to 6 months. After that, the safest sleep outfit is a little sleeping-bag suit without a hood.

Don't start to wrap a baby after 4 months and don't keep a baby wrapped all day: only for winding-down time just before sleep and while they're asleep. Babies, especially if more than 2 weeks old, need to practise wriggling around a bit, to stretch their arms and legs, and to feel the fresh air on their skin.

The wrap should be firm but not tight

Wrap a baby in nappy and singlet only in summer and light cotton 'grow-suit' in winter, so they don't get too hot. As with all babies, a wrapped baby should be placed on their back to sleep (see more on safe sleeping positions in Chapter 8, Baby Sleep).

~~~~~~~ **more info** on wrapping a baby ~~~~~~~

To practise wrapping before your baby arrives, use a teddy bear! There are lots of videos online, but choose one of the links below for an approved source. Also see Chapter 8, Baby Sleep, for tips on safe sleeping.

rednose.com.au
Search 'safe wrapping' on the main page of this non-profit charity (formerly SIDS & Kids), which teaches parents how to greatly reduce the risk of sudden infant death syndrome. The *Safe Wrapping* brochure is available to download in several languages.

raisingchildren.net.au
Search 'wrapping a newborn' on the main page for diagrams and instructions or the video of how to wrap a baby, with narration in many languages.

~~~~~~~~~~~~~~~~~~~~~~~~~~~~~~~~~~~

'fourth trimester'

This is a term for an idea that some people find comforting: pregnancy is three trimesters (of three months each) and then, the first three months of a baby's life can be seen as the 'fourth trimester'. The general idea is that babies aren't quite ready to come into the world, but have evolved to come out ready after nine months so they can still fit through their mum's pelvis on the way out. Some new parents find it useful to think of that first three months as a time when the baby's getting ready to come fully into the world. A new bub is still soothed by any womb-like environment and wrapping, and by fuzzy noises; still acting on instinct; and still needing lots of help. One counterintuitive point here: many babies just love being outside in the open air, whether carried or in a pram.

You're done with the placenta

Placentas are only useful to you and your baby while you're still pregnant and giving birth. Once your bub is breathing, and it's outside you, the placenta is useless.

'Lotus birth' – a nice name for the bad idea that a baby can stay attached, via their umbilical cord, to the placenta for a few days – can cause and has caused dangerous infections in babies. Cutting the umbilical cord doesn't hurt a baby because there are no nerves in it.

Eating or liquefying and drinking your placenta is also a bad idea and a waste of time. The risks range from mess and expense to infection. The 'service' costs up to a couple of hundred dollars or more for capsules made from your dried placenta.

Some (not all) mammals eat their placenta straight after birth, which is believed to be a protection against predators smelling it and attacking while the mother is weakened. Humans traditionally don't eat their placenta. Lions often do but they often eat the baby as well, so I wouldn't look there for inspiration.

Placenta bits used in 'traditional' medicine were not given to the new mother, but to others in the belief they had special powers.

Placenta capsules have fewer vitamins or minerals than a multivitamin pill. Hormones taken in this way can't survive the mother's stomach acids. Placenta capsules cannot prevent or cure postnatal anxiety or depression, boost breastmilk production, shrink your uterus, or 'balance' your hormones. Placenta capsules may have a psychological effect, but that is a matter of coincidence, or faith, not a physical or hormonal change.

In rare cases, an infection in the placenta will be ingested in capsules by the mother and transferred to the baby via breastmilk. Though many 'encapsulation' services say their process is safe, they are not covered by medical regulators. If you do have problems with milk production see Chapter 4, Breastfeeding, for solutions; and if you have feelings of anxiety or depression, as many of us do, please talk to your child & family health nurse or your doctor, and see Chapter 11, Getting Through Tough Times.

'You've created a boss. A newborn baby knows nothing of schedules and appointments and can only vocalise hunger and discomfort.' ANTHONY

Good things about babies

* Their head smells of Baby.
* Their tiny starfish hands.
* That little hollow at the back of their neck.
* Their excellent chubby thighs.
* The way they bend time when you're sitting holding them in a quiet place.
* They stare at you and you can stare back.
* They hold on to your finger.
* Their toothless grins.
* They have amusing hair or they're bald.
* They look kind of Star Trekky.
* There's so much potential in such a small package.
* They have hilariously short arms.
* You can read stuff into their faces: 'mmm, wise', or 'flabbergasted'.
* They mimic facial expressions.
* They snore, but not very loudly.
* They have a total body response when they're excited.
* You are keeping another human alive.
* You are creating new love in the world.
* The green poo stage doesn't last long.

 wise

 staring

 flabbergasted . . .

tummy time for newborns

You can help 'train' your baby to be able to lift their head and move it, and their mouth, if they're on their tummy. You also need to help them develop the right muscles, using 'tummy time'. Several times a day from birth, pop your bub on the floor on a rug or towel, and encourage them to lift their head and 'play' by looking at you while you talk or show a toy or book.

It's harder for a baby to do this on a softer surface such as a bed or cushion. Never leave your new baby unattended on their tummy, as they may not be able to move their head well enough to get a good breath. Babies younger than 4 months can 'cheat' by having a rolled-up face washer or bunny rug under their chest to lift it slightly, and you can pop their elbows underneath their shoulders so their weight is resting on their forearms. Some babies will get cranky, but you still need to do it. You can build up from less than a minute of tummy time at each go. By 6 to 8 months, a lot of babies just like to hang about on their tummies. Once a bub can move into and out of a tummy position by themselves, and lift their head up and down and turn their head easily, they'll just do it themselves from then on if given a chance.

BLAST FROM THE PAST
'Baby's first clothes must be drawn on over the feet, for luck. When first taken out it must be carried upstairs or upwards in the street, not downstairs or down the street, before coming down so that it will rise in the world. It's unlucky to cut the baby's nails or hair in the first year.'
– From a wrap-up of superstitions in the Launceston *Examiner*, 1895

---

premmie babies

Bringing home a tiny baby can be awfully daunting – especially after seeing so many tubes and machines doing things to and for your bub in the hospital. Sometimes it can help to be introduced to great, hulking, galumphing teenagers who were once as premmie as your wee baby. Your hospital should have a website link, a handbook or at least a pamphlet on premmie babies, which you can take home; or contact your nearest major-city maternity hospital.

Ask your midwives and paediatrician (specialist children's doctor) whether your baby needs special handling, but don't be afraid to touch your bub, no matter how fragile they seem. Almost constant skin-to-skin contact (which is called 'kangaroo care' because the bub is nestled against the mum or dad) and soothing, comforting soft songs and voices are known to perk up a premmie baby in the early days.

Your bub may have especially pale or red skin, a distressing thinness and prominent veins, but when they put on weight these will disappear. Very early babies may be covered in the tiny hairs (called lanugo) that all babies have in the womb: it's temporary. Your baby may have difficulty sucking so if breastfeeding isn't possible, it's okay.

You mustn't be hard on yourself about being emotional or feeling overwhelmed: after what you've been through that's absolutely normal. Many people feel scared of their premmie babies and daunted by the responsibility. DO get help if you feel that the difficulties are constant and never-ending: see Chapter 2, Your Help Team, and 'More info on premmie babies' coming up.

These days so many babies are born prematurely and survive and thrive that doctors and nurses know a lot about premmies. If you have trouble making enough breastmilk, your hospital may have a 'milk bank' where you can get trusted milk that is donated by other mums who have extra supply.

Early arrivals can have physical difficulties, including lung trouble and pooing problems, and might always be a smaller size than other kids of the same age. Make sure you fully understand from midwives and doctors, including your ongoing paediatrician or family doctor, what you might expect as your baby grows into a toddler, a preschooler and beyond. Some premmies never have a problem: it often depends on how premmie they are.

Premmie clothes

Most of the small sizes in baby clothes will be too big at first. Your baby will soon grow into them, but in the meantime you'll need the softest cotton things you can find: little hats are important to keep a tiny head warm. Many hospitals are given clothes specially made or knitted for premmie babies by wonderful volunteers. Be careful that wool isn't causing an itch the baby can't tell you about. Specialist online shops and maternity hospitals carry a limited range of clothes for premmie babies, sometimes labelled size 0000. (Search 'premmie' on US sites.)

Common premmie characteristics

The following features are usually temporary.

⭐ Premmie babies weigh less and look tinier and skinnier than boombah full-term ones.

⭐ They're tired, and tire more easily.

⭐ They like to stay curled up and be asleep a lot.

⭐ They're doing what they'd be doing if they were still inside: growing and developing.

⭐ They're not big on facial expressions, eye contact or reacting to being touched. They can be a bit irritable at arriving earlier than anybody expected.

⭐ They can be rather wrinkly and seem frail, with relatively large heads and hands.

⭐ Their skin can be pale and blood vessels can be seen beneath their skin (when they put on more fat this will change).

⭐ They're covered with a layer of fine downy hair, called lanugo.

⭐ Feeding may need some work, and their cry will sound weak – some say almost kitten-like – until their lungs puff up and get stronger.

'My firstborn being a premmie scared me a lot. I hated anyone touching him and breathing near him. I was too scared to put him down. I spent a whole day without eating because I couldn't leave him. It didn't occur to me that I could hold him (in a sling) while I made a sandwich! I think I lost half my brain when my baby was born!'   TRACEY

Your emotions about having a premmie

You may feel:

★ guilt at not 'holding on longer' or being a 'good mum' who got to the 'right' week; this is common but not fair to you – treat yourself as you would a best friend going through the same thing

★ sadness and stress at the separation, if you have to go home while your baby remains in hospital for a few days or weeks of special care

★ disconnected from the baby

★ frightened of touching the baby, of not feeling the 'right' things, and of taking the baby home and being alone without all the help of the hospital staff

★ incredibly tired, physically and emotionally, especially if you have had a caesarean or traumatic birth.

Partners may have any of these emotions, plus a sense that they are irrelevant. They may feel frustrated that they can't solve the situation or fix the baby. In fact they have an incredibly important job: being there for the baby as much as possible and supporting their partner.

Partners and friends can be indispensable for getting expressed breastmilk to the hospital when the mum has gone home before the baby but is exhausted and needs rest and recuperation. Partners can also be in charge of gatekeeping both at hospital and at home (letting people know if and when they can visit, according to the mum's wishes), and can take photos to show rellies who can't yet see the baby.

~~~~~ **more info** on premmie babies ~~~~~

raisingchildren.net.au
Search 'premature' from the main page for info on bonding with your newborn, other practical info and support, and advice about development.

prembaby.org.au
The National Premmie Foundation has a focus on research, and on info for parents.

normal newborn stuff

In the first days our babies are so new to us we hardly recognise them. And they're so teeny-tiny and so unlike the big, robust babies crawling around on TV ads (they're all 6 months old) smiling, grabbing things and signing modelling contracts. It's easy to stress out about newborns. What follows is some stuff we tend to worry about that is probably, actually, usually, completely, okay.

Worries about how your baby looks

Because of the birth experience babies may have a squashed or bruised face; puffy, closed or even bloodshot eyes; scrunched-up ears; or a pointy head. Almost all weird-looking stuff disappears quickly: ask your doctor if something worries you.

Foetal pozzie

Babies have been in that womb for so long and have been so cramped at the end that they keep their foetal position for a while, and they like their little hands closed tight. Things gradually uncurl by themselves: you don't need to stretch or pull any bits.

Private parts

Well, there's nothing very private about a baby's bits. The festival of hormone production that happens at birth can lead to some rather swollen genitals on boy and girl babies, and even a slight, period-like bleed from a baby girl's vagina – just some of her own tiny, tiny womb cells coming away. This will stop in a few days. If anyone is proud that their son has an enormous pair of testicles they should know it's usually temporary. And feel free to roll your eyes.

When 'girl or boy?' isn't so easy to answer

Almost two in every 100 babies born in Australia has genes or genitals that don't automatically suggest they're male or female. A specialist medical team can help accurately predict how each kid is likely to identify. It's often described as DSD (differences of sex development) or 'intersex'. Make sure you get a referral to specialist help and support.

There's lots of reassuring info on how to choose a name, why not to rush into surgery, what to tell people and more on these sites: rch.org.au/endo/differences-of-sex-development; ihra.org.au/parents and dsdfamilies.org (UK).

Eyes

gummy eyes   Squirt on some of your own breastmilk (a traditional remedy) or squeeze some sterile saline from the chemist onto cottonwool pads or gauze patches, which don't fall to bits as easily as cottonwool balls. Use a new one for each eye so you don't cross-infect, and wipe gently. The problem should clear up: if not, see your doctor.

dry eyes   Little babies sometimes don't cry actual tears, and sometimes the tear ducts are blocked. These should right themselves in the first few months. Babies should be able to produce tears by about 2 months old. If there are still no tears by then, ask your doctor about it.

watery eyes   If your bub has 'watery eyes' and is prone to eye infections in the first few months, their tears may not be draining in quite the right way behind their eye, because a little membrane they don't need is in the way. This can sometimes be fixed by a simple, gentle massage technique of stroking your finger from near the inside of the eye and down the side of the nose. Ask your doctor or child & family health nurse to show you, and if the problem is still there at 6 months, talk to your doctor again.

wandery, squinty eyes   Babies don't really focus their eyes when they first come out into the world. This should sort itself out by 6 months. If one eye doesn't move from a certain position, see a doctor straight away so that it can be fixed.

changing-colour eyes   Some people claim all babies change eye colour in their first year. Utter piffle. And all babies are *not* born with blue eyes despite what they tell us in old textbooks and on websites written by white folk. Some babies change eye colour, some don't.

Skin

jaundice   If a baby is jaundiced their skin and the whites of their eyes usually look a bit yellow. It happens to more than half of newborn babies, who should then be routinely checked by a paediatrician. Although the liver usually breaks down some extra red blood cells by the time bubba's a few days old, sometimes the liver is on a go-slow, and that makes the skin look yellower. This is more common in breastfed babies. It's not a reason to stop breastfeeding, because if you can, that gives your baby extra nutrients and protections even if they slightly match the daffodils for a while.

Sometimes the getting-rid-of-the-yellow process is given a kick along in hospital by laying the baby under bright lights. Some experts dispute that this helps, insisting that jaundiced babies sort themselves out in their own good time, in a few days or weeks, or up to 3 months. Jaundice is generally considered ho-hum unless the baby is also floppy and not feeding well, or unless it's unusually severe or long-lasting, in which case, off to your doctor, with perhaps a further referral to a paediatrician.

birthmarks   Many babies have 'stork marks', a red, rash-like mark on the forehead, eyelids and back of the neck. (The idea that a stork's beak made the marks dates from the days when people pretended babies were brought by storks to avoid any mention of s-e-x.) 'Stork marks' are visible blood vessels close to the skin and usually fade quickly. But they can hang around or 'reappear' as the blood vessels bulge away harmlessly when a kid holds their breath, yells a lot, or is hot or stressed. I've heard of some that last until towards the end of primary school or perhaps longer, despite some books and websites saying that they all disappear in the first months.

Some babies of Asian heritage or who have dark skin are born with bluish-grey pigment spots on their buttocks, back and sometimes arms and legs. These spots fade.

Other birthmarks can be more permanent, although most are removable by laser later in life if that's important to the child. You should talk about the marks with your doctor and have them identified. If in doubt, get your doctor to give you a referral to a paediatric skin specialist.

nappy rash   This is usually caused by wee or poo irritating the skin under a nappy. Wash everything off with a baby wipe or a cottonwool ball/pad soaked in a bot-cleaning lotion or water, pat or air-dry, and apply a barrier or nappy-rash cream from the pharmacy or supermarket. It doesn't have to be flash, or have fancy herbs or fragrance or special ingredients, so feel free to get a straightforward, generic one. Don't rub it in: the idea is for it to be generously applied as a visible extra layer on top of the skin – that's why it's called a 'barrier' cream. Disposable nappies are less likely to cause nappy rash because they absorb more moisture. You may notice little square or round clear crystals around the bot in a disposable nappy. They're part of the absorbent stuff the nappy is made of: seeing them means it's past time for a change. (For more on all this see Chapter 6, Nappies.)

'cradle cap'   You can remove this rather crusty layer or flakes on top of a baby's head, but it may keep coming back for a few weeks or even months. It's not contagious, or dirty or dangerous. If it doesn't bother you, leave it alone and it will probably go away by itself (often after the bub is 3 months old). To get rid of it try a paste of 1 teaspoon of bicarb of soda and about half a teaspoon of cold tap water. Make the paste a consistency you can apply with a cottonwool ball. Rub it into the baby's scalp lightly and gently, leave it on for five minutes, then wash the head with baby shampoo and rinse it out.

The 'cradle cap' is often on top of that soft bit of your baby's head, the fontanelle. It's okay to massage it gently. Softly comb through the baby's hair or rub the scalp gently to loosen the flakes so they fall off, or wait for them to fall off by themselves. Beware if you rub the area with olive oil, mineral oil or 'baby oil', as some people recommend, that the oil will then probably get on everything else, including the curtains and the lady at the post office. If the 'cradle cap' is anywhere apart from the scalp, see your doctor as your bub might need some treatment for dermatitis (a rash).

thrush   This is a white rash, usually in the mouth or on the bot, and is caused by a fungus. Try an over-the-counter treatment from a chemist or get your doctor to prescribe a cream.

spots   Little pimples, whiteheads and other spots are pretty standard for babies, and often last for about three months. You just need to make sure it's not an infectious illness or insect bite (in which case you'll need to use screens, a mozzie net or another non-chemical strategy in the baby's bedroom). See your child & family health nurse or doctor for a diagnosis.

sucking blister   Some babies get a small blister on their lip from sucking. It might make the bub a little antsy while feeding, but should heal by itself.

veins   The thinner a baby, or the thinner their skin, the more you may be able to see veins or a bluish tinge where the blood vessels are close to the skin. It's really normal on bubs.

Head

Babies' heads are big compared with the rest of them: this lasts well into childhood. Babies who were pulled out with a vacuum device or forceps may have heads that look a bit pointy or dented. Ask your obstetrician how long this is likely to last. It's usually very temporary.

fontanelle   This is the squishy bit on your baby's head where the skull plates haven't meshed together yet. It makes it easier for your baby's head to go temporarily pointy when coming down the vagina during birth. It will grow over (sadly, unlike your vagina) and you won't notice it in a few weeks' time – although the plates don't fully fuse until the second year of life. The fontanelle requires the same amount of careful handling as the rest of a tiny baby. If it looks higher or lower than the rest of the head, see a doctor: it could be swelling or a sign of dehydration. (There are actually two parts to the fontanelle, a front one, and a smaller one towards the back of the skull, so if you feel both, that's just a normal noggin.)

head size   Don't even think about taking notice of the head circumference measurement unless a nurse or doctor tells you there might be a medical problem (this is very rare).

hair   Some babies have a headful, some have none. Others have baldy patches. The first baby head hair sometimes falls right out and is replaced later. Body hair (called lanugo), which is often found on the back and shoulders, is normal and will fall out.

Heartbeat

Okay, it's got nothing to do with how they look, but you may want to know that babies' heartbeats are faster than adult ones.

Teeth

Apparently some babies are actually born with teeth. Let's hope they keep them to themselves during breastfeeding.

Umbilical cord

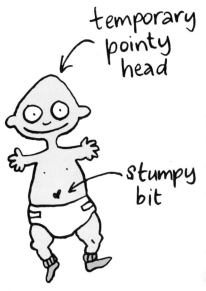

temporary pointy head

stumpy bit

What a strange little stumpy thing they send you home with on the front of your baby: the blackened remains of the umbilical cord fastened with a plastic, well, peg. It looks absolutely revolting. At some time during the first couple of weeks, perhaps even after a few days, the cord stump will fall off, peg and all.

Usually you just clean the tummy button and stump with lukewarm tap water, and gently pat and air-dry afterwards. If there's a bit of blood after the stump falls off, continue cleaning the area in the same way once a day and it should come good in a few days. Have the tummy button checked out by your doctor if there is pus, or inflamed redness around the area, or it's smelly and seems to have a fleshy lump within the tummy button. This is a standard condition called 'umbilical granuloma' (because why not make everything sound scary, doctors, hmmm?) and family doctors can cauterise it with silver nitrate (there are no nerves in the umbilical cord, so it's painless).

An 'umbilical hernia' is when there's a bulge or lump on or around the tummy button with no infection. This can make you feel a bit frightened, but it's not dangerous. As a baby's muscles grow stronger and are better able to hold in place all their inner organs, it usually goes away on its own. In rare cases, simple surgery is needed, usually after your 'baby' turns 3.

Noses

nose 'choking'   Milk that a baby is trying to swallow can sometimes come 'up' into their nose and cause a blockage, which can make your bub a bit distressed. If your bub splutters and goes red, with milk coming out of each nostril, just pick them up, wipe their nose, turn them over on their tummy and pat their back until it is cleared and they calm down again.

blocked nose   You know how babies can't blow their noses, or understand that they're supposed to? Brace yourself. All over the world, mums clear the mucus from a baby's blocked nose by personally sucking the snot out. It's all right, it isn't compulsory. It will eventually clear by itself but instead you can use a 'nasal aspirator' bought from pharmacies, whether you get a bulb-design one or a newer syringe-with-tube type. You should scrupulously clean your apparatus, making sure it's dry inside and out afterwards.

Ears

Don't squirt or poke anything into an ear, including breastmilk, a cotton bud or a finger. Ears clean themselves. Ear experts say deafness should be detected as soon as possible, so ask your hospital to do a hearing test before you take your bub home, or ask your child & family health nurse to do one. (For more info look up 'ears' and 'hearing' in the index.)

more info on newborn health

raisingchildren.net.au
Click on newborns, then 'Health & daily care' for fact sheets from this reliable, Australian government–backed website.

Newborn breastfeeding and bottle-feeding apps

Many people find them useful, others reckon they just cause anxiety. When babies are new, they're the ones who decide how often they breastfeed – it could be a more 'snacking' rhythm every hour or so, or every three to four hours. You don't need to time the length of breastfeeding – if they've got a good grip on your nipple with their little mouth, and your milk is flowing well, they'll slow down to a stop or detach themselves suddenly. Then you just use the other breast for the next feed. (A brooch or safety pin on your top can be swapped to the side you should start on next to remind you.) Your child & family health nurse or family doctor can help with checking how much formula to use each time. See Chapter 4, Breastfeeding, or Chapter 5, Bottle-feeding, for lots more.

Weight & length

Midwives and child & family health nurses have to weigh and measure babies, but the numbers don't matter to us unless there's a problem, and there rarely is. It's only important for you to have a feel that your baby is generally healthy and happy and getting bigger, or not. If your baby is anywhere on the chart they're somewhere in the normal range.

Some babies are darling roly-polies with dimply buttocks, others can be surprisingly lean yet healthy: this is mainly a matter of genes. Babies with Pacific Island, Indian or European heritage will often differ widely in size, for example. As long as the baby is not distressed or lethargic, or not getting enough milk, weight is not a problem.

Babies should steadily put on weight – but you don't need to constantly weigh them yourself. Some weeks there'll be more growth than others. Suddenly going backwards may indicate a problem, but growth spurts are pretty normal. Regular visits to the child & family health nurse will pick up any problems.

Baby noises

Babies often make odd snorky breathing sounds, just getting used to breathing with their little tubes and lungs. Sneezes, hiccups, grunts and general snorkiness are all perfectly normal.

The baby slept longer than normal

It's probably just your baby's first big sleep. Most parents know the blind panic on the first morning the baby misses a night feed and 'sleeps through', before racing in to find a hungry but healthy bub. As long as the breathing seems regular and untroubled, and there is no fever, it's almost always best to 'let sleeping babies lie'. They can be quite cross at being woken up.

Is my baby hurt?

Babies are very resilient. Usually everything's fine, but of course if you do drop your baby, or they receive a knock, go to the doctor immediately. A baby who's floppy or sleepy after a drop or knock is a worry, and if they can't be roused, they stop breathing or they have a convulsive fit, call an ambulance on 000.

Rough play

Some parents and relatives – often men – think it's a great idea to throw babies up in the air and catch them: they must be stopped. It is not a matter of opinion. This shouldn't happen to babies at all and certainly never to newborns, whose brain and eyes can be badly damaged by being rattled about. This is the same damage that can be done by shaking a baby.

Is my baby sick?

You'll find info on gastro, colds, fever and convulsions, in particular, in Chapter 33, Health (and you can look these up in the index).

Call an ambulance on 000 if:

* your baby has difficulty breathing or has stopped breathing for 20 seconds (usually causes a blue or purplish tint)
* your baby has a convulsion or 'fit'. (☎ The emergency number in New Zealand is 111.)

Take your baby to the doctor if:

* your baby seems to have a fever and/or is distressed or floppy and uninterested
* there are signs of dehydration (dry, pinched skin; sunken eyes and fontanelle; fewer wet nappies than usual; dark, stinky wee)
* your baby has been repeatedly vomiting
* your baby has a wheezy cough
* your baby suddenly doesn't want breast or bottle
* there's something that looks yucky or pus-oozing somewhere
* your baby seems in pain or otherwise screams for a long time no matter what you do
* you're worried about anything
* there's something you haven't seen before such as a rash or lump.

Is the weather too hot for my baby?

Signs of a too-hot baby include crying, a red rash and dehydration. Make sure your baby has lots of fluids on a hot day. This means breastmilk or bottle milk. Some older people might suggest a few teaspoons of cooled boiled water, but this is outdated advice. If you're breastfeeding, make sure you're drinking lots of water in hot weather, too.

To cool down an overheated baby, get their clothes off and lay them on the floor or bed, sponge them with room-temperature water and perhaps use a fan – but not directed right at them – to move air around. The change should be relatively gradual, so don't use ice or cold water. A hot bedroom at night can be cooled by air conditioning (if you have a thermostat, about 18 to 20 degrees Celsius is standard); by wetting towels and hanging them over the edge of the cot; or by using a fan not directly pointed at the baby.

If a baby is really hot and cross, you can sponge them with water that's at room temperature – never ice cold.

Babies in the tropics, especially visiting babies, can be more susceptible to skin problems such as infected scratches, thrush, rashes (including 'prickly heat') and impetigo (a contagious bacterial infection that causes sores). Don't overdress them.

Is my baby too hot?

See the 'Fever and High Temperature' section in Chapter 33, Health.

Is my baby too cold?

Most of the cases of 'prickly heat' in Australian babies don't occur in the tropics, but in cold areas where the babies have been so bundled up to the eyebrows in woollies that they're sweating under all their layers. This particularly happens with bubs who are dressed for the cold outside and then brought into shops or homes that are heated. As long as your eyes are on the baby, you can put a bunny rug or fleece square over them, in your arms or in a pram, rather than dress them in extra clothes. Much easier to whip on and off.

Quite a lot of a baby's surface area is head, so a hat is a good idea, especially out-side in the cold or wind. Keep the face uncovered. The general rule is if you need a long-sleeved top, a small baby needs a hat. Another general rule is that little babies need at least one extra layer than we do to feel comfortable outside. (When they're toddlers and they're on the move they can start having the same number of layers as we do.)

While you walk with the pram you're warming up, but not so the baby being wheeled about. Small babies can't run around to warm up, or throw on more clothes, so you need to be aware that a too-cold baby may start out crying but then become very quiet and still.

Hypothermia in babies is rare. If a baby does get too cold, they'll be floppy and won't cry or feed. Wind chill is what can make a baby too cold too quickly.

To check how cold your baby is, feel their face: if it's cold, feel their tummy, and if it's cold too that's unusual. Warm up a too-cold baby (or toddler or small child) with a hat and direct skin-to-skin contact under rugs pulled around you both, in a warm room – but not directly in front of a heater and not with a hot-water bottle, which is too much heat too suddenly. A baby's room on a cold night should be kept warm, not hot. Make sure that the room is aired well between sleeps (and that the baby is too!).

~~~~ more info on worries about newborns ~~~~

See your child & family health nurse, your family doctor or the parent helplines in Chapter 2, Your Help Team.

Sudden infant death syndrome (SIDS)

It's normal, but awfully tiring, to keep waking up and leaning closer or creeping next to your baby to check whether they're still breathing. In the past few years there's been a steady drop in the number of babies dying from an unknown cause that makes them stop breathing, called sudden infant death syndrome (SIDS). (It used to be called 'cot death' and is often now also called SUDI, sudden unexpected death in infancy.) It's believed that the babies who die have a respiratory problem that means they can't fight for air if they have trouble breathing or if their mouth or nose is blocked; of course, very young babies are unable to move their bodies at all by themselves. Most SIDS deaths happen before the baby is 6 months old. At about 6 months babies start to move in their sleep, which means they will almost certainly be able to shift to a better position if they can't breathe, unless they have a respiratory problem.

There is no causal link between vaccinations and SIDS and there is no causal link between breastfeeding (or not) and SIDS. Awake babies can be regularly placed on their tummies for 'tummy time' to help them strengthen their necks.

The marked drop in SIDS cases is because of the publicity campaigns warning parents about the risk factors for SIDS. Researchers and doctors now recommend a checklist (coming up) that emphasises babies sleeping on their back and not co-sleeping, and other hints such as keeping fluffy toys out of the cot. (Also see Chapter 8, Baby Sleep.)

You cannot go into the cot!

Anti-SIDS checklist

✽ All babies should be put on their back to sleep, not on their tummy. As babies get older and can move their head to the side themselves and shuffle around changing position in bed – at about 6 months – they might choose to sleep on their tummy themselves. This is rarely a problem.

✽ Sleep in the same room as your baby for the first six months, but not in the same bed. (See 'Co-sleeping or sleeping "apart"' in Chapter 8, Baby Sleep, for the lowdown on this.)

✽ Avoid overheating.

✽ A sleeping baby should never have their face covered, and shouldn't have a doona or any other puffy paraphernalia such as pillows. A doona can cut off the air supply and smother a baby. The easiest way to make sure babies don't get tangled up is to use a bottom sheet, tightly tucked or fitted sheet with nothing on top. Up to 3 or 4 months old your bub can be wrapped securely in a muslin or cotton cloth. After about 3 months you can leave a baby's arms out of the wrap, and when your baby's worked out how to roll over (about 4 to 6 months), stop wrapping. After that they should be put to bed in a safe sleeping-bag suit with arms but no hood (from babies' wear outlets).

✽ If you feel that your baby needs a bedcover as they get older, two or three cotton blankets that can be firmly tucked are safest. The cot should be made up at the bottom end with the baby's feet pointing to the bottom, so there is no danger of the baby wriggling down under the blankets (new babies tend to wriggle in a direction away from their feet). Babies in hot climates, however, can drift off to sleep in a singlet and nappy, or just a nappy.

✽ If the baby is sleeping unattended, they should always be in a modern safety-standard cot (look up 'cots' in the index). Many cot designs and secondhand or vintage cots are potentially dangerous. Babies can be trapped, or be injured on sharp protrusions, or get stuck down between the mattress and the side of the cot.

✽ A mattress should be firm and fit snugly, with no more than a 2 centimetre gap between it and the cot on all sides. Other important factors include the spacing of the bars (a baby shouldn't be able to fall through), the security of a drop side, the efficiency of wheel brakes, and the position of the mattress relative to the height of the sides.

➜

Anti-SIDS checklist (continued)

✳ To keep the airflow going and to cut down on the chance of smothering, avoid bumpers (padded cot liners), fluffy toys and similar objects. Babies don't need fluffy toys when they're tiny; they need the comfort of having a parent or carer nearby and on call.

✳ The baby should never be left to sleep unattended in a car, a car baby seat or a pram, or in an adult bed.

✳ Never let a baby sleep on a couch or an armchair, even if someone is there.

✳ There should be no smoking by anyone near the baby or inside the home, the car or any other environment. The parents and carers of the baby should be non-smokers.

✳ Keep an eye out for any interrupted breathing or rousing problems and see a doctor about them straight away.

more info on safer sleeping for babies

Make sure you also see Chapter 8, Baby Sleep.

rednose.com.au
24-hour grief and loss support: 1300 308 307
The national website of Red Nose (formerly SIDS and Kids), Australia's non-profit info and research organisation. The site includes all the up-to-date info you need on safe sleeping positions and sleepwear, and has FAQs. Red Nose provides counselling and help if a baby dies, whatever the reason.

raisingchildren.net.au
On the main page of this independent, government-funded site, choose 'newborns', then 'Sleep', then 'Minimising SIDS risk' for a video on how to put bub to sleep, and other hints.

Worries about circumcision

Circumcision of boys

Male circumcision is the removal of part of the penis foreskin with a scalpel. This is usually done in the first few days of a boy's life, with an injected 'local', not a general, anaesthetic. Some religions require circumcision for cultural reasons.

Once almost routine, now only about 10 per cent of Australian and New Zealand baby boys are circumcised.

Male circumcision advocates say it can be a cultural need that represents religious identity and freedom, that very few side effects occur or are lasting, and that it means a lower risk of sexually transmitted infections later in life (although only condoms can prevent STIs).

Anti-circumcision arguments say that although complications are rare, they can be devastating and effects can include pain, shock, infection, damage to the penis and severe bleeding. They say it is a barbaric, outdated practice that is not prescribed by religious texts. They say parents should wait until a child is 18 and let them make their own decision. 'Reclaim-the-foreskin' groups say circumcision will result in the penis having up to 75 per cent less sensation during sex.

The official position of the Royal Australasian College of Physicians is that in normal circumstances there are no compelling health reasons for circumcising a baby, but that parent choices should be respected.

Some boy babies are born with a fusion of the foreskin to the penis that in time will cause pain or friction. Corrective surgery is the same procedure as a circumcision. Many doctors recommend that babies are 6 months or older when they have this operation so that they can have a stronger anaesthetic.

Any circumcision should be performed by a qualified, trained, specialised medical professional.

~~~~~~~~ **more info** about circumcision ~~~~~~~~

racp.edu.au
Search 'circumcision' to download a brochure for parents of boys from the Royal Australasian College of Physicians.

Female genital mutilation (FGM)

Female genital mutilation, sometimes called 'female circumcision' or traditional cutting, is the removal of or deliberate damage to the clitoris, clitoral hood and/or labia, usually with a knife or razor blade. It is sometimes accompanied by a process called infibulation in which the vagina is stitched closed or mostly closed. It is a cultural practice based on the belief that it will stop a future woman's sexual desire, and keep her from wanting sex or being seen as shameful or unmarriageable.

FGM predates organised religion. It's denounced by many religious and ethnic leaders, both Christian and Islamic. It's sexual assault, child abuse and a traumatic and dangerous procedure that can cause infection and death, permanent disability and incontinence, severe psychological problems, pain during sex, and distressing difficulties in childbirth. It is illegal in Australia, as is travelling overseas for the purpose of having it done.

~~~~~ more info on FGM ~~~~~

www.nofgmoz.com
Hotline: 1800 522 707
No Female Genital Mutilation (NoFGM) Australia has info for medical professionals, including midwives, nurses and doctors, who are caring for a woman with damage to her own genitals, or anyone else who may know babies and girls at risk. They also offer confidential support for women who have undergone FGM for any reason.

Feeling angry & frustrated with your baby

Most parents know the inexplicable rage that sometimes comes over you when you're spectacularly tired, you've tried EVERYTHING to make the baby happy but they're still crying. I can remember shouting at my baby to shut up (you don't see that on the nappy ads, do you?), which was just nutty but I was at the end of my rational self. In normal circumstances you'd never take out your frustration on a baby. But in these days of isolation and lack of sleep, your coping skills are sometimes hard to find. Remember, feeling angry and overwhelmed is a normal response, but it means you need support.

You must not shake or hit the baby. Chapter 11, Getting Through Tough Times, is all about how to deal with this, but you must immediately get help because the situation will probably happen again, and you'll need a strategy to get you through the next time. Talk to your partner, or get right on the phone to a relative or friend you can ask for some practical assistance, not just a sympathetic ear. For parent helplines and services see Chapter 2, Your Help Team.

> 'Sometimes courage is the quiet voice at the end of the day, saying "I will try again tomorrow".' MARY ANNE RADMACHER, quoted by a mum, ALYSSA

a grab-bag of worries

Fears that something awful will happen to the baby

We all get those. If you find that you're often anxious, see your doctor.

People who undermine your parenting

There's no one right way to do everything. You'll learn. It's okay. Nobody knows what to do at first: even people who've been midwives get a shock when the baby is their own and they can't go off shift! Comments or criticism can stir fear or lack of confidence. Never let a passing comment ruin a second of your day. It's about them, not you.

Worries about baby getting a 'flat head'

Some babies develop a 'flat head' effect at the back or on one side because they are lying on their back so often to sleep. Doctors call this by a scary name, 'positional plagiocephaly', but it's pretty common and can be corrected without pain or much palaver.

Vary the side the baby's head is turned to each time they're laid down on their back to sleep. Vary your baby being in a pram or a carrier. If the flatty bit stays stubborn, or your baby seems to automatically pick one position for their head no matter what side you choose for them, sometimes they can wear a cute helmet for a while.

If you're worried, talk to your child & family health nurse or a doctor about it before your baby is 9 months old. Always put your baby to sleep on its back regardless of worries about flattiness. 'Tummy time' is helpful to avoid a flat spot, too (see 'Tummy time for newborns' earlier in this chapter).

Crying

Oof, it's tough, sometimes, isn't it? See Chapter 9, Crying, for lots of useful info.

Phone 'radiation'

Radiation from phones and its effect on baby brains hasn't been studied but it's best not to keep a phone near a baby's head anyway. It's so hard to get vomit out of the charging port.

'You will get back to doing the things you love that aren't baby-related. You will get yourself back. You will be rested enough to think clearly again, I promise. It just doesn't feel like that now.' KARA

'When I came home to my toddler after giving birth to number two I felt completely overwhelmed and thought how can I manage this?! The baby health care nurse who visited me said, "Take things one feed at a time" and that really helped.' SARAH

YOUR HELP team

You'll be needing a hand, then. Some people are
lucky enough to have trusted relatives and friends
close by who know what to do with babies.
Your back-up team can also include the
army of people listed here, and a few butlers and
footmen if you've married into European royalty.

midwives

Midwives are registered nurses with specialist knowledge and training in pregnancy, birth, mums and babies. Most women will have a midwife as a birth attendant. Maternity wards are staffed by midwives who will advise and help after the birth. Midwives must have at least three or four years of medical study and training.

child & family health nurses

These nurse specialists are also known as maternal & child health nurses in Victoria and used to be 'mother-and-baby nurses'. In New Zealand they are Plunket nurses, which is simply more fun to say. Depending on where you live, they'll do an initial home visit within the first few weeks of the birth to see how you're settled in, and then see you for regular appointments at a community health centre to check you, and your baby's development and health. The appointments get further apart until your baby is a toddler or preschooler depending on what's provided where you live. Your hospital or local council should give you the contact details for your nearest nurse service. You should also be able to call the nurse at any time to ask questions if you are worried. Nurses have the standard nursing qualifications, topped up with extra training and experience in their specialty; many are also qualified midwives.

Nurse visits will get you out of the house and talking to somebody who understands what you're going through. If you're coping well it's fun, and if you don't feel you're coping they should be both sympathetic and helpful. They see a lot of babies and frazzled, exhausted parents, and can be full of reassuring, indispensable baby knowledge. They're an on-tap reality check.

Nurses can give the impression that statistics are important because they're required to keep them. But baby length and weight measurements don't matter a bit to you, unless the results are very unusual.

Part of a nurse's job is to try to help you persevere with breastfeeding if you can. If you're having a great deal of trouble and your baby is losing weight you may need extra help, so see Chapter 4, Breastfeeding, or Chapter 5, Bottle-feeding.

your family doctor

Yep, you're a family now, even if there's only two of you, and that means you need a family doctor: a GP, meaning general practitioner. Ask around to identify a local doctor who's a parent favourite, or ask the clinic desk staff who has a special interest in 'paediatrics' (baby and kid health). This doctor will usually know which germs are 'going around', which can make diagnosis easier. Many family clinics have a policy of bulk-billing the public health scheme, Medicare, for consultations involving children so there are no 'out of pocket' fees.

Family doctors are your first line of defence in your baby's health. They've completed a five- or six-year university medical degree with further training and experience, and at least two to three more years of training and experience in general medicine, including some specialist training with babies and kids. Pick a kind one if you can.

If you feel concerned about your baby's health, have it checked out by a family doctor during the day if possible. All good GP clinics have a policy of seeing a baby or child on the day a parent calls. It doesn't matter if it turns out there's probably nothing wrong. It will help get your child used to going to the doctor, and let the doctor know what your kid looks like when they're not sick, which helps in future diagnoses – and a check-up is never a bad thing.

Kids tend to get sick quickly and get better quickly, but if they take a turn for the worse there is no time to lose. At night, your options are more limited for medical help and can involve more difficulties and longer wait-times in a difficult atmosphere, in, say, a hospital emergency room.

If possible, avoid those 'out of hours' phone service doctors who come to your house. They will almost certainly not have the breadth of training, qualifications, experience, local knowledge or continuity of care as your own GP, and it's always better to be seen at a medical facility. See the start of Chapter 33, Health, for when to call an ambulance or go to the doctor.

In a shared clinic, see if you can settle on one or two doctors who you like. If you're not happy, go to another doctor – never feel you have to stick with one who doesn't 'feel right' for you. After all, you'd switch hairdressers if you weren't happy. No, don't go and look in the mirror. This is no time to think about hairdressers. I'm sorry I mentioned it.

paediatricians

A paediatrician – a doctor who's a specialist in children's health – should check your bub before you leave hospital. On top of their five-year medical degree, they have usually done two to three years of hospital training, then another two to three years of specialist paediatrics training, study and exams.

obstetrician-gynaecologists

Your obstetrician-gynaecologist or local doctor should check you and your bub six weeks after the birth. An ob-gyn is a specialist in women's health, including pregnancy and birth. They have a five-year medical degree, then two years of practical training in a hospital, then probably another six years of specialist study and training. They may then sub-specialise in, say, IVF, ultrasound, gynaecological problems or women's weeing.

breastfeeding advisers

If you're given conflicting advice about breastfeeding in hospital, pick a midwife you like and only listen to that one. When you're home, you can get breastfeeding advice from your child & family health nurse. A professional breastfeeding adviser is known as a lactation consultant, and has completed specialised education and training and will teach you how to twirl tassels on your nipples. Just seeing if you're still awake. See 'More info on medical helpers', below, for more.

Speak up

Always express your worries to a child & family health nurse or doctor. They've heard it all, and there is no such thing as a dumb question. We're all beginners. (One nurse was equally puzzled during a home visit by the green marks on a baby's feet during a home visit, until the resident toddler owned up to drawing them on.)

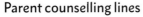 **more info** on parent counselling

Parent counselling lines

Parent helplines are run by charities, some with religious affiliations. They're usually funded wholly or partly by government, and sometimes by donations.

Parentlines

These are for counselling and referrals for parents, not immediate health information about babies.

ACT: (02) 6287 3833
NSW: 1300 1300 52
Queensland & Northern Territory: 1300 30 1300
Tasmania: 1300 808 178
South Australia: 1300 364 100
Victoria: 13 22 89
Western Australia: 08 9368 9368 or 1800 111 546

Urgent counselling lines

Lifeline: 13 11 14 (general emergency 24-hour helpline)
Australian family violence helpline: 1800 RESPECT or 1800 737 732
Lifeline New Zealand: 0800 543 354 (general emergency 24-hour helpline)
New Zealand family violence line: 0800 456 450

more info on medical helpers

Midwives

Midwives are regulated by the National Nursing and Midwifery Board of Australia, and can be found through the Australian College of Midwives at **midwives.org.au**.

Child & family (aka maternal & child) health nurses

Call your community health centre, state government health department, local state member or, in Victoria, the local council.

Family doctors

The Royal Australian College of General Practitioners site is **www.racgp.org.au**. Your GP can refer you to a paediatrician – a specialist baby or toddler doctor.

Lactation consultants

'Lactating' means breastfeeding. Lactation Consultants of Australia & New Zealand is the professional association your consultant should be accredited with: **lcanz.org**. Private health insurance may cover them. See Chapter 4, Breastfeeding, for more.

more info on parent helplines staffed by qualified nurses

These health information lines should be staffed by qualified nurses who can help with practical, physical, mental and developmental concerns.

National Pregnancy, Birth and Baby helpline: 1800 882 436
24-hour helpline staffed by experienced, qualified midwives and child & family health nurses for the Australian Health Department. A website service is also offered at: **www.pregnancybirthbaby.org.au**

National Health Direct helpline: 1800 022 022
24-hour daily helpline for any medical issue, staffed by registered general nurses for the Australian Health Department. A website service is also at: **healthdirect.gov.au/healthdirect**

NSW
Karitane: 1300 227 464 or 97942350
Karitane parent service line staffed by maternal & child health nurses. They usually take a message and call back in 24 hours.

Tresillian: 1300 272 736
Tresillian parenting service line, 7 a.m. to 11 p.m., 7 days. Live Advice chat service at **tresillian.org.au**, operating long hours Monday to Friday.

Queensland: 13 432 584
24-hour daily helpline staffed by registered general nurses for the Queensland state government.

South Australia: 1300 364 100
Parent helpline mostly staffed by registered nurses for the state government's Women's and Children's Health Network.

Victoria: 13 22 29
Maternal & Child Health Line staffed by specialist maternal & child health nurses for the state government.

New Zealand 0800 933 922
24-hour daily Plunket helpline, staffed by specialist maternal & child health nurses for the NZ government.

doulas

Doulas, or mother-helpers, are private freelancers hired to help a woman before, during and after a birth. Anybody can call themselves a 'certified' or 'credited' doula. A doula may have done a weekend course or a six-day course, or simply watched a video or joined an association online, or be, as described on one doula website, 'self-trained'. They usually don't have nursing, medical, counselling or lactation consultant training. They are not a replacement for your child & family health nurse or family doctor.

Doulas should not attempt to diagnose or treat any medical conditions for mother or baby. They can be lovely, helpful, calming influences who offer continuity of kind support, and/or dangerous, inexperienced anti-vaccination activists who advise against medical treatment. Most doulas in Australia have a philosophical motivation and a sincere belief in natural therapies. Unlike a medically qualified person they are more likely to recommend homeopathy, and 'placenta pills' (look them both up in the index to find out why they don't work).

natural therapists

A natural therapist can help complement your medical care but can't take the place of a medical doctor, especially at this vulnerable time. Your doctor should know of any natural therapies or supplements you are given, and should make a diagnosis of any condition before you consult a natural therapist. Herbal remedies and supplements can be dangerous for children, so even over-the-counter remedies should be checked with your doctor. 'Homeopathic remedies' are often advertised as 'safe', but this isn't always true; in any case they do not work and should not be given to babies or toddlers. Chiropractors should not advise on medical care for, or 'treat', babies or toddlers. There's more on this in Chapter 33, Health.

family & friends

Family and friends can be a fantastic help or not much chop at all, depending on personality and how familiar they are with babies and kids. They can also help in other ways, such as doing housework and hunter-gathering. Someone who has a child a little older than yours can be helpful to tap for info.

All families are different. Some in-laws and grandparents might just want to pop around every few months to wave from the other side of the room; others may want to roar in and take over the week you get home from hospital. You are in charge of how much help or advice you want to ask for. The trick is to recognise the people who'd like to get to know the baby and learn how to help look after and enjoy the bub as a developing person, and those who are genuinely not interested or are benign but fairly useless onlookers. (Which is probably fair enough. To be utterly candid, before I had a baby myself I used to be more interested in people's dogs.)

Uncles, aunts, godparents or special adult friends can have more defined roles than others. Perhaps they can take the baby for regular outings and have preferred-babysitter privileges. And be told when to bring the chocolate.

parent groups

Your child & family health nurse will give you the contact details for a local group of parents (sometimes only mums, but there are mixed-parent and dads groups, too) with babies or kids about the same age as yours. These meeting or play groups can be great for parents who feel isolated, and for making friends and sharing experiences (although some parents find them a hotbed of judgemental remarks and dull conversation: feel free to try another one or decide it isn't for you). Children don't play 'together' much until after they're toddlers, but after several months babies are at least interested in looking at each other, and meanwhile you can hang out and chat. Groups meet in local halls, cafes, parks and each other's houses.

'Not every elderly neighbour who stops to talk to you and your baby is going to criticise you and give you conflicting advice. Some of them are just the village reaching out to support you.'
JO

parenting help websites

I am astonished at the wrong and sometimes terrifying information on some flash-looking, mainstream parenting sites with lovely designs and lifestyle photos. Just in the past three weeks I've read that the pricked-heel blood tests done to a newborn will tell you if a baby is allergic to dairy products (no, they don't!), that a plastic-sided Kmart garden trolley is good for taking a baby to the beach (no, it's dangerous and too hot for babies to sleep in!), and that a candlelit dinner is a good fun idea for toddlers (why not just call the fire brigade now to save time?).

Many baby-care websites are so swamped with ads that they're more advertising than independent information. Many sites use unpaid bloggers and writers, sometimes billed as 'experts', who push their own product, theory or therapy because they believe in it, or they make money from it. Other articles are 'tied' to, or written by, sponsors. Beware of cheap, syndicated 'content' that can range from simply annoying (a zillion pictures of seemingly cloned, suspiciously clean kids) to dangerous (decorating a cot with jolly, strangle-risk bunting).

Parent website forums

Even the most fancy-pants, celebrity-sprouting or medical-sounding parenting site can have unhelpful, wrong and dangerous advice that's posted by other parents. Most sites say their forums are not intended to be used for medical advice: unfortunately, this doesn't stop people from using them in that way. As with many website forums, some parents' queries remain unanswered for weeks, months or indefinitely. Some forums are unmoderated, or checked only for swearing and abuse, not wrong information. If you have any concerns about feeding, sleeping, crying, development or medical issues, ask your child & family health nurse or doctor first, and double-check any public forum advice with a professional.

'You can't have a clean house, a happy child, and your sanity: pick two. Clue: don't pick the first one!'
JANET

~~~~~~ **more info** on parenting help websites ~~~~

raisingchildren.net.au
Backed by the Australian government's Health Department; heaps of info on new bub
and toddler care, development issues and local services. On the main page search for
'newborns', or choose from the A–Z list of topics.

pregnancybirthbaby.org.au
Australian Health Department site for health info and advice on pregnancy, birth,
babies and toddlers. On the main page you can make an audio or video call to a
specialist midwife or nurse, or use the drop-down menus or A–Z list of topics for
everything from 'flat feet' to 'vegan'.

https://jeanhailes.org.au/what-were-we-thinking/
The *What Were We Thinking!* blog by the independent women's health
organisation the Jean Hailes Foundation has lots of useful stuff.

🥝 **plunket.org.nz**
New Zealand's Plunket Society is a government-funded hub
where you can arrange nurse visits for advice on parenting,
get referrals for other help, organise baby and child car-seat
rentals, find parents' groups, and more.

🥝 **parentscentre.org.nz**
Advice line: (04) 233 2022
Parents Centres New Zealand is a non-profit organisation
that offers help with childbirth education, parenting and
parent support, and referrals.

...that can't be right, surely?

3

LOOK after yourself

That's an order. Especially you, mum, after what you've been through, and how much you need to be there for your bub now. You and your bub will have a check-up with your doctor about six weeks after the birth. (I recommend you wear flowers on your nipples and a party hat , just to indicate you're doing fine.) The baby's important, but so are you. You are a confused woman in elasticised pants. You deserve to be looked after, too.

recovery from the birth

Even though medical care in Australia is tippety-top, childbirth is still a big health risk for women. Don't be surprised if body and soul take a while to recover from such a stressful event. Even if your experience was relatively easy, your mind and physical self will still need time to heal.

After your baby is born, you experience vaginal blood loss (sort of like a period; its medical name is the lochia). This is so that all the blood and tissues from the wall of your uterus, which nourished the baby, can come out. This will go on for two to six weeks, and starts off as a heavy period with some small clots, then gets darker, and trails off to nothing. During this time don't use tampons, as in rare cases they can cause an infection.

Tell your obstetrician immediately if:
- ⭐ the bleeding doesn't happen
- ⭐ it suddenly turns bright red and becomes heavy again after being paler for a while
- ⭐ there are large clots
- ⭐ it has a yucky smell.

As your uterus contracts to help expel the lining and shrink down to its normal size, you may feel some cramps like period pains. Your cervix is slowly closing, too. You should be healing well: any bruising or stitches should be dissolving. If you can, have therapeutic massages. Treat yourself as you would your best friend who's just been through the same thing. For heaven's sake don't be leaping about with a netball trying to prove you can do it all.

Women who have had a difficult labour – or an emergency caesarean – will probably need to talk and cry about it, and then move on when they are ready. Many women feel traumatised by birth, or for not having the 'right' sort of birth. Unrealistic or ill-informed expectations ('If you do yoga you will have a natural birth' or 'If you follow your birth plan there should be no need for medical intervention') can lead to an unfair feeling of failure or alienation from friends who did it differently – by luck or design. There's much more on this in Chapter 11, Getting Through Tough Times.

A 'natural birth' can result in a too-long labour, pelvic injury, a forceps delivery or tearing of the perineum, with later complications including prolapse of the vagina, and incontinence. A caesarean creates equivalent stress on the body and recovery to another surgical operation or to a car accident.

Other after-effects of birth can include bullying or a lack of support from relatives, the shock of an orderly life become 'out of control', shame at any of the feelings that occur or seem overwhelming, and managing your own and the expectations of others. You might have a bald patch in your hair or some darker spots on your face. Please don't compare your life and your body changes with the pretend perfect lives on social media. Emotional recovery is also an issue for a lot of people, mums and dads included. Many physical and mental after-effects can be sorted, cured or managed when you reach out for help.

Talk with your friends and family, mothers group, child & family health nurse, or a postnatal counsellor at the hospital or one that your doctor can refer you to. If you are fixating on the birth rather than the present and the future, ask for help.

ways to move on from a difficult birth

⭐ Talk about it.
⭐ Acknowledge any feelings – fear during the birth, disappointment afterwards.
⭐ Ask questions about anything you didn't understand.
⭐ Find the things to be grateful for and contemplate them.
⭐ Identify what you're looking forward to as a mum.
⭐ Get help for any residual anger, sadness or guilt.

recovery from a caesarean

You may have just had a baby, but you have also had major abdominal surgery. The injuries caused are significant ones: they've cut through several layers of your body. Your scar will be itchy and may heal as a ropey line. Good, healthy food will speed recovery. Having a caesarean makes it much harder to look after a baby in the house, especially if it's not your first child. You'll need help: ask for it. Go easy on yourself.

Make sure you find out from your doctor what you can't do: usually no picking-up of anything except your baby for six to eight weeks (that includes the shopping and the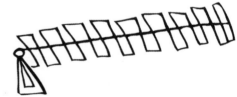

washing basket), no reaching above your head to lift anything at all, no driving or heavy housework or other work for a few weeks – that sort of thing. Don't tire yourself out. Do half as much each day as you think you 'should'. You'll be shuffling about from the pain of your wound. Make sure your obstetrician or doctor gives you some effective pain relief for the first week or two at home.

Stay home rather than visit other people – get them to bring the shopping.

more info on recovering from a caesarean

betterhealth.vic.gov.au
On this reliable and practical website, choose 'Healthy living', then click on 'C' in the 'A–Z of healthy living' box, then click on 'Caesarean section' for info, and hints for special care for you and your baby.

babycenter.com.au
Choose 'Pregnancy', then 'Labour and birth', then 'All about caesarean birth', then 'Recovery after a caesarean birth' for practical and emotional suggestions.

BLAST FROM THE PAST
'The glorious event of motherhood with its expectant joys now, by the aid of science and a government thoroughly awake to its responsibilities, is practically safe,' – An optimistic if unrealistic letter to the editor, *Cloncurry Advocate*, Queensland, 1936

'The shock of not being able to go walking for the first 16 weeks stung. I felt isolated in my own home. I wish I'd known this was common and just a phase. Best advice was just to lie outside with baby in the backyard and get some sunshine.' MELISSA

new mum nutrition

'Everyone has a battle.
Just not everyone talks about it.
Celebrate the small wins.'
LISA

Eat as well and as heartily as you can, particularly if you're breastfeeding. Special breastfeeding or 'women's' vitamins are probably a good idea, because then you'll know you're covered for anything extra you need, like a boost of iron, and vitamin D, which is mainly created by your body when it's exposed to sunlight. You might need extra vitamin D, especially if you live in a wintry area or generally wear full-cover clothing. Any vitamin you don't need, below an overdose level, will just be wee-ed out without doing any harm. Your pharmacist can advise you about local, reputable brands and the right formulation. Try to keep up with your body's needs, which will be higher if you're breastfeeding.

Stock up on things you can eat easily in the middle of the night if you get ravenous, snack-monstery feelings: a few swigs of soy milk and a banana perhaps, or a vegetable muffin. Or indeed a giant block of Toblerone. Sorry, no. Try to eat a range of different-coloured vegies and fruits, as that ensures a broader range of nutrients – don't get stuck on just carrots and zucchini. Try to get some protein in at every meal: cheesy omelette, tuna sandwich, boiled egg, tofu mountain, entire leg of lamb (possibly not – I'm writing this before lunch). Rice with protein and vegies is filling and quick, as is a potato or a sanger. Chicken and vegie soup is sublimely useful. And great hunks of toasty, crusty bread can be dipped into oil and dribbled on a passing sailor.

See your doctor if:
- ★ you have a worry
- ★ anything is swelling up or getting redder
- ★ you have any stinky or yucky discharge from your vagina or your caesarean wound
- ★ you have a high temperature
- ★ you have any shortness of breath
- ★ you find a lump in a breast (this could lead to mastitis)
- ★ you're depressed
- ★ you're never hungry.

your postnatal fitness

Maternity hospitals all have physiotherapists on board, and many have postnatal exercise classes that teach the basics. Your maternity hospital should have already given you a pamphlet or link to some sort of information on exercise and physio. There will be different stuff to do, depending on whether you had a vaginal or a caesarean delivery. A physiotherapist can help you work out what exercise to do to recover from a caesarean. You can ask your obstetrician or midwife for a referral to a physio.

If you take up or resume exercise at a class or gym, it's important to be supervised by a specialist in postnatal exercise, so make absolutely sure the person you choose is not just a general instructor. Take any exercising slowly and tell the instructor you're recovering from a birth.

Your back and your 'core'

The most important priority for you is to protect your back, especially after a caesarean. Your core muscles – abdominal and lower back – may now be very weak, leaving you vulnerable to lower back injury or strain.

Useful 'core' muscles can be built up through specialised yoga, pilates or other exercises. You mustn't do any 'abdominals' such as sit-ups, if your rectus muscle has separated during the pregnancy (a common, hernia-like condition): ask your doctor about it.

Make sure all your baby equipment, such as the bath and change table, is at a good bench height for you. Always lift heavy things with bent knees, and squat down instead of bending over for actions such as picking up bub from the floor. (If you have a toddler, squat in front of the stroller to fasten or undo the straps: don't bend forward.) Your baby is just going to get heavier, so start strengthening your back now, or at least avoid injuring yourself.

Sneezy wee

Your pelvic-floor muscles may be so weak that you do a little wee if you sneeze, cough or laugh. The pelvic strain is caused during pregnancy by the weight of the baby on your trampoliny pelvic floor, which stretches undrneath your pelvic organs.

To avoid a small wee, try tensing, sitting down or crossing your legs before the sneeze or laugh. The only way to really stop it from happening is to tighten your pelvic-floor muscles by exercising them.

Pelvic-floor exercises

Different midwives and obstetricians have different guidelines, but here's a start:

* lie down if possible – the muscles don't work as hard if you're standing up
* squeeze your pelvic-floor muscles for a count of four, then relax them for a count of four
* build up to doing this for five minutes twice a day – but keep breathing!
* and keep doing them – it can take up to three months to build better bladder control, but exercise does make a difference.

Only your vaginal muscles should be working: you shouldn't be also tensing your buttocks or your abdominal and thigh muscles. Although one means of identifying the muscles is to wee and then try to stop halfway through, it's not a good idea to practise pelvic-floor exercises that way: once is enough. (A better way to check is to put a finger in your vagina and squeeze: if you're exercising correctly you should feel the muscles tightening around your finger. Best not to do this in a cafe.)

Current wisdom (which keeps changing) is to do the exercises as often as you can until it's tiring. Some people put red sticker dots around their house and do the exercises every time they see one. (In a similar exercise, you can scream every time you see the federal treasurer on telly. It does nothing for the vagina, but I find it passes the time.) If all else fails, you can buy thin panty pads in case of unscheduled wees, and get a doctor's referral to a specialist physio.

more info on your pelvic floor

continence.org.au
National Incontinence Helpline: 1800 33 00 66
The Continence Foundation of Australia is a non-profit organisation that helps mums recover their continence after birth.

thewomens.org.au
On the home page of Melbourne's Royal Women's Hospital, type 'pelvic floor' into the 'How can we help you?' box, then scroll down to and click on 'The pelvic floor'. The Women's has lots of info on all aspects of health that you might find useful.

the new you

You're still you, even if you feel a bit lost for the moment. You probably won't suddenly want to make giant macramé owls for the rest of your life (unless you do, in which case, no, I do not want one for Christmas). But some things inevitably change.

Some changes are temporary, like squirty bosoms, the kind of tired you feel, the fact that pretty much every cup of tea goes cold before you can drink it, always thinking you can hear a baby cry if you're in the shower or using the hair dryer, and bursting into tears while watching the news or a sad movie (or a TV ad for air freshener).

Some changes may be permanent: an expansion in the amount of love you can feel, the darker colour of your nipples, a feeling of empathy with other parents, and, well, the fact that pretty much every cup of tea goes cold before you can drink it.

having sex again

As I said in my pregnancy book, *Up the Duff*, because some doctors say 'No sex until after the six-week check-up', a lot of chaps think 'Whacko, that night my sex life will resume and go on like it used to!'

Oh dear.

Many women feel that their body has been through enough, and has enough to do, and they want a rest from sex. A fall in libido is probably a mixture of hormonal changes and wanting a rest for your body, or more sleep. Some women are worried about what their body looks or feels like now – please believe your partner when they say they still find you gorgeous. Sex should be mostly about how we feel, not whether we look particularly like Heidi Klum modelling lingerie in high heels. Otherwise only Heidi would be having sex, with herself.

Well, some people do resume energetic and regular rumpy-pumpy pronto, but a great many women (yes, it's more likely to be the women) are feeling too leaky, bulky, sick of their body being required on demand for feeding and seemingly everything else, and desperate to adjust to hideous broken-sleep patterns and the draining, droning tiredness, to be able to find any clean knickers, let alone put on lingerie. Generally. Not. Up. For. It.

'Don't worry if you feel, like I did, that your brain is being sucked out through your nipples.' CLARE

Hormonal contraception or ordinary old post-baby hormone changes can also squash your desire to have sex. Vaginal bleeding can go on for up to six weeks after the birth, so most women don't feel all that frisky soon after a six-week-long 'period' sitting on maternity pads. Penetrative sex not involving a penis (or a man at all) is also off the table (and the bed).

Even with a straightforward birth, or one that didn't require stitches for a tear or cut to the vagina, the general area needs time to heal. Perhaps if men could imagine their penis being stretched to ten times its normal size, then being torn down the middle, having an orange being passed through it and being sewn back up again, they might empathise with their partner and understand that some rest and recuperation is required. Why not describe that to him.

Some women who've had a traumatic birth or a long labour and stitches are frightened of having sex. Please talk to your doctor to make sure everything's physically ready, and wait until you're mentally ready. Partners may have to be a little patient. (Of course they may be a bit knocked around themselves in the sleep department.)

If you don't feel like sex, talk with your partner about why: the best way to keep the relationship working is to talk about your feelings. And work out ways you might become less tired.

Vaginal dryness might be a problem for breastfeeding women, caused by drop in oestrogen levels. If so, use a lubricant. But if you're using condoms for contraception, your lubricant must be water-based.

Ask your obstetrician when you can have sex again after the birth: usually you're told four to six weeks. Some blokes say they've been told it's four to six years. But the real answer is 'when you want to'.

Possible feelings about sex after childbirth

* Never again.
* I'm too tired.
* Leave my body alone: someone's already getting milk out of it and it's recently been inhabited. I want it to myself for a while.
* I may have sex again if I ever want another child.
* I can't see the point now I've had a baby.

Misunderstandings can crop up if you and your partner don't discuss this stuff openly. Here are some she says/he says – or she thinks/*he thinks* – translations that might be going on:

He only wants me for sex, so when he kisses and cuddles me I wriggle away because I'm not up for it.
(I'm just happy with the cuddle and the kiss.)

She couldn't possibly want sex with me. She saw something come out of my vagina, and I haven't had time to doll myself up for weeks, and I haven't lost my baby tummy.
(She doesn't realise she still turns me on.)

She doesn't want me any more. She just wanted the baby.
(Of course I still love him and find him attractive. I'm just too exhausted to feel sexy right now.)

I want it to be like it was before.
(Things change. That doesn't mean it's bad. Just different.)

Oh my God, I'll never have sex again.
(This is temporary.)

Are you awake? (ZZZZZ.)

Are you awake? (ZZZZZ.)

Are you awa— oh forget it.
(ZZZZZ, snonk.)

Contraception

Please use it unless you want to get pregnant again. Breastfeeding is NOT a guarantee you won't get pregnant: some people ovulate in the first few months and get caught out.

Some forms of contraception can have the effect of lowering sexual desire. Many breastfeeding women are prescribed the Mini Pill as it's less likely than the stronger Pill to cancel out the hormone prolactin and so interfere with the breastmilk supply.

Women on any Pill should still look out for the symptoms of ectopic pregnancy, which happens when a fertilised egg implants itself outside the uterus (usually in a fallopian tube). Symptoms, which tend to occur at about six weeks, may include abdominal pain, either on one side of the abdomen or more generalised, and that comes and goes; spotting or bleeding; dizziness, faintness, paleness and sweating; nausea and vomiting; sometimes shoulder pain; and sometimes a feeling of pressure in the bum.

Please have condoms near the bed and use them if you suddenly get frisky, unless you're just fine with the idea of two kids under 3 (or more if you have twins!). Talk to your doctor about contraceptive options.

~~~~~~~~~ **more info** on having sex again ~~~~~~~~~

Your GP or nearest Family Planning Clinic can advise on contraception.

mariestopes.org.au
This independent organisation provides info on contraception options, vasectomy and terminations for unwanted pregnancy.

'Embrace your after-kids body because you are never going to see the before body again, even if you do lose the weight.' STEPH

'After breastfeeding 3 kids my breasts aren't what they were – a bit flat-pancakey. But I also think, well, that's part of life and I wouldn't change them – they're testimony to my motherhood!' MANDY

your post-baby body

Is there a worse moment than when somebody asks 'When's the baby due?' and you've already had it? Medical experts say we should feel fine about taking a year to get back to our pre-pregnancy weight – and all post-pregnancy women have body changes that will be companions from now on forever. The older you are, the less likely your body is to 'go back to where it was'. Big tummies can last for weeks, for months or forever. Post-caesarean tummies can continue to have a double 'bump'.

I used to be a pear, now I'm a quince

Don't be guided by friends or by family expectations, what celebrities do, social media, or a nasty inner voice that sounds like the mean girls from high school.

Here's what I said in my pregnancy book, *Up the Duff*, about your post-baby body. It's all true. You've either had a major body shock (labour) or surgery akin to a serious injury in terms of damage and bruising (caesarean). People can be jailed for making workers sleep as little as you are. You're keeping a new baby alive. This is no time for star jumps. You don't need a strict exercise regime, or a demanding plan, or a personal trainer who wakes you up before dawn and shouts at you.

BLAST FROM THE PAST
'Until your muscles are firm again, wear a well-fitting corset.'
– M.A. White, *Woman's World* magazine, Australia, probably early 1950s

'I don't love the spare tyre under my belly button. I always wondered why Mum had her body shape – now I know ...'   SAM

Body-image boosters

1   Understand that pregnancy changes the body – the breasts especially – forever, whether or not you can breastfeed. Remember to have your bra size re-measured after pregnancy and when you finish breastfeeding: your breasts will change and may not go back to their original size.

2   Don't compare your body with a celebrity's. Or with your sister's or your mum's or a friend's. Everyone is different. And celebrities lie through their whitey-white teeth about what they did to lose weight and how healthy it was. They are demented. Stay away from stories about celebrities who are the shape of lollypops with gravity-defying bosoms a week after the birth.

3   Don't obsess about what your body looks like: this means don't keep checking the mirror.

4   Acknowledge that it takes weeks to lose the extra blood volume, fluids, fat tissue and other reserves you needed for pregnancy.

5   Keep reminding yourself that any sensible weight-loss scheme means that losing a kilo a week, max, is realistic. (It may need to be even less for you – check with your doctor.)

6   'They' say breastfeeding causes weight loss, especially after the first four months of it: this doesn't work for everyone. Don't believe claims such as 'Breastfeeding burns 500 calories a day' because (a) it's bollocks and (b) this is no moment to find the time to count calories or kilojoules.

'I hate the permanent front-cover message BEST EVER BABY BODY from women's magazines accompanied by the waif-thin new mother that make the rest of us feel totally inadequate.'   ANNIE

'Lots of stretch marks but can't complain too much because it helped me make two beautiful children.'   JULES

~~~~~~~~ **more info** on your post-baby body ~~~~~~~~

haescommunity.com
The Health At Every Size community site concentrates on health instead of size, and is run by Linda Bacon. Her book by the same name is a bestseller and has helped many women re-think how they feel about, and talk about, their physical self. She talks about 'compassionate self-care'.

bodyimagemovement.com
Founded by Aussie mum Taryn Brunfitt, this joyous site supports her philosophy of acceptance, and sports a blog as well as info on the movie she made, *Embrace*, and her books. There's also a Facebook page.

ifnotdieting.com.au
Has calming, practical, sensible ideas from Dr Rick Kausman, the author of *If Not Dieting Then What?* (Allen & Unwin, Australia), about ending the war with food and guilt.

about-face.org
A media-challenging US site that calls out stupid ads and presents positive images of women. The slogan is 'Don't fall for the media circus'.

~~~~~~~~~~~~~~~~~~~~~~~~~~~~~~~~~~~~~~~

activity suggestions for new mums

★ Be active. It's good to be fit and strong to do the things a mum has to do. Don't think of exercise as being only about weight loss. Walking quickly is much harder when you have a baby and other children. That's okay. If you can't use a double-decker pram, you can maybe arrange with a friend to mind each other's kids so that you can take it in turns to walk. Or do your exercise before your partner goes to work or after they return, or on your way home from work.

★ Accept that the key goal is fitness, flexibility and vitality, not slimness or a magic weight or dress size.

★ Don't plan to exercise when the baby is asleep. In the early days sleep when your baby sleeps.

★ Ask your doctor at the six-week check-up about any activity you plan to get into.

⭐ Wait until you feel ready to start.

⭐ Get fresh air and sunshine whenever possible – much better to get out than to be inside a gym. It's a proven blues-buster, too.

⭐ Consider free or cheap exercise: walking, dancing in the lounge room, swimming at the local pool (maybe on a season pass), joining a fun sports team with other mums or locals.

⭐ Organise a walking date with friends or a new-mums group: you're more likely to go, and the adult company will do you good. Get a fancy three-wheel pram if that will help.

⭐ Keep things moderate. Vigorous or high-impact, high-energy gym routines or running can make you sore and haggard. Fatigue is a special risk if you're breastfeeding.

⭐ Don't feel you have to pay for a special program with a special baby- or mum-relevant name. These can be very expensive and reinforce self-esteem problems because they keep telling you you're not the right shape or size. It's better for your baby to go on a walk with you and hear you chatting to them. These 'programs' can give you unrealistic expectations about how quickly your body will recover. You're still producing a lot of the hormone relaxin, and this can cause back and pelvic pain or other stresses and strains.

BLAST FROM THE PAST

'The slogan of unionists is One Man, One Job, but this does not apply to mothers.'
– Letter to the editor from 'Mother of Three', *Westralian Worker*, 1921

⭐ Don't give up if you can't do an hour a day – do half an hour a day,
or an hour three or four times a week or whenever you can.

⭐ Don't give up because you have to wrangle a toddler as well as a baby.
Get a double pram for walks, or ask for babysitting help so that you can
get active and have some fun.

⭐ You need to eat well if you are convalescing from childbirth, breastfeeding
or exercising – and here you are, possibly doing all three. Eat. Forget about
fad short-term diets with low kilojoules or calories. If you need help to work
out a healthy, long-term eating program, ask your GP for a referral to a dietician.
(See also 'More info on your post-baby body' earlier in this chapter.)

⭐ Don't dismiss your needs. If you feel you can't take 'me-time', look at exercise
this way: a fit mum with a healthy immune system is good for the kids.

'As a mum, enjoy your pre-baby body for its aesthetics,
but rejoice in your post-baby body for your strength,
resilience to all the physical challenges of babies.'   BETH

'My boobs have simply deflated since breastfeeding two
children. I can honestly roll them up now.'   ROS

'Somewhere on the internet there is always someone
telling you that you're doing it wrong. So just turn off
technology, "listen" to your baby and instincts and call
on your circle of trusted pals.'   'FULL TILT NANNA'

4

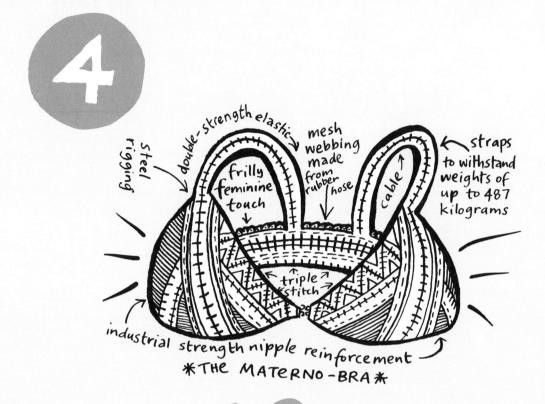

steel rigging

double-strength elastic →

frilly feminine touch →

mesh webbing made from rubber hose →

straps to withstand weights of up to 487 kilograms ←

cable ↑

← triple stitch →

industrial strength nipple reinforcement →

✳ THE MATERNO-BRA ✳

BReastFeeDING

A newborn baby is as new to this bosoms-with-milk business as you are. Together you'll work it all out. And if that's not possible, off to the next chapter with you, which is Bottle-feeding.

why breastfeeding is recommended

Breastmilk has so much good stuff in it the scientists haven't even worked it all out yet. Not only is it full of exactly the right combination of vitamins, minerals, fats and other compounds for optimum health, but it also has boosters for a baby's immune system, anti-infection stuff and agents to help digestion. Literally hundreds of elements are all packaged perfectly to be absorbed properly and quickly by the baby's body. Many of these components can't be reproduced in formula milk.

It's believed that babies will get some of breastmilk's benefits even if you can only breastfeed for a short time, but they'll probably get the most advantage if they're breastfed for at least 6 to 12 months.

Good points about breastfeeding

⭐ Breastmilk has all the necessary ingredients.

⭐ Breastmilk has important health and immune system benefits.

⭐ Breastmilk is portable and on tap.

⭐ Breastmilk is free.

⭐ Breastmilk is always the right temperature.

⭐ There are no bottle contamination risks.

⭐ Breastmilk is best for babies, as babies' bodies have evolved to accept it.

⭐ Breastfed baby poo smells better than bottle-fed baby poo.

⭐ It's very, very rare for a baby to be allergic to breastmilk.

⭐ The baby usually doesn't get constipated.

⭐ There's an immense feeling of pride in being able to keep your baby alive and healthy, just with your own body.

'One day when I was struggling with breastfeeding, three people asked how I was and each time I burst into tears. However, I was determined. It took three months and lots of help, nipple shields and more tears but I eventually got it. It's one of my proudest achievements!'   ROBYN

'Breastfeeding is something you both need to learn to do.'   LIBBY

Possible drawbacks of breastfeeding

This list is longer, but breastfeeding is best if you can! A lot of these are rare.

⭐ It can be hard work to establish.

⭐ It can result in problems for some women, such as the infection mastitis.

⭐ Breastmilk will carry drugs or illnesses from you that can affect the baby.

⭐ People assume that breastfeeding is a contraceptive. For some women this is true for about 18 months, for others it is never true. If you want to avoid another pregnancy for the time being, make sure you use condoms: you can't be on some of the Pills as the hormones will go through your breastmilk to the baby (ask your doctor).

⭐ Your breasts can leak at embarrassing moments.

⭐ If you want someone else to feed the baby, you'll have to express the milk. Actually, this is not so much a drawback as a rather splendid idea.

⭐ You have to wake up (sometimes barely) for every night-time feed. In the early days this can be incredibly draining and put you into a brainless, starey state that only gradually, gradually gets better as you start getting more sleep.

⭐ You get short-term memory loss, extreme fatigue and other symptoms such as putting the car keys in the crisper.

Some reasons why it might not be a good idea for you to breastfeed

⭐ You can't make enough milk to keep your baby growing. Some women don't produce enough prolactin, the hormone that controls the milk supply, so they can't make enough milk for their baby. (Luckily this is rare, and you could well be able to combine breastfeeding and bottle-feeding.)

⭐ Your baby can't suck effectively: some babies have a real problem with learning to suck properly, and a few are never going to get it together.

⭐ The difficulties you have experienced trying to breastfeed are affecting your relationship with your baby, which is more important than your baby's relationship with your bosoms.

> 'I ended up doing it to keep my husband happy, even though my son and I would both be in tears trying to get it right.'
> **MOTHER WHO BREASTFED FOR SIX MONTHS**

★ You've tried everything, received help from all sorts of groups and individuals and it still isn't working.

★ You are so against the idea of breastfeeding that if you do it you will resent the baby.

★ Breastfeeding or its side effects (such as chronic mastitis) are consistently making you ill or depressed.

★ You've had breast surgery: any kind can make it physically difficult or impossible to breastfeed, although some women who've had breast surgery can breastfeed.

★ You have an illness that could be passed to your baby through the breastmilk.

★ You need to be on a medication that will go through to the breastmilk and won't be good for your baby, or that interferes with milk production. Check with your doctor. Many drugs, including some antidepressant drugs, are okay to use while breastfeeding. (See next section)

★ You smoke, drink alcohol or take non-prescribed drugs: even if you don't do this often, you shouldn't be breastfeeding. Some people have an occasional glass of wine – but this does 'go through' to the baby.

If you've decided you need to bottle-feed, tally-ho onto the following chapter, all about bottle-feeding.

Medication & breastfeeding

Many medications are okay to take while breastfeeding, but always check with your GP and pharmacist about any medical or herbal preparation, whether prescribed or off the shelf. Many herbal preparations as well as drugs can be very dangerous for pregnant or breastfeeding women because of possible damage to the baby.

'I am lucky – breastfeeding came very easily to me and is a part of babyhood I savoured, and missed dreadfully once they were weaned. [But] it's your decision alone, and nobody else's business!' TIFFANY

~~~~~ **more info** on medication & breastfeeding ~~~~

Medicines Line: 1300 633 424
The national 'MedicineWise' Medicines Line, backed by the federal government, provides info on medicines in pregnancy and during breastfeeding to women and their doctors. It's usually open during business hours for the cost of a local call from anywhere in Australia.

Poisons Information Centre: 13 11 26 (24-hour hotline)
0800 764 766 (1800 POISON) (NZ 24-hour hotline)
These services can also advise you on drugs and breastmilk.

https://toxnet.nlm.nih.gov/newtoxnet/lactmed.htm
The US National Library of Medicine Toxicology Data Network database of drugs and breastfeeding lists reliable info on medication, drugs and chemicals (including antidepressants) and their likely levels and effects in breastmilk. Your doctor should also check it when deciding which version of a medication is best for you while breastfeeding.

breastfeeding straight after the birth

Colostrum

Breastmilk doesn't 'come in' until three or four days after you've given birth, as your body switches from baby-inside-you hormones to baby-outside-you hormones and pumps out its new, large output of prolactin, allowing your body to make breastmilk. But your bub still gets to eat because in the meantime some yellowy stuff called colostrum comes out of your breasts, which is really good for babies. Human colostrum is full of antibodies and mysterious ingredients that help the baby's digestive system gear up for a totally new way of ingesting, now that the whole umbilical-cord thing is out of fashion. There's not a lot of colostrum, but it's packed with special goodies, so it's perfect for babies with little tums.

Newborns lose weight

It's normal for your bub to lose some weight before the milk 'comes in', then steadily start to gain weight again when feeding is established.

getting started with breastfeeding

Most people have some sort of trouble getting started: like anything, breastfeeding takes practice to find a successful technique. After all it's quite possibly the first time you've had to do tricks with your bosoms. The fact that it's 'natural' to breastfeed doesn't mean that knowing how to do it comes naturally. Puberty and menopause are also 'natural' and they can be a pain in the everything. We don't see women breastfeeding around us every day, so don't be surprised if you feel awkward! Most mums take a while to get used to breastfeeding.

Mums who've had more than one baby say that breastfeeding depends on the kid: with some it's easy, with others it's hard. It doesn't seem to get easier or harder with each child – it's just the luck of the draw. So you mustn't blame yourself if it's difficult.

Many women have some kind of problem, but many go on to breastfeed for a year or more – even ones who have inverted nipples or painful breast infections. The first month or two are usually the hardest. Expect some hurdles and know you'll usually be able to get over them, with help.

Feeling a bit panicked is a normal response to not being able to feed your baby enough breastmilk, but it's okay. Your baby will also thrive on formula milk. If you can't breastfeed, there's the bottle, and always feel you've got the time to have a second or third go at a new technique: your baby won't starve as long as you are under the care of a good lactation consultant, child & family health nurse, or doctor.

It's always much better if you can have someone show you. Often midwives or well-meaning friends and relatives will tell you different things: maybe one will recommend the 'American football hold', perhaps another will say wait until the baby opens up for a yawn and then whack them on the nipple. Choose a person whose approach you like, and only listen to them.

The hospital where your baby was born has an obligation to help you with breastfeeding even if it discharges you before your proper milk comes in. If a hospital tells you its lactation consultant is busy or on holidays or can't come until next week, kick up a stink. If you're too tired, get your mum or your partner or an in-law or a friend to do it.

'They played a video in the hospital when I had my first son, over and over, "Breastfeeding should be 100 per cent pleasant and comfortable", until I almost threw something at the TV.'
PENNY

learning how to breastfeed

After a few weeks you'll probably be able to breastfeed upside down on the monkey bars at the local park, but in the beginning you may need to set up a comfort zone at home. Choose a comfy chair as your breastfeeding HQ. Next to the baby's bed is perfect, especially for middle-of-the-night feeds. Make sure the room is warm enough before you start. You need to drink a lot during the day if breastfeeding, and you'll sometimes feel thirsty during a feed when you can't get up.

You may also want a pencil and notebook or a safety pin to swap sides on your front if you're recording which breast you need to start on next time, and how long each feed is. You don't have to do this, but I found it quite useful when I was brain dead. (It hadn't actually occurred to me that if the baby fed every four hours I would have to be awake every four hours.)

The lack of sleep makes everything harder – including trying to remember which bosom you started with last time. After a while you'll gain confidence and forget to make notes. Later you can look back and laugh at your funny lists with 'L 25 min.' and 'R 17 min.' on them.

Breastfeeding equipment

You might use:

⭐ maternity bras – supportive, stretchy, your new size and front-opening

⭐ a lanolin-based nipple cream or one that's okay for a baby to swallow (some people use pawpaw cream) – ask your pharmacist

⭐ breast pads – little disposable or washable pads to put in your bra to soak up any leaking milk

⭐ a spare top and bra and spare breast pads in your bag in case you do leak

⭐ pillows to help support your baby and your back

⭐ warm (not hot) wheat-filled fabric packs that can trick your brain into sending the right message so your milk will come, although it doesn't work for everyone; you can also use them as cold packs to stop your breasts becoming engorged

⭐ a hand pump in case your nipples are sore – you can express some milk (see the 'Expressing breastmilk' section coming up) and give it in a sterilised bottle

⭐ a nappy or cloth for putting over your shoulder in case the baby throws up a bit during a break or straight after feeding.

Breastfeeding checklist

⭐ Drink a big glass of water and have another one within reach.

⭐ Put a cloth over your shoulder for when you burp the baby.

⭐ To bring the baby up to the right level without getting aching arms, and to help if you've had a caesarean, put a couple of pillows on your lap and lay the baby on this high, comfy 'tray' (while still holding on to them so they don't roll off).

⭐ Talk to your baby and explain what you're doing.

⭐ Sit up straight.

⭐ Find a feeding position for the baby that's comfy for you.

⭐ Start on the breast you didn't start with last time or the one that is fuller.

⭐ Get your baby to open wide by tickling their cheek or under their chin, so that they take a big mouthful of areola as well as nipple when they latch on.

⭐ As your baby opens wide, aim your nipple towards the roof of their mouth.

⭐ Reattach if the attachment is not a big mouthful, feels wrong or hurts.

⭐ Let the baby have as much as they want on the first breast, and then however much they can take on the second.

Getting pouty

If your baby's mouth doesn't open automatically when you tickle their cheek to a shape that looks like a duck-faced selfie pout, or the curved right-hand side of this letter 'K', get yourself to your nurse or doctor just in case there's a common physical problem that can be fixed or worked around.

How to breastfeed

Choose whatever works for you and your baby. Speak to your baby soothingly and encouragingly. Trying to get breastfeeding going can be stressful if the baby is crying with hunger, and I know it can be hard, but staying calm will help you both.

Take a few deep breaths. Sit up straight and make sure your lower back is supported. This means you need to bring the bub to your breast rather than hunching over, round shouldered, to deliver the breast to them.

'Using a U-shaped pillow to support the baby for breastfeeds made it easier.'
AMY

positions   You can try various feeding positions, including laying the baby sideways across your lap, face up, then turning them gently so the bub is facing you and is tummy-to-tummy with you. Another common one involves holding the baby on their side, under your arm and facing your body, then bringing them forward to the nearest breast, as if you're holding a hungry surfboard (this is the 'American football hold' or the 'French loaf hold' – or any term suggesting carrying something under one arm – that is often referred to). Experiment until you find a position that feels good. Some people prefer to breastfeed lying down, but this seems an unduly restrictive position to have to be in every time.

Support your baby's body and neck, either with your arm or pillows. Remember that tiny babies can't hold their heads up by themselves.

nipple attachment   Tickle your bub's cheek to create the sucking reflex: their mouth will open. Try to get the breast in when the mouth is open wide. The baby needs to get a big mouthful of areola (the coloured circle around the nipple) as well as nipple, not just suck on the nipple itself, which will be painful for you. If they latch on to only the nipple, slip your little finger into their mouth to break the suction and gently dislodge it from your nipple. If you just pull the nipple out, it can really hurt.

swapping breasts   Start with the breast you didn't start with last time. After a while you may be able to tell by feel which is the fuller one; otherwise, jot the info down or put a safety pin on the side to start on next time to remind yourself. If being seen in public with a safety pin above one bosom worries you, why not substitute a priceless ruby brooch in the shape of a small potoroo? Let the baby suck for approximately 20 minutes or more on the first breast. Some advisers say there isn't any point in going much over 20 minutes on each breast, but others say a newborn can take up to an hour to get everything they need while they're working up those jaw muscles and swallowing skills. Helpful, ain't it? Some babies suck faster and the milk is squirted out more quickly. (It might be half an hour each side, and then by three months it could be about 15 minutes.) So it's probably best to be guided by what your baby seems to want to do, and ask for help if you still feel bamboozled. The baby will pull away when they've finally had enough, and then you can burp them (or not) and bung them on the other bosom until they've had enough there.

burping   A lot of babies don't need to be 'burped', and it's unknown in many cultures. In fact, some babies will not burp but hiccup. If you want to, you can burp or 'wind' the baby when they have a rest during the feed and then get back into it. After the feed or between bosoms hold your baby upright, peeking over one of your shoulders, and rock and pat until there's a burp – but don't worry if there isn't one. The theory is that burping stops 'wind' from causing tummy pain.

How often to breastfeed?

Newborn babies usually feed eight to twelve times in a 24-hour period. In the early days you will have to try to muddle through, but your aim would be to feed the baby when they seem hungry, probably about every three to four hours during the day and when they wake and cry during the night – unless they wake every hour or two, in which case they may just be feeling a bit freaked out about not being in the womb and need a rock back to sleep.

Breastfeeding as often as you like in the first weeks will help you build up a constant, replenishing supply of milk, but it will leave you a zombie if you wake up every couple of hours to feed the baby. This may be easier after the first three or four weeks. Sometimes a baby may genuinely need a feed in two hours, but often this is because they've had a bit of a sniffle and got tired feeding, so for a day or so they'll want shorter feeds at shorter intervals.

Wanting feeds within three hours might be more of a habit of comfort sucking but it's unreasonable to expect you to be able to 'diagnose' this: nobody really can. Be aware that you can get yourself into a vicious circle of feeding your baby little bits too often: you'll need to gradually extend the time between breastfeeds. Try to give a complete feed at intervals of three to four hours rather than get the baby used to snacking or top-ups every two hours. If it's only been two hours since the last feed, remember to check whether your newborn's grizzle might be caused by an annoying noise from next door, or a farty feeling or a pooey nappy, instead of hunger.

How long is a breastfeed?

In the early days feeds tend to take between 30 and 50 minutes in total (both bosoms). The time usually gradually reduces. Eventually you'll probably be feeding only 7 to 10 minutes on each breast: older babies can be gulpy speedsters.

If you've chosen to breastfeed you need to allow yourself time and energy to concentrate pretty much solely on that, as well as to get to know your baby, give yourselves some fresh air and recover from the birth. Eventually your baby will develop a rhythm of feeds. If you can't delegate the housework, as one lovely doctor consultant on this book (and a mum) says, 'The dirty laundry doesn't give a toss and probably quite likes it on the bathroom floor . . . But you will treasure this time forever, the getting to know your baby.'

Breastfeeding privacy

You can breastfeed anywhere you like. If it makes others uncomfortable, they can not look, or move away. If you'd rather go into another room while you have visitors, that's okay too.

Some shirts and singlets allow for easy side access and some women feel more comfy if they drape a scarf over bosom and bub, when they're around strangers. Up to you.

It is illegal everywhere in Australia to tell somebody not to breastfeed in public. This includes restaurants, cafes, shopping areas, bus stops, flash-mob dance routines, cinemas, school grounds, parliament houses, and the top of flagpoles. You may ignore any request to cover up or go elsewhere. If you think somebody is giving you the stink-eye (that's an extreme dirty look), poke out your tongue at them. If they laugh, they're on your side. And if they don't, well, I'm glad you poked your tongue out at them. They deserve it.

If you're out shopping and need to feed your baby, go to a large shopping centre or department store and use their ladies' lounge or mothers' room, which should have a couch or armchair to sit on. Otherwise a corner of a cafe will do fine, or even a park bench or the car.

'If you're out, plan to be in the bigger shopping centres around feedtimes: these days they have excellent parenting facilities at most of them.' FIONA

~~~~~~~~~ **more info** on breastfeeding ~~~~~~~~~

breastfeeding.asn.au
1800 686 2 686 (1800 MUM 2 MUM)
The 24-hour advice line of the Australian Breastfeeding Association (ABA) is staffed by specially trained counsellors – usually mums talking to you from their own homes. The website has info about breastfeeding, and the shop site, **shop.breastfeeding.asn.au**, has equipment and downloadable booklets on specific aspects of breastfeeding.

betterhealth.vic.gov.au
On the home page of this government health site, search 'breastfeeding' to find lots of useful info on breastfeeding, including expressing and storing breastmilk, the first days, travelling and breastfeeding, breastfeeding at work, and troubleshooting problems.

raisingchildren.net.au
Search 'breastfeeding videos' to find a video on 'good attachment' to help work out the deal with 'latching on'. Also search 'breastfeeding'.

www.thewomens.org.au
On the main page of Melbourne's Royal Women's Hospital website, type 'breastfeeding' into the 'How can we help you?' box – there's a wealth of special-interest variations to choose from, including nipple shields, breast and nipple thrush, tongue-tie and more.

lcanz.org
Lactation Consultants of Australia and New Zealand can point you to a qualified private consultant. (If you have private health insurance, check to see if it's covered.)

plunket.org.nz
Plunket helpline: 0800 933 922
You can talk to a Plunket nurse about breastfeeding.

lalecheleague.org.nz
(04) 471 0690
La Leche League New Zealand provides breastfeeding help from a 'peer counsellor' and info on all areas.

breastfeeding.org.nz
The New Zealand Ministry of Health site.

Breastmilk supply & demand

Unless you have a problem, the more a baby sucks, the more milk your body will produce. This is how people are able to feed twins, and were able to become 'wet nurses' – women who fed other people's babies as well as their own.

If you stop breastfeeding for a few days, the milk will 'dry up' and you may not be able to get the flow going again, although breastfeeding organisations will help you to try: many mums have been very successful. This can be a problem easily fixed, or it may come good after trying a few things – or there may be nothing you can do, despite all your best efforts and hopes. Get lots of help so you know you've tried everything, and if you still can't continue breastfeeding, off you skip to Chapter 5, Bottle-feeding.

Women who conceive using medically assisted conception can find their body isn't geared up for maximum milk supply.

breast size   Bosom size is irrelevant to breastfeeding – even the titchiest ones are up to the task. All breasts get bigger for breastfeeding.

A wish list for easy breastfeeding

⭐ As much rest as possible.

⭐ No other commitments apart from baby, at least for the first six to eight weeks.

⭐ A healthy diet.

⭐ Extra food. (Everyone I know gets the munchies at 4 a.m. in the early days.) Soy milk, rolled-oats porridge and bananas are good.

⭐ No obsession with losing weight – you need fuel for breastfeeding, although you shouldn't be actually gaining weight. Your protein requirements are higher now than they were in pregnancy.

⭐ Lots of fluids – but not gin. Or coffee. Or too much tea.

⭐ Support from family and friends.

⭐ Perseverance: nearly everyone has early problems to overcome.

⭐ Help: even champion breastfeeders can come across temporary problems.

⭐ Luck: you need to be one of the people who can do it.

Perseverance with breastfeeding

Everyone bangs on about perseverance but perseverance itself won't get you through. You need perseverance *and* good technique (as well as no physical problems) or you will just keep persevering with something that isn't working. But it's true that, all going well, what at first feels clunky and by the book at first becomes something you can do without even thinking about it, simply with repetition and practice.

breastfeeding troubleshooting

Breastmilk supply problems

The reasons can include:

- ★ a mum not getting enough fluids and nutritious, filling food
- ★ going back to work
- ★ being run-down, tired, ill or stressed
- ★ smoking
- ★ taking some medications (always check the fine print and talk to your doctor and pharmacist about the effects a medication might have on breastfeeding)
- ★ using cabbage leaves too much to reduce engorgement, which can have an adverse effect on supply
- ★ the baby could be ready to eat stuff and want less milk – some time between 4 and 6 months babies show signs of wanting more in the food department.

'Both my babies had bottles and breast quite happily from a few weeks of age, which meant less stress all round and longer night-time sleeps and a bonding opportunity for dad. Handy hint: allocate said bonding opportunity to the 2 a.m. feed.'   MARY

Lactation cookies & other 'supply' products

Some people and companies produce special products said to 'help' or 'support' breastmilk supply. In the past, products such as 'stout' were popular. Some sellers are just trying to make money by identifying a worry and meeting a demand; others might really believe their product is special.

There is no magic ingredient that guarantees or boosts milk supply in everyone. The good base ingredients for breastmilk are: good food and enough water so you don't get thirsty, rest, genetic luck, frequent 'emptying' from your breasts so your body knows to top up if it can, and perhaps a 'breastfeeding' multivitamin (to supplement, not instead of, good food). With any vitamin supplements, make sure you get a mainstream Australian-produced brand, or are otherwise able to check sources and ingredients that are subject to national laws.

Part of the cookies' popularity is that they're portable snacks. Always check claims, and anything you're taking to boost milk supply with your medical advisers. Herbs and supplements claiming to do this can cause other problems.

The following things are *not* magic breastmilk makers and there's no scientific evidence they boost supply: commercially sold biscuits, homemade ones, fenugreek supplements, raspberry leaf tea, thistle herb tablets. 'Placenta' tablets don't increase milk supply.

more info on breastmilk supply

breastfeeding.asn.au
The Australian Breastfeeding Association has booklets for opposite problems called *Your Supply* and *Lactation Suppression*. A handful of Australian maternity hospitals have 'breastmilk banks' to help mums who can't breastfeed. You can ask about donating at your hospital.

Lactation consultants can help:

Those things on your front are bosoms

Aieee!!

Milk not coming?

Try thinking about babies, thinking about your own baby, listening to a baby cry, smelling a baby's head, and/or putting hot face washers on your breasts and drinking lots of water. My friend Kate used to let down her milk in the supermarket if she heard someone else's baby cry. 'It's my "feed the world" reflex,' she'd say.

Baby still hungry

If the baby still seems hungry after having the lot from one breast you can offer the other one, too, but remember to start with that breast the next time.

Short feeds and refusals

If your baby 'refuses' the breast or turns their head away, but otherwise seems like their normal happy self, just shut up shop and try again a bit later. Repeated breast refusal needs to be checked out quickly by your child & family health nurse or doctor. If baby only does five minutes on one breast, it may not be cause for concern: it's quite possible they've had most of the available milk volume anyway.

Baby pulls away from the breast & cries

It's perfectly normal for a baby to pull away and cry during breastfeeding. There can be a number of causes. The 'let-down' of milk could be too slow, they might be distracted by noise or other people, or they could want to poo. 'They' say babies baulk at the taste of your milk if you've had an unexpected curry, onions or garlic – there's no evidence of this. Having different tastes in breastmilk is a way babies get to know variation. If something you've eaten doesn't agree with them, babies might show distaste but are more likely to have farty problems, indigestion or diarrhoea.

The baby might have something making their mouth or throat sore. Get your GP to check for baby health problems such as thrush.

Some newborns come off the breast at the start or during a feed when they get big squirts of milk (this could be messy, so keep a cloth handy). Your supply will sort itself out and your baby will get used to it.

If your baby has a blocked nose they might find it hard to breathe while breastfeeding, in which case try to clear the nose very gently by using a – oh dear – snot sucker device from the pharmacist.

The baby could just be so hungry they're cross and confused, or they could be feeling pain caused by a windy tummy, a tooth coming or something else. Use the usual calming techniques, including burping, soothing chat, swaddling and going to a quiet, dim room for a slow, rocking cuddle. Not easy, but you're supposed to stay calm.

If your baby continues to pull away and cry, get some advice from your child & family health nurse or a lactation consultant. The Australian Breastfeeding Association has a booklet called *When Your Baby Refuses the Breast*, which has hints for encouraging a baby back to the bosom (see 'More info on breastfeeding' earlier in this chapter).

Very zingy or buzzy pain in the breast

This is a normal feeling early on in your breastfeeding career and is caused by your body doing as it should, creating a 'let-down' of the milk – and telling you you're full of goodies and ready to go. In the first days while feeding you might feel contractions of your uterus as it shrinks. If you have sharp pains in your breasts or underarm area, especially accompanied by a high temperature, you could have a blocked milk duct causing the infection mastitis – or just the flu and a few normal bosom twangs. If you have a fever, flu-like symptoms and unusual pain in your breasts or under your arms, see your doctor.

Inverted nipples

It can be difficult to coax those shy, inverted suckers out at first, but most women with 'innies' can breastfeed successfully after some initial nipple pain. Lactation consultants and breastfeeding groups have heaps of hints on how to 'pop out' your nipples so the baby can really latch on. The underarm hold is often recommended for women with inverted nipples, but many women find the underarm hold quite difficult. Nipple shields (see 'Cracked, sore nipples' above) may also help. Don't accept 'it will all be fine' if it isn't fine for you, and expect some pain when establishing feeding.

Thrush

This common fungal infection loves warm, wet areas such as babies' mouths and bots, and mums' breastfeeding nipples. It causes white spots or areas which when wiped can leave a painful red rash. Your pharmacist will have over-the-counter creams and drops, but the rash should be seen by your doctor. Rarely, thrush turns up inside the milk ducts, which causes a shooting pain between feeds (so it can't be a 'let-down' pain, if anyone tries to tell you that). Off to the doctor for an antifungal medication. Part of the romance of parenthood is hearing words like 'antifungal'.

Blocked milk ducts & mastitis

A blocked milk duct can cause a sore red mark or hard lump on a breast. If it becomes infected, which is called mastitis, it can progress to cause pain, a fever and body aches and chills, and infection in the bloodstream. If the blocked duct is still there after a whole day or you recognise mastitis symptoms, you probably need antibiotics. Don't try treating it with natural therapies alone. Homeopathic 'remedies' are useless.

Your body makes milk and sends it down tubes – called ducts – to your nipples. If milk stays too long in your breasts, when your body makes new milk the first batch has to go somewhere, and some of the milk can bulge into a blockage. Then the next new milk backs up behind it.

To help clear a blocked duct:

* Keep breastfeeding often from the affected side first, when the baby is sucking more vigorously. Express any extra if your breasts feel too full or there's a longer gap between feeds.
* Apply heat packs before a feed (warm, not hot), or aim warm shower water at the lump or redness.
* During and after feeds, massage the lump towards the nipple.
* After breastfeeding use a cool pack or cabbage leaf (from the fridge, not the freezer) to reduce inflammation.
* Vary the position of your baby during breastfeeding, as different milk ducts are drained by the way babies suck. Some swear by pointing the baby's chin at the site of the blocked milk duct to help clear it, but you can't really put a baby on the breast upside down if the lump is straight above the nipple, so it's not always possible.

If you have mastitis:

* Call your GP's office and explain why you need an immediate appointment.
* Take the antibiotics and rest; eat healthy food.
* Leave your bra off and wear a loose top if that helps the pain.

Cracked, sore nipples

These are almost always caused by the bub not being attached with a big mouthful. It will NOT help to 'toughen up' nipples by scouring or pinching them! The only real cure is to get the baby positioned in a different, mouth-fully way. This is best done with a lactation consultant, midwife or child & family health nurse watching you and advising. The most common methods of treating the pain and keeping breastfeeding going are rubbing on naturally based ointments from the chemist; using nipple shields; massaging breastmilk into the cracks and sores; briefly exposing your bosoms to sunlight (but most certainly not to sunburn); and resting your nipples from feeding for 24 hours and expressing milk for your baby instead.

Hilarious but brilliant thin, bendy plastic nipple shields, worn while the baby is breastfeeding, can help prevent and heal cracks, and can mean the difference between being able to breastfeed and not. Always get the large ones, however small your nipples are.

Painfully full breasts

This is also known as 'engorgement'. Don't worry, most new mums get this rock-hard, possible-exploding-bosomry feeling while the breasts are trying to find the right amount to keep in readiness for the baby. After a few weeks the bosoms will settle down and feel quite normal in between feeds instead of being all hard and bursty just before each one. As for a blocked milk duct, you can relieve the pressure by putting a warm face washer on your breasts and leaning over the bathroom basin to let a bit of milk dribble or squirt into it; conversely a cold (not icy) pack should calm things down. A cabbage leaf cupping each breast is also said to work wonders – many maternity hospitals keep them in the fridge (not freezer).

'Cabbages, cabbages, cabbages. Let's be honest, your chest starts to take on the appearance of a bad Renaissance painting by the time your milk starts coming in.'   TRACY-LEE

'Against advice I used nipple shields the entire time. I guess once he got used to this he wouldn't do it any other way.'   JOANNE

One breast not behaving

This is very common and often has something to do with the baby preferring one side over the other (who knows why – babies keep their secrets about this sort of thing), so your body produces less on one side. You can feed with only one breast if you absolutely have to, but get help from your child & family health nurse or doctor if the situation continues for longer than a couple of weeks.

Is my baby getting enough breastmilk?

A baby should be growing and putting on a certain amount of weight each month (depending on their individual size). This is one of the reasons you go to those regular weigh-ins at a mother-and-baby health centre. Babies shouldn't stay the same weight or go backwards between visits.

The other major sign of a problem is screaming or floppiness. A baby who is hungry will tell you by yelling. Unfortunately the baby doesn't know how to yell so specifically that you get the picture immediately. A baby who is really starving will stop yelling and become far less alert.

A young baby getting enough to drink should need six to eight nappy changes in a 24-hour period, and have regular poos.

Babies do go through hungry periods and growth spurts, when they seem to want more, and then the rate drops back a little.

Vegan breastfeeding

If you're a vegan mum who's breastfeeding, get your GP to check your vitamin B12 levels, essential for baby development. If you're low, you'll need to take a supplement.

'I'd advise perseverance. For me it was mastitis and cracked and bloodied nipples early on, but this sorted itself out in due course and the convenience of not having to prepare countless bottles countless times a night is a good trade-off.' KARINA

your breastfeeding body

What do your bosoms look like?

Breastfeeding boosies can look like a road map of Norway, with the veins pushed closer to the surface by all the milk ducts and milk in there. Large breastfeeding bosoms hopefully don't get too much larger, but expect to go up a size. That is, if you start out a 12B you might be a 14C in a maternity bra. What that will settle down to after breastfeeding is anyone's guess. Some breasts get smaller than before, some stay bigger.

Pregnancy itself makes the breasts bigger – everyone has floppier, softer, less pert and pointy-out breasts afterwards, whether they breastfeed or not. Cosmetic surgeons who want your money call this 'deformed'. Billions of partners around the world beg to differ and love you and your bits just the same. Celebrities who claim pregnancy made their breasts permanently bigger, firmer and perkier deserve only one reply: liar, liar, pants on fire. And probably bosoms as well if they get too close to a naked flame.

Nipples

Nipples have lots of holes, like a sprinkler, for feeding. The areolae appear darker (they will stay darker forever now) so it's easier for the baby to zero in when the light is dim. Your nipples will stay more prominent.

Does breastfeeding make you lose weight?

Yes. No. Depends. Some breastfeeders start to lose weight after three months, some snap back into pre-pregnancy weight within weeks, and others hold on to every extra kilo with a white-knuckle grip no matter how much they breastfeed. The best way to lose weight after a baby is slowly, with self-respect, and by doing whatever you enjoy. Most of the celebrities who lose 27 zillion kilos in the first three weeks after their baby arrives don't breastfeed. (Half of them didn't even have a pregnancy, and the other half live on lettuce ends and cigarettes.)

BLAST FROM THE PAST
'The nursing mother should cleanse her nipples before and after each feeding with boric acid solution.' – US government in the 1950s

expressing breastmilk

Mums who want to go out or go 'back' to work can 'milk' themselves with a handheld or electric breast pump that can be hired or bought from chemists and lactation consultants.

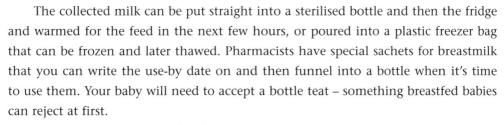

If you're going to be expressing milk a lot, get an electric pump. The hand pump can give you a very sore hand from repetitive action. The machine will make a noise (sort of a cross between a sucking noise and a vibrator, from memory). You can hook yourself up and read while it's rhythmically pulling a nipple into a soft silicone nipple shield attached to a bottle. The electric business seems quite contraptiony, but it's very simple. A lactation consultant or video instructions should be able to help you learn how to use a hand pump or an electric one. The electric pump is hands-free, although it's hard not to say 'moo'. You usually pump both breasts, one after the other, to keep them 'even', as you would if you were breastfeeding directly.

The collected milk can be put straight into a sterilised bottle and then the fridge and warmed for the feed in the next few hours, or poured into a plastic freezer bag that can be frozen and later thawed. Pharmacists have special sachets for breastmilk that you can write the use-by date on and then funnel into a bottle when it's time to use them. Your baby will need to accept a bottle teat – something breastfed babies can reject at first.

Some parents give a bottle of expressed milk a day, or in the night-time to serve the dual purpose of giving mum a rest and getting the baby used to a teat. Some breastfeeding advocates say this can cause 'nipple confusion', with the baby not wanting to go back to the breast, which can be harder to suck on. Others say they had no problem with back-and-forth.

Remember that the more you express, the more extra milk your body will make, so don't go overboard and try to fill heaps of bottles, freezer bags or sachets all at once. And take breastmilk pads with you when you go out, to pop in your bra in case you leak.

How to store breastmilk

Try to build up a store of frozen milk for emergencies – for instance, if a bottle is spilled or you can't get home in time for the next feed.

Freeze or store the breastmilk in single-breastfeed amounts to avoid waste or having to use part of a thawed, second freezer bag or sachet for a feed. The bottles or sachets you express into will have markings on the side so you'll know when to stop.

Do label the milk properly at home or at work, and let everyone who uses the freezer understand not to tamper with it. Write 'BREASTMILK' and the date you pumped it. You might also like to put a sign on the freezer saying 'Keep freezer closed as much as possible! Breastmilk inside!' if it's used by lots of people.

Storage times for breastmilk

Breastmilk should always be put in the fridge immediately after it's been expressed. Stored expressed milk will 'separate', but it's still okay – you just need to turn it upside down once or twice before giving it to your baby.

According to the Australian National Health and Medical Research Council, breastmilk can usually be kept:
- at room temperature (26 degrees Celsius or lower) for 6 to 8 hours
- in the fridge, stored in the coldest part (usually the back; 4 degrees Celsius or lower), for 72 hours
- in a freezer compartment inside the fridge for 2 weeks
- in a self-contained freezer with a separate door for 3 months
- in a deep freeze (maximum of minus 18 degrees Celsius) for 6 to 12 months.

The guidelines also say:
- if milk has been frozen then thawed at room temperature, use within 6 to 8 hours
- if milk has been frozen then thawed in the fridge, use within 24 hours
- if milk has been frozen then thawed, do not refreeze
- once a baby has started on a thawed batch of milk, any left in the bottle must be thrown away.

> 'Angus is now 6 months old and while breastfeeding we have listened to talking books from the library: *The Hunchback of Notre Dame*, a variety of the Brontë sisters' works, lots of Agatha Christie radio plays, and Robert Hughes reading *The Fatal Shore*.'   KATIE

Milk that will be used within a day is better off in the fridge than the freezer because 'the antimicrobial properties of human milk are better preserved with refrigeration', the La Leche League says.

~~~~~~~~~ **more info** on storing breastmilk ~~~~~~~~~

breastfeeding.asn.au
On the main page of the Australian Breastfeeding Association site search 'expressing and storing breastmilk'.

raisingchildren.net.au
Search 'expressing breastmilk' to find a wealth of info.

How to thaw breastmilk

- ★ You can take a batch out of the freezer and leave it in the fridge overnight to thaw.
- ★ Or you can put the frozen container into a saucepan, bowl or sink of warm water to thaw. Boiling water will curdle the milk and it will be spoiled.
- ★ Don't use the microwave to thaw or heat breastmilk: 'research suggests that microwaving changes the immunological and nutrient quality of breastmilk', according to the Australian Breastfeeding Association.
- ★ Don't boil your breastmilk. The milk should be thawed and brought gradually up to room or body temperature, and not made any hotter.

Some babies are happy to take milk at room rather than body temperature. This is handy when you're out.

breastfeeding & going back to work

If you want to work outside the home and continue breastfeeding, you'll need to be very organised. Breastfeeding support organisations (see 'More info on breastfeeding' earlier in this chapter) have lots of hints and info about how to accomplish this. Workplaces should provide a place for mothers to express milk so they can lock the door and don't have to be in a toilet.

breastfeeding twins or more

I know it sounds daunting, but lots of people do it and have milk to spare – it's amazing how most women's bodies can keep up with supplying the milk demand, although if you are an older mum you might not have the milk supply you would have had when younger.

And if you don't want to do it, here's official permission: you don't have to. It's more important that you're well rested and enjoying your babies and coping well.

See Chapter 15, Multiples, for contact details for the Australian Multiple Birth Association. The Australian Breastfeeding Association has booklets and can put you in touch with people who have done it or are doing it, as can the Multiple Birth Association; the La Leche League website has FAQs and other info about breastfeeding twins or more. (See 'More info on breastfeeding' earlier in this chapter.)

dropping breastfeeds

As your baby gets older the feeds will become further apart. The first feed to 'drop', if you can manage it, is obviously a night-time one so you can all sleep longer. When people say a baby 'slept through' they mean the baby stayed asleep from, say, a 10.30 or 11 p.m. feed until, say, 6 a.m. Eventually many mums get down to just a breastfeed in the morning, the time when their breasts are fullest, or perhaps one in the evening as a comfort before the baby goes to sleep (obviously that one can become a hard habit to break).

Chapter 12, Baby Routines, has suggested feeding schedules for babies of various ages, which could suit you. Talking at playgroup to other mums with babies the same age, or to your child & family health nurse, can also help you to establish a routine that fits your needs and your baby's and is adjustable as time goes on. Some babies sleep through as early as 6 weeks old, others at 3 or 4 months, or not until 18 months or later – which is why people seek help (see Chapter 8, Baby Sleep).

> 'After three days of not feeding I felt as though I had postnatal blues again and cried for a while – I guess my hormones were settling down. I wasn't expecting this.'
> MEI

weaning

Weaning from the breast

Everyone who breastfeeds will need to wean their baby – end breastfeeding – eventually. Many mums have the luxury of weaning gradually, others have to wean suddenly because of illness or another reason. Some babies wean themselves gradually, others stop suddenly with no warning.

Do remember that if you wean a baby from the breast before 12 months, you'll need to get them onto formula bottles, not straight onto cow's milk, or they won't be getting everything they need. Any weaning should be done after a chat to your child & family health nurse or doctor about how to replace the breastmilk.

Most mums of older babies wean the baby directly onto a cup. Some breastfed babies refuse the bottle anyway. You can buy special cups with lids ('sippy cups') at the chemist and some supermarkets so that the baby can start with a spout, then progress to a normal open cup. This way you can avoid bottles with teats altogether. Sippy cups need to be fully dismantled and sterilised often, as mould can grow in the bits you can't see.

If you know you'll be weaning onto bottles, try beforehand to get your baby used to the artificial teats – and maybe someone else feeding them – by giving a bottle of expressed milk or formula once a day.

The most common reasons mums gave me for weaning their kids were:
- the baby gave up themselves (many mothers described their reaction to this as 'horror at the feeling of rejection')
- the baby got teeth and bit a nipple (some breastfeeding encouragers say you just need to say 'no' sharply, but some babies find this simply hilarious)
- the mums reached their breastfeeding goal – most often set at 1 year
- another baby came along and they didn't want to feed two
- the mum 'wanted her body back'.

Expect to have an emotional response to weaning, which can be affected by hormonal changes. Some women feel an aching sense of loss and disappointment, others rejoice in a new-found freedom and independence. For others, it's a bittersweet mix. Everyone does it differently.

Self-weaning babies

Australian kids with parents who care have a fabulously varied and nutritious diet and access to plenty of yummy food and drinks. It's not surprising that many wean themselves. Try not to take it as a rejection, or the end of close, good times with your baby. You're still your baby's most favourite mum of all, and they shouldn't be made to feel they're doing the wrong thing when they tell you they're getting enough nutrition elsewhere and it's time to take your bosoms away. If your baby weans independently, feel exultant – you've done your job brilliantly. Self-weaning can happen as early as 8 or 9 months, although it's most common at about 1 year – but some babies will happily go on breastfeeding into their second year or longer. If you definitely want to continue after 8 or 9 months and your baby loses interest, check out some strategies to continue (see 'More info on breastfeeding' earlier in this chapter).

If you talk to your child & family health nurse or GP about your baby self-weaning, they'll be able to make sure the baby hasn't temporarily lost interest in breastmilk because they have a sore mouth or some other physical cause.

Many babies wean themselves when their mum is pregnant with the next one. This could be due to the supply, the taste or other factors being affected by the mum's different hormones.

BLAST FROM THE PAST
'Weaning time usually comes when baby's between eight and nine months old . . . weaning should be delayed until the summer is over. All milk should be brought to the boil and boiled for 10 minutes.'
– *The Women's Weekly*, 1953

'One day he just thought my breast was the funniest thing he'd ever seen and kept laughing when I tried to give it to him. I can take a hint.'   JULIE

'Unless there is a great rush, drop a daily feed every two weeks.'   CAROLINE

Fast weaning

If you have to wean immediately or relatively quickly (over four or five days) for any reason you'll probably spend a couple of days with rock-hard bosoms, wearing a one-size-too-small sports bra to 'bind' them and standing over the basin in the bathroom a couple of times a night with a warm face-washer compress, letting out just enough milk from each nipple to stop the painful pressure, but not enough to let your body think it still has to feed a baby.

The danger of fast or sudden weaning, apart from the possible shock all round, is that it leaves the breasts mightily engorged and vulnerable to blocked milk ducts and mastitis (see the 'Blocked ducts & mastitis' box earlier in this chapter. Keep an eye on yourself. To help breasts during sudden weaning:

⭐ massage any lumpy bits

⭐ use warm compresses to let a little milk leak out to relieve the pressure

⭐ use cold cabbage leaves to help relieve too-full bosoms

⭐ wear a tight bra, or a very tight shirt over a handtowel wrapped around your breasts – the pressure can help to relieve the pain, and some milk can leak into breast pads or the towel.

Semi-fast weaning

The following method, compared with fast weaning, is much kinder to you, and your bosoms and your baby. It involves dropping one feed each day every four days and replacing it with a bottle-feed.

⭐ On the first day of dropping a feed, express a little bit of milk until you feel more comfortable.

⭐ On the second day of dropping a feed express a little again if you are not comfortable enough.

⭐ On the third and fourth days don't express.

⭐ Then drop another feed, but not one on either side of the first one you dropped.

'I expressed in the shower every morning, just enough to take the pressure off. I massaged my boobs during the day to push lumps out. Sometimes I leaked a bit in my bra. It took about ten days to be really comfortable and about three weeks for the milk to totally dry up.'   FIONA

After the last breastfeed is stopped:
- ⭐ express on the first day to comfort level
- ⭐ don't express for the next 48 hours
- ⭐ express again to comfort level
- ⭐ don't express for another three days
- ⭐ express again, then don't for the next four days, and so on.

> 'I'm still breastfeeding at 20 months much to the disgust of parents/in-laws who have been encouraging me to wean since she was 9 months old.'
> NICKI

When you get down to only being able to get about 20 ml from both breasts in total, you can 'leave the rest to nature to reabsorb'.

When your baby hasn't had any formula before you wean, you're less likely to have the bottle chucked back at you if the first bottles you give them contain expressed breastmilk, or half expressed breastmilk, half formula. Gradually increase the ratio of formula until your baby's happy to have 100 per cent formula. (See Chapter 5, Bottle-feeding.)

Gradual weaning

Most mums who weaned gradually suggested dropping a daily feed – say, the middle-of-the-day one – for a week, then dropping the late-night one, then the evening one, then the morning one. This way you cut down gradually over a few weeks and the supply adjusts without your bosoms getting a fright. Many mums advised only giving the breast on request, apart from a morning or before-bed feed, then phasing those out too.

Weaning an older baby or toddler

Mums tend to agree that if you don't wean by about 1 year, either by baby's or mother's choice, it becomes much harder later as toddlers start to use the breast for comfort, often demanding a breast to suck or fondle in social situations. But of course, some mums are happy to go on and on. When you're ready, ask your child & family health nurse for tips: they've helped lots of mums when they're ready.

Sadly, breastfeeding an older child is often commented on by others who somehow believe it to be their business or that they're being 'helpful' in sharing their opinion that 'he's too old for that' or 'you should stop when they get teeth'. Find support among breastfeeding communities online if you need a bit of sisterhood. Some regard it as an act of defiance against parents and parents-in-law, who see it as a discipline or social acceptability issue. Other mums are embarrassed and wish they could find a way to stop: if that's the case for you, reach out for help.

~~~~~~~~~ **more info** on weaning ~~~~~~~~~

breastfeeding.asn.au
Search 'weaning' on the Australian Breastfeeding Association site for fact sheets.

'I loved it. Absolutely loved it. Didn't want to stop: was in danger of ending up like the woman in the comedy sketch breastfeeding her adult son in public! Gave up when he was tall enough to stand up and latch on to a boob when I was sitting down!' ROSIE

'He got a tooth and two bites later the breastfeeding stopped.' LEANNE

'I realised it would be much easier to wean them onto a cup and bypass bottles if I fed them till around 12 to 15 months. There seems to be a crucial point at which you can wean them and they'll forget about breastfeeding altogether, whereas friends who continued till the child was older, say 18 months to 2 years, found that even after they were weaned the kids still wanted to comfort-suck.' MERONA

5 BOTTLE-feeding

Bottle-fed babies thrive and grow up to be happy, healthy, smart kids. Although breastfeeding gives special benefits to babies, a bottle-fed baby also has a huge head start in life in a developed country such as Australia, with safe, nutritious formula, a good public health system, a safe water supply and access to fresh, healthy foods.

bottle-feeding is your own business

If you can't breastfeed, for whatever reason, don't feel guilty about it. It's not a failure. Many studies have shown that kids who were breastfed are statistically less likely to get a range of illnesses, but do breastfed kids 'perform' better in IQ tests? It depends on the test. When it comes to intelligence, other factors in life are crucial: genes, lifestyle and access to good medical advice and education. Breastfeeding gives babies advantages, but it's not a guarantee of anything. Many breastfed children have allergies and asthma, and many bottle-fed kids get all As in school.

If you've given breastfeeding a red-hot go and it doesn't work for you, move on. As I said in my book about pregnancy, *Up the Duff*: look at the adults around you. Can you tell who was breastfed and who wasn't? In the past, if you couldn't feed your baby with your breasts, you paid for a 'wet nurse' or your baby died. These days, you can use formula to keep your baby happy and healthy.

Good points about bottle-feeding

⭐ You know exactly how much the baby has drunk.
⭐ Someone else can feed the baby and enjoy the loving bond and eye contact.
⭐ You can sleep through the night while someone else gives the night feeds.
⭐ Babies tend to sleep longer on formula.
⭐ Your body is more your own again.

'Don't let anyone make you feel guilty if you can't breastfeed. You can still maintain closeness with your child.' WENDY

'The cuddles continued, the closeness, the holding, so it was just the menu that changed.' MAREE

'Oh my God, you feel bad enough already without people judging you as if you've made an easy, selfish decision. I am so glad my maternal & child nurse understood, and helped me.' LAUREN

Drawbacks of bottle-feeding

⭐ Formula doesn't supply the immunity to some infections and some of the other goodies that breastmilk does.

⭐ Formula's not as easy for the baby to digest.

⭐ You have to sterilise bottles and teats.

⭐ You need to be careful with quantities and measuring, and sterilising bottles.

⭐ A baby on formula does smellier poo.

⭐ Going out and travelling requires more planning.

⭐ When you're away you're dependent on local water supplies and need to find somewhere to heat up a bottle.

⭐ It costs money. Bosoms are free.

⭐ Formula is more likely than breastmilk to cause allergic reactions.

⭐ Some bottle-fed babies are more prone to constipation.

Some babies who are used to the breast reject the artificial teat when they swap over to formula, and refuse the bottle for the first several tries. This can be distressing for you but it's usually overcome by hunger and having someone other than the mum feed the baby. (The theory goes that a baby smells mum and expects breast, if that's what they're used to, but they're more likely to realise they've never had any bosom action from dad or aunty.) Some babies are really stubborn – get help from a friend who's been through it, or your nurse or doctor.

Many people who fear a lack of bonding when forced to give up breastfeeding are thrilled to find that, in the absence of stress and the faff about faulty breastfeeding, bottle-feeding is a tender time that can be spent quietly enjoying the moment, free from pain or worry. You can't do 'bonding' without time, and calm and space to enjoy each other's company.

As one mum, a doctor, says: 'Some parents need professional permission to step away from exclusive breastfeeding, and in some instances the occasional top-up with formula means the breastfeeding can go on longer in a mum who was about to stop. Find a non-judgemental doctor or child & family health nurse. Breast is best but not at all costs, when the cost is maternal and child health.'

Things you get from bottle-feeding as much as from breastfeeding

⭐ The knowledge that you're doing your best for your baby and making sure they're as healthy as possible.
⭐ The baby enjoys the sucking reflex.
⭐ Intimacy.
⭐ Bonding with your baby.
⭐ The feeling that you're sustaining your baby.

BLAST FROM THE PAST

Owing to our long summers we have formed the habit of boiling our milk . . . consequently our children rarely suffer from tuberculosis of the bones and joints, common in people who have the unclean habit of drinking raw milk.'
– *The Morning Bulletin*, Rockhampton, 1931

---

bottle-feeding equipment

Some pharmacies, online stores, baby shops and supermarkets will only carry one brand, but there are several brands to choose from.

Bottles

If your baby will need, say, six bottles a day (see the formula instructions under 'Formula milk' coming up), buy those and a couple of spares in case you lose any or get behind in the washing-up. Get all the same brand so the parts are interchangeable. Soon enough you'll be going up to 250 ml of milk in a bottle, so get the full-sized ones. Buy bottles with a wide neck as these are designed to reduce the air bubbles that can be gulped down and might cause tummy-aches.

'The more pressure I put on myself to breastfeed the worse I felt, and in the end I put my babies on formula and never looked back.' JEANETTE

Teats

Check out the age-related teats – there are ones with tiny holes for newborn babies, and ones with bigger holes that allow slow, medium and fast flows, with maximum flow for older babies. More expensive doesn't necessarily mean better. Check teats regularly to make sure they don't have bits falling off, especially after your bub gets teeth. Buy as many teats as bottles plus a few extras.

Sterilising equipment

You can buy a special electric steam steriliser – a bit like the size and shape of a rice cooker – that you can use to sterilise the bottles, tops, teats and anything else that will touch the formula. It acts like a mini-dishwasher that sits on the bench and does the lot and then drains them dry. There are also microwave sterilisers. For travelling or emergencies you can get sterilising tablets to dissolve in water, but they make things taste nasty and chloriney.

Once a baby starts putting everything in their mouth (around 6 months) or crawling around and getting a nice supply of immune-system-building germs, there's probably not much point in sterilising everything that goes into their mouth – but make sure to use very hot water and detergent to wash out all skerricks of milk from bottles and teats, as 'off' milk can cause dangerous bacteria. Check your bottle manufacturer's instructions to see if your dishwasher will sterilise the bottles (some don't get hot enough and some might melt the plastic).

Bottlebrush

There are some cunning designs of bottlebrushes designed to scrub all traces of milk out of bottles, tops and teats before they go in the steriliser.

Worries about plastic bottles and BPAs

Reports have raised questions about the safety of baby bottles that contain a polycarbonate chemical called bisphenol A, also known as BPA. Australian and New Zealand food standards authorities have investigated the claims and say there's no danger to babies and children. But many people choose 'BPA free' bottles and storage containers.

formula milk

The important thing to know is that there are plenty of people who make squerzillions of dollars out of formula, the upside of which is that they have a lot of employees working for their companies trying to make the best formula and get it as nutritionally close to breastmilk as they can, with some extras such as iron supplements. Formulas, obtained at the chemist or supermarket, usually come in a big tin with a plastic pop-off top, a measuring spoon inside and instructions. Generally the tins are divided between formulas for babies under 6 months and those for babies over 6 months.

The instructions folded inside or printed on the side of the formula tin will guide you how much you need to give a baby of a certain weight or age (weight is always a better indicator as babies range from dear wee premmies to lovely big armfuls). Your child & family health nurse can help you with the weight. Follow the instructions carefully. Your baby cannot read the tin, so they might have another idea of how much they want to drink. If you're worried they're not having enough or want too much, talk to your child & family health nurse or your doctor.

Some companies do a ready-made liquid formula. It's much more expensive and needs to be used within 24 hours of opening. Travellers or parents on the go can buy formula sachets, which can be added to ready-measured water that's boiled before you leave home then cooled in the bottles.

Most people have a night-time ritual where they sterilise the used bottles from the day in the six-bottle steamer thingie (which takes ten minutes or less) or a boiling cauldron of some description. Then they make up the bottles for the next day, plus one with just boiled water in case they need to go out and make one on site somewhere.

Which formula?

Start with a standard formula unless you have a doctor's diagnosis of an intolerance, allergy or other relevant condition with an accompanying specialised formula recommendation. Most words in formula titles such as 'gold', 'optimum', 'sleep', 'colic' or 'comfort' are just marketing. The more 'standard' it is, the more likely it will be easier to find.

Don't switch formulas because a friend recommends one or your baby seems to go 'off it' for a couple of feeds. Check with your nurse or doctor first. Choose a reputable brand from a well-regulated country that is suitable for your baby's age and weight (check the label). In most cases, regular formula is a better choice for babies than soy-based formula. If your baby has been diagnosed by a child & family health nurse or your doctor (not by you or a relative) as having an intolerance, you can use a special formula such as a lactose-free one or one based on soy or goat's milk.

'Organic' does not mean a formula is healthier, and you should check the claims: maybe only one ingredient is organic. Soy-based formula is not the same as soy milk. Ordinary formulas are based on cow's milk, but have a reduced salt content as a baby's kidneys don't cope well with salt. Formula has more iron and vitamin D than breast-milk does, but this doesn't make it better than breastmilk. All babies over 6 months old need iron in their 'solid' food or formula.

You can't use unsterilised tap water or bottled water for formula feeds.

Formula amounts

Don't try to guess formula amounts. Follow the instructions on the can and measure carefully. Recommendations can vary between brands. Too little formula powder can result in hunger and distress; too much creates an overload and the baby will feel uncomfortable and too full and will be much more likely to 'posset' – otherwise known as baby up-chucking. You are not doing more for your baby by adding more, and babies should never be put on a 'diet' of watery formula. Adding an extra spoonful or putting in less than the recommended amount can make your baby very sick in the long term.

Keep checking the label as your kid grows, because they will need more formula milk. (Your baby will probably let you know too, as they're better able to communicate with reaching and pointing). It will still be essential to get the proportions of water and powdered formula right as directed, but your baby will drink more of it – it's not like throwing a good-looking amount of Milo into a glass of milk and stirring.

'The back of the tin may not always get it right. Ninety-five per cent of the time your child will self-regulate. If you think they may be having too much or too little see your family & child health nurse or child-friendly GP.'
CHILD-FRIENDLY GP MELITA

Babies on properly prepared formula – or on breastmilk – are never too fat. They are supposed to have those lovely jubbly rolls, or not, depending on their individuality.

'I was worried to tell the nurse that I had decided to bottle-feed, and she was wonderful.' DONNA

Formula 'alternatives'

The only alternative to commercial baby formula is the first and best option: breastmilk. After a year babies tend to come off formula and start to drink cow's milk, or a substitute such as calcium-enriched soy milk if necessary, as their solid food should be providing them with most of the nutrition they need. You must use a commercial formula made especially for babies. Don't ever try to make up your own formula using cow's milk or soy milk or rice milk – or anything else. Your baby's life depends on it: babies have died when parents wanting to be 'natural' have made their own 'formulas'. After they're 6 months old you can use a bit of cow's milk when cooking for babies, and give them other dairy products such as yoghurt and cheese – but don't give milk to them as a drink until after they turn 1 year old.

Raw (unpasteurised) milk is extremely dangerous for babies and children, and in recent years in Australia and the US has caused severe stomach problems and some deaths.

Other drinks for babies

Babies under a year should not be given any 'alternative' milks to drink: no kind of high- or low-fat cow's, goat's, sheep's or soy milk, or rice, oat, bean, seed or nut 'milk' (aka juices or crushes), or dried, powdered, long-life, evaporated or condensed milk, or fruit juice. A few rare exceptions can be made by a doctor.

'I cried for a year because I "failed" [to breastfeed] and it was such a waste of energy!' JOANNE

How to make formula milk

★ Sterilise all equipment – if you are using a saucepan for this, the water needs to boil for at least five minutes.

★ Boil water for making up the formula for five minutes, then let the water cool down.

★ Wash your hands with soap and wipe them on a clean towel.

★ When the bottle or bottles are cool enough, take them out of the saucepan or steriliser using sterilised tongs.

★ Fill a sterilised bottle with the amount of freshly boiled water recommended on the formula label (for example, to the 125 ml mark).

★ Spoon in the exact amount of formula powder recommended on the label, using the measuring spoon provided. Scoop the powder up and then, without packing it down, level off the top with a sterilised knife. (You can just pour some freshly boiled water over the knife to sterilise it, if you like. You can use the same method to sterilise tongs.)

★ Fit the sterilised teat through the plastic bottle ring using the sterilised tongs, then screw this combo onto the top of the bottle, and snap on the protective see-through bottle cap.

★ Shake the bottle until the formula is well mixed.

★ Immediately put the bottle in the back of the fridge so that it cools down as quickly as possible.

★ Keep all formula powder in the fridge once a can is opened.

★ Warm a bottle just before you serve it. Prepared bottles should only be heated up once.

How to warm formula milk

Formula milk should be at body temperature when it's given to your bub – you can check by squeezing a little onto the inside of your wrist. If the milk feels cold, heat it up a little more and test again. If it's too hot, allow it to cool down and test again before giving it to your baby. The milk should be gently warmed up to the right temperature and should never be scalded, cooked or boiled.

'Make it a quiet time to cuddle and enjoy rather than have the TV blasting.'
SUE

The best way to warm formula milk is to place the whole bottle in a saucepan, bowl or sink with hot (not boiling) tap water up to about the level of the milk in the bottle if possible, and then let it sit for a few minutes. Shake the bottle gently or turn it upside down once or twice to distribute heat through the milk, without causing bubbles – or let any bubbles subside – before testing.

Not too hot

Never give your baby a bottle without testing the temperature first. It can be a good idea to occasionally give a baby a bottle that hasn't been warmed. If your bub is used to this happening now and then, it will increase the chances of them accepting a colder bottle, warmed under your arm (or a bosom!), in an emergency.

Avoid the microwave

Heating a bottle in a microwave can lead to burning-hot spots in the milk. If using a microwave is unavoidable because no hot water is available, make sure the milk is left to stand for a minute, then turn the bottle upside down ten times (rather than shaking it, as that will create air bubbles). Test the milk's temperature carefully on your wrist: the formula should feel tepid, not warm or hot.

how to bottle-feed

* Sit down comfortably, holding your baby in one arm (holding on to your bub all the time!). You can 'balance' your baby on one or two pillows to bring them up higher: this can be particularly helpful in the early weeks if you've had a caesarean.
* Support the baby's head and neck.
* Tickle the baby's cheek to make them open their mouth.
* Hold the bottle on enough of an angle so that milk always totally covers the inside of the teat to make sure the baby is sucking milk and not air.
* Let the baby suck at their own pace, resting as many times as they'd like. (Sucking is hard work when you're new at it, or if the teat has a too-small hole, or your nose is blocked and you have to breathe.)
* Immediately after the baby has had the last drop of milk, gently disengage the teat from their mouth with your little finger so they don't start sucking in air.

⭐ After a pause in the feed or at the end, put a tea towel or a cloth nappy over your shoulder and, letting it hang down your back in case of a little vomit, hold your baby upright so they are looking backwards over your covered shoulder, and rock and pat them until there's a burp (or not). The theory is to stop that 'wind' from causing pain.

Bottles & bed

Never leave a baby in bed alone with a bottle. If they're tiny it's because they might choke, and as they get older it's because it will damage their tooth enamel, which can cause pain and expensive dental treatment, including possible tooth extractions.

Transporting formula milk

Because warm milk is a breeding ground for germs, it's best when you're out or travelling to heat a bottle right before a feed rather than carry a warm one around with you like a thermos. Before you go out, take a bottle from the fridge, wrap it in ice or a cool pack from the freezer and a tea towel, put a rubber band around it (or you might want something more sophisticated, such as an insulated pouch), and place it upright in your handbag or baby bag.

In case of hunger spurts, an accident to the bottle or the original bottle being rejected (if you've already heated it once, you can't reheat it), you could take an extra bottle with just the right amount of sterilised water for one sachet of formula, and add the sachet of powder right before the feed. Because a sachet is always the right amount for a big bottle, after you've made up the formula you might have to pour some of the made-up milk out so you can offer your younger baby less than the whole 250 ml. (A few sachets could be left in the baby bag at all times, just in case.)

'Being the mother of twins I found it easy to make up the formula all at once in a jug and then pour it into individual bottles and keep them in the fridge until feedtimes.'   ASHLEY

Storing bottle formula milk

A made-up bottle can be kept in the fridge for 24 hours. if it's not used, throw it away. Most powdered formula is unsuitable for freezing as the ingredients separate and won't mix properly. It won't hurt the formula, but your baby will probably not like it. Make sure you check use-by dates as you go.

Formula 'shortages'

Some professional shopper-sellers are emptying Australian supermarket shelves of formula milk and shipping them to China (usually), where the supply is not as trusted to be free of contaminants. Some supermarkets restrict sales to a limited number of tins a day. If you've been affected, some tactics include: keeping spares in the cupboard (I know, that can be expensive); ordering home deliveries; having a standing online order; having a private arrangement with your local pharmacy or supermarket; and asking family and friends in another area to pick up a tin of 'your brand' when they see it.

troubleshooting for bottle-feeding

If you need help with bottle-feeding, see your child & family health nurse or doctor. (See also 'More info on bottle-feeding' at the end of this chapter.)

Constipation

This sometimes happens when bottle-fed babies are little or you've just made the switcheroo from breastmilk. Also check you're not putting in too much formula powder. If you're in a very warm climate or it's been unusually hot, check with your nurse first to see if they recommend a little sip of boiled, cooled water from a sterilised bottle – just 3 ml, or about half a teaspoon a day.

> 'I found my baby slept better through the night as the formula is thicker and fills tummies better.'
> SHARON

Baby poo

I'm afraid I'm about to describe poo consistency. Ready? Baby poo is generally mushy and not formed into shapes. Babies on formula should poo every one or two days. If it is formed into a shape or seems to be causing pain, you might need a different formula. See your child & family health nurse or doctor if there are other symptoms (like vomiting or not seeming perky).

Diarrhoea

This can be caused by a tiny speck of unclean milk or other agent contaminating the milk or by a common 'bug' – a virus or, more rarely, a contagious bacterium (which is the singular of bacteria, and makes me sound all doctory). If the diarrhoea is frequent over an eight-hour period, take bub to your doctor. In the meantime, keep up the milk supply. (For more on diarrhoea, look up 'gastro' in the index.)

Weaning from the bottle

As your baby gets close to 1 year old, talk to your child & family health nurse or family doctor about when's a good time to stop formula-milk feeds.

As when weaning from breast to cup, those sippy cups with a detachable spout top can be good to start your kid on, before they graduate to a cup with one or two handles. (Again, take sippy cups completely apart often and wash in very hot water and detergent. They can go mouldy inside the sealed bit you can't see.) It's also not a bad idea to teach your baby to drink from a small bottle of water or milk with a pop-up top, and then a normal cup as soon as possible. Don't take milk drinks around with you – they spoil quickly and are more likely to result in hideous cleaning-the-vomit-in-the-hot-car scenarios, not to mention very bad bus incidents.

Babies (and toddlers) shouldn't be given fruit juice, either freshly squeezed or at a juice bar, or in boxes with straws (they are also full of sugar). Juice can badly damage

'After realising that he wasn't thriving at 12 weeks I tried a bottle and he looked at me with absolute marvel that I had finally given him a decent meal. It's a shame the breastfeeding wasn't a success as I really enjoyed it and am looking forward to trying again next time.' GRACE

first teeth, and then second teeth, with its swishy acidity. And because it lacks fibre, juice isn't a healthy substitute for bits of fruit.

One of the most important gifts you can give your kid in life is so easy: always water as their main drink, and never establish the idea of a 'soft drink', fizzy drinks or juice as a treat or party drink – they contribute to acid damage and cavities in teeth. (See Chapter 36, Teeth, for more.)

more info on bottle-feeding

betterhealth.vic.gov.au
This is a Victorian government website with basic info on bottles and sterilising, and handy hints. From the main page search 'bottle-feeding'.

raisingchildren.net.au
This site is backed by the federal government Health Department. On the home page, type 'bottle-feeding' (note the hyphen) into the search box to find info and videos.

Guilt-free Bottle-feeding by Madeleine Morris with Dr Sasha Howard (Finch Publishing, Australia)
An Australian book designed to take the guilt and uncertainty out of bottle-feeding. Billed as 'helpful information and support for mums who bottle-feed', it is also useful for dads and other carers of a bottle-fed bub, with topics such as 'Why your formula-fed baby can be happy, healthy and smart', and practical info on choosing, and safely storing and using, formula.

thefullbottle.org
A compilation of personal stories to support breastfeeding and bottle-feeding parents.

'I changed from a bottle to a non-spill cup at 18 months (or I'd do it earlier) before they became emotionally attached to the bottle.' MADISON

'One night she went to sleep without her bottle, and didn't wake during the night for it, so I just stopped giving it to her and she didn't miss it.' RACHAEL

6

Nappies

Suddenly you need to deal with someone else's bottom. Here's a bracing fact. A baby can go through six to eight nappies a day (that's nearly 60 a week). An older toddler will have perhaps three to four nappy changes a day and, once toilet trained, some kids still need a nappy at night until they're 4 or older. That's approximately several million berzillion nappies per kid, until they turn 3.

how often babies wee & poo

All babies are different but generally really new babies wee a lot – often more than 24 times a day in the first 6 weeks. Most are little wees. A slightly older baby wees in larger amounts about every three hours, in between each feed, and has quite pale wee. Babies should have a poo every day or second day, and it should be messy. Some breastfed babies only poo twice or even once a week but check with your GP or child & family health nurse if you're worried. Baby poo doesn't start forming into more solid shapes (sorry) until they start eating their first foods. Formula poo is generally less messy but should still be 'unformed'. (Oh for heaven's SAKE.)

reusable versus disposable nappies

In the long run, reusable nappies are cheaper and better for the environment. Disposable nappies are way more convenient but will probably mean your baby stays in nappies a bit longer. What you do with those facts is probably more about the philosophy or lifestyle you already have – the percentage of parents who choose disposables in Australia is in the 90s.

If your philosophy suggests you prefer reusable nappies but you find yourself overwhelmed and struggling with new parenthood in general, you have the universe's permission to switch to disposables, either sometimes, or all the time. The blame for environmental pollution, and lagging biodegradable technology, is not on new parents. It's on big companies, governments and regulators.

Almost all info about nappies online is on commercial sites, and therefore probably biased. Ignore extremist unsupported nonsense on some reusable nappy websites stating that disposables 'cause asthma or infertility'. And ignore suggestions from disposable-nappy websites that their brand has more absorbent secret magic than other brands. Sometimes you're just paying for the brand name because it has already achieved some market dominance or paid for more supermarket shelf space, creating an assumption that it 'must be good' if it's so popular. Some manufacturers of disposable nappies boast that as well as their products being biodegradable, they are unbleached, and made from plant material.

'I always knew I'd use reusable nappies – I had hand-me-downs from friends.'
HUDA

reusable nappies

Entrepreneurs, many of them mums, have roared into the smaller reusables market with a selection of 'modern cloth nappies'. Many companies now offer different sizes, covers (pants) to go over the nappy with gathered leg holes and absorbent liners, and coloured patterns and catch-all swimming nappies. There are also 'biodegradable' disposable liners that take days or weeks to break down instead of years. Materials include wood pulp, cotton, bamboo and compostable materials.

The advantages of reusable nappies

★ They don't go to landfill.
★ They're cheaper in the long run.
★ If it's mostly sunny where you are, they're easy to get dry.
★ You can reuse them for other kids if they don't fall apart (the nappies, I mean – the kids will definitely fall apart sometimes, and go wah a lot).

If you choose reusable nappies you'll need:

★ A 'starter pack' or selection of nappies for newborns, which are 'one size fits all'. Ask pals for recommendations for the most sturdy and poo-containing ones. They're going to be washed a grizillion times (approximately – I made that up. But it will feel like that).

★ Any over-pants, covers or liners you choose to go with the nappies.

★ A wet-proof, smell-proof bag for hauling dirty nappies home.

For cleaning you'll need:

★ rubber gloves, a plastic spatula for scraping poo into the loo, nappy-soaking buckets with tight close-fitting lids that no kid can get off and antibacterial soaking/washing powder, or waterproof bags.

★ a washing machine with a hot function (some people choose cold if they use antibacterial powder)

★ clothesline space and fine weather, or a clothes dryer.

★ waterproof undersheets for the cot – this will save having to replace the cot mattress.

disposable nappies

'I used cloth nappies for my first baby, disposables for my second.'
BRIONY

Cheaper brands are usually not as absorbent but mid-range brands can be as good as expensive ones. Top-range ones have slimline construction, maxed-out fancy absorbency, anti-leak flanges, colour-change indicators, and cartoon-merchandising gender-mandated tie-in characters printed on them. Millions of nappies go to landfill (they take up about 3 per cent of household waste), and they take years to 'break down'. Some 'biodegradable' nappies take longer than advertised to decompose, depending on where they end up.

Toddlers in disposable nappies or 'pull-ups' are drier and more comfortable than their mates in cloth, and often don't feel as much incentive to get out of nappies and graduate to the loo.

Advantages of disposable nappies

⭐ They don't use water for cleaning.

⭐ They have absorbent compounds that draw moisture away from the skin, so they don't need to be changed quite as often.

⭐ Your bub may get less nappy rash and so sleep longer at night.

⭐ Obviously, you chuck them away instead of washing them. The nappies, not the babies.

If you choose disposable nappies you'll need:

⭐ two packets of the right-sized nappies (the size is marked on the packet); different ones are sold for boys and girls – something to do with the spouty effect of a willy (in a shopping emergency this not a big enough difference to matter)

⭐ two waterproof undersheets for the cot (one spare if the other's in the wash)

⭐ plastic bags for disposal.

~~~~~~~~~~~~ **more info** on nappies ~~~~~~~~~~~~

choice.com.au
Choice (aka the Australian Consumers' Association) is non-profit and non-partisan. On the home page, type 'nappies' into the search box to find articles on cloth v disposables, and product tests on disposables. Other independent consumer advice on 'diapers' is at **consumerreports.org** (US) and on nappies at **which.co.uk** (UK).

thankyou.co
Non-profit social enterprise brand Thankyou makes disposable and reusable nappies in all sizes. Nappy profits go to reputable maternal health projects in developing countries. If your supermarket doesn't have them, email info@thankyou.co or buy online at thankyou.co/products/little-dreamer. You can track where your money goes using a label code on your purchase.

australiannappyassociation.org.au
The member organisation for cloth nappy companies and entrepreneurs. See the blog for 'cloth nappy tips'. Click on 'members' for Aussie nappy sellers and manufacturers that have signed up to a code of ethics, and available laundry services in your area.

~~~~~~

Fresh-air bots

Whenever possible – say, when your baby is lying on a rug inside, with a towel folded underneath, or outside under a shady tree or umbrella – let their bot run free and give them a rest from the heat and padded feeling of a nappy. (See 'Sun care' in Chapter 33, Health.)

when to change a nappy

Change your baby's nappy when you smell the poo or feel the wetness. Check it every now and then, or if your bub seems uncomfortable or cries between feeds. To avoid nappy rash, change a nappy if there has been any wee or poo even if your bub is happy.

Babies can sometimes do a wee or poo straight after you've changed them: never assume they're dry because you only changed a nappy five minutes ago.

A nappy can be changed when a baby is asleep. This prevents the nappy being really wet and nasty when they wake up later.

how to change a nappy

Keep within reach of the change table or the bench or table you use for changing nappies:

- ★ new nappies
- ★ alcohol-free baby wipes or cottonwool balls, and other bot-cleaning needs such as baby lotion and tepid water
- ★ a barrier or nappy-rash cream in case of nappy rash
- ★ a lined bin or plastic bag for the rubbish
- ★ clean clothes for the bub. Sometimes the pooing or weeing escapes in explosive or mysterious ways.

Lay your bub on the change table, always keeping a hand on them. Open the dirty nappy and clean the baby's bot with a baby wipe or cottonwool balls dipped in baby lotion or tepid water. Make sure bub can't sit back into the dirty nappy. Throw away the baby wipe or cottonwool balls and put aside the soiled nappy. Pat or air-dry the bot. Smear on some barrier (nappy-rash) cream, creating a thick, visible layer, before fastening the new nappy. Deal with a pooey cloth or disposable nappy as soon as you're free to do so but don't leave the bub alone on the table while you go to the bathroom, laundry or rubbish bin.

If the baby has done a ballistic poo, give them a bath after a thorough wipe-down. You might like to have one yourself.

nappy rash & skin irritations

Nappy rash is chafing caused by wetness – wee or poo, but more usually wee. The rash can be irritated by some skin products. Change the nappy as soon as you can after it's wet. When washing your bub, use a soap substitute or soap-free liquid wash on the bot bits, and use baby wipes that contain an oil or lanolin but not alcohol. If you have reusable nappies, use sensitive-skin washing powder or liquid in the washing machine.

A barrier or nappy-rash cream will protect the baby's skin from the worst irritation caused by wee. Cheaper creams are available: they don't have to be organic or smell fancy. Nappy-rash or barrier cream has to be spread thick enough that it can be seen – if it's rubbed in, it won't make a 'barrier' between the skin and the wetness. Gently wipe off and reapply after each wash.

Ditch the talcum powder

Talcum powder can cause particles to go where they shouldn't – up little noses and vaginas – so doctors advise against using it. Its fine particles are a known risk for damage to anybody's lungs, but especially susceptible or premmie bubs. Tell grandparents, childcare workers and babysitters not to use talc.

Oh my God, it's someone else's poo

Yes, well, just make sure you don't talk about it to other people unless they ask. There's nothing worse than a parent banging on about their offspring's poo unless it's to another interested parent. Yes, even if it's green.

---

baby poo facts

⭐ Breastfed newborns can poo six to eight times in 24 hours, and this can go on for up to 3 months.

⭐ Breastfed babies can sometimes go a few days without a poo, or they might poo a couple of times a day, but bottle-fed babies tend to reliably poo at least once a day, or every two days. Babies tend to be individual poo-ers, so be more aware of a difference in your own baby's 'normal' than of comparing yours to somebody else's.

⭐ If the baby cries when pooing, the poo is hard, there's blood in the poo or there's any other poo worry, see your child & family health nurse or doctor.

⭐ Babies can look like they're straining or concentrating when they're pooing: this is normal and not a problem.

⭐ Breastfed baby poo is that classic mustardy/orangey 'baby poo' colour; surprisingly it doesn't smell too bad.

⭐ I am sorry to say that sometimes baby poo is green. All I know is it's not a problem and I'm happy to go with that.

⭐ Bottle-fed baby poo can be bigger, browner and smellier than breastfed baby poo, and constipation is common when you first switch to formula.

⭐ See your doctor if the poo is very frequent and/or watery (diarrhoea) and this goes on for longer than 24 hours. (See Chapter 33, Health, or look up 'gastro' in the index.)

⭐ Huge, stinky poo? Your child is now on solids, possibly meat.

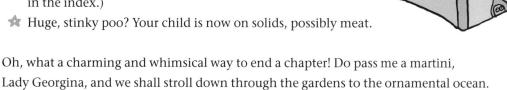

Oh, what a charming and whimsical way to end a chapter! Do pass me a martini, Lady Georgina, and we shall stroll down through the gardens to the ornamental ocean.

7

THROWING UP

Euwww. I know. When a baby throws up a bit, it's called 'posseting'. Because 'posset' referred in Elizabethan England to a warm, curdled, fermented-milk drink. I repeat, euwww. Babies most often throw up a bit straight after a feed or in the middle of it (or during burping). Parents and carers get really used to this and usually have a tea towel over one shoulder for, oh, a year or so.

why do babies throw up?

A baby usually vomits because all the bits of their digestive system aren't in full working order yet. Or because they drank too much milk at once. Repeated throwing up that seems to be a rejection of the milk can indicate an allergy to cow's milk protein and can be most tedious and mad-making for all concerned, so if you're sick of sick, see your child & family health nurse or doctor.

happy vomiting

The state of mind of some babies can best be described as la, la, la, happy, happy, enormous vomit, la, la, la, happy, happy. In other words, there is a kind of vomiting the baby doesn't mind in the least, and which poses no threat to anything but the warranty on the washing machine. It's only a problem for the baby if they're losing weight because they're vomiting up lots of milk. Most babies vomit a tiny bit when burping.

Some babies also seem to be on a hair-trigger and vomit if they choke slightly on some milk, or later on solids, or someone puts a finger too far into their mouth to check for teething action. It makes perfect sense for babies to be quick to vomit in this way, as nature is preventing them from choking.

babies who throw up a lot & cry ('reflux')

A lot of babies are diagnosed with 'reflux', meaning a vomit reflex to breastfeeds or bottle-feeds that causes acidic discomfort (like 'heartburn'). Only a tiny percentage of babies who are 'fussy' have a digestive problem, or 'reflux'. Some doctors prescribe certain medication in case it's 'reflux', and because parents are desperate to try something. But it's now accepted that 'reflux' is hardly ever the cause of crying in the first few months, and there's evidence that 'anti-acid' treatments for babies are almost always unnecessary, work no better than a placebo and could cause other health problems.

'Old' advice, such as trying to make the baby feed more slowly or for longer, or to elevate their head, is sometimes given by well-meaning friends or rels, but there's no evidence it helps. Unfortunately, this search for a 'reason' for 'fussy' babies has also resulted in some wrong diagnoses of 'allergies', often by those who shouldn't make such a diagnosis, including said relatives and friends, and some 'natural health' practitioners.

Babies who cry a lot, throw up, bend their legs and arch their back when they're upset are behaving like babies, not necessarily displaying symptoms of 'reflux'. Milk neutralises baby tummy acid for two hours after a feed, so they're not getting heartburn or irritation if they're spitting up soon after a feed. After ruling out a medical diagnosis, the best treatment for parents with fussy babies is support and help from family, friends and baby health professionals, medical advice on fiddling with feeding techniques, getting more sleep and not blaming themselves.

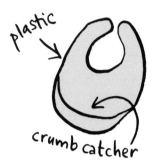

plastic
crumb catcher

There's evidence that wrapping helps settle some (not all) babies; gentle massage helps many more. Chiropractic and homeopathic 'treatments' do nothing to help, and can be dangerous.

If your baby is diagnosed with 'reflux' by a doctor, and you breastfeed, a lactation consultant can help you learn to feed with the baby held somewhat upright rather than lying down – bottle-feeders can try the upright pozzie too. A truly 'refluxing' baby will probably prefer smaller feeds, more often. Some medical treatments include a special thickened formula milk (do NOT try to make one up yourself), but there is little evidence to support this, or the use of 'anti-acid' or anti-vomit drugs, for almost all crying babies. Adult antacid treatments of any kind must not be given to babies.

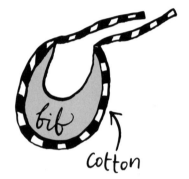

bib
Cotton

velcro
towelling

more info on 'reflux' or crying & throwing up

See your child & family health nurse or doctor, armed with the info above. Other sections of this book will be helpful, including Chapter 8, Baby Sleep; Chapter 9, Crying; and Chapter 10, Loving Your Baby.

The Discontented Little Baby Book by Pamela Douglas (University of Queensland Press)

Dr Douglas, a Queensland specialist GP and lactation consultant who runs a clinic for unsettled bubs and their demented parents, says her research shows tried-and-true techniques for the first 4 months for settling 'fussy' and crying babies who have been misdiagnosed with 'reflux'. The book contains info on breastfeeding technique, bonding, and ideas for a better night's sleep.

8

BABY SLEEP

The sleeping habits of a newborn baby are perfectly logical and sensible – unless you're an adult, in which case they're completely and utterly insane. And, luckily, temporary. Very new babies can't sleep for a long time because they have such tiny tummies, and they get hungry. They are usually 3 to 6 months old before they 'sleep through the night'.

your baby's attitude to sleep

All babies come with ready-made personalities. Some are sleepy, placid bubs, and some are alert little tykes who will always fight sleep. Your baby is probably not an exactly average sleeper – so any sleeping strategies from a parenting adviser or 'sleep school' will have to be tailored to you and your bub, usually by a bit of trial and error and over time. If a theory or method doesn't work for you, it's not your fault – or your baby's. Blame the theory and try something else.

newborn sleep facts

Newborn babies will go to sleep just about anywhere. Once they're asleep they're initially very deeply asleep, then they have peaks of being easily roused before going into deeper sleep again.

Some babies are born with a pattern of being soothed to sleep while you're walking around (amniotic bouncing) and waking up when you're still asleep. That's why lots of people end up rocking their baby in their arms, pushing a pram backwards and forwards or driving around aimlessly in a car trying to get the baby to sleep.

Newborns love to hear a heartbeat. If you don't mind them sleeping in a strap-on baby carrier, you can do other stuff – but this is not the answer if you need to sleep when they do, early on. Look up 'baby carriers' in the index; they're in Chapter 31, Kid Equipment.

it's too early for a routine

Don't try to be all stricty-pants about routines in the early days. It doesn't hurt to start heading towards some sort of pattern to make more sense of your days, as long as you know it will go out the window on the whim of a newborn, and almost always in later days if a baby or toddler is sick. (See Chapter 12, Baby Routines.)

> 'I don't want to take a "nap", goddammit. I want to SLEEEEEEEP!'
> **A NEW MOTHER**

baby sleep patterns

In the first 6 months the 'average' baby wakes two to three times a night, then between 6 months and 1 year old they wake one to two times.

Most babies older than 6 months will be having one long stretch of sleep, perhaps six to eight hours, and will be getting enough milk during the day not to need a night feed. It's good to try to get this long sleep to last until the dawn or early-morning feed. Most babies over 6 months will have a morning and afternoon nap, and then just the afternoon nap from whatever age it suits them – could be at 10 months, or 4 years old. Depends on the kid. Older baby and toddler naptimes usually range from about 45 minutes to two and a half hours. They often sleep longer when they seem to be having a growth spurt and eating more too, also known as 'on the fang'.

what a baby needs to get to sleep

Here's a reasonable checklist:
- ⭐ a quiet wind-down time
- ⭐ a feeling of comfort and safety – often a firm tucking-in or swaddling (ask your child & family health nurse how to wrap a baby for sleep). If your bub resists swaddling, make soothing noises and keep trying. But don't swaddle a baby who reeeeally seems to detest it: that's your little individual!
- ⭐ a dry bottom
- ⭐ a full tummy
- ⭐ a ritual – words, pats, music, swaddling
- ⭐ a blackout blind
- ⭐ a dim night-light.

BLAST FROM THE PAST
'The ideal [amount of sleep for a baby] is twenty hours a day, gradually reduced to sixteen by one year of age and further reduced to twelve by five years of age. Complete darkness, no rocking, and no sleeping with the mother.'
– H. Meredith, *The Modern Home Doctor*, 1935

Signs of baby tiredness

* droopy eyelids
* slow blinks
* stiff and jerky movements, like a clockwork figure
* frowning
* a long-distance blank stare
* whinginess and irritability
* yawns

When the baby is a bit older, add:

* rubbing their eyes
* pulling their earlobes or hair
* hyper-style hysteria or aggression
* looking bored with toys
* mood swings
* clingy behaviour
* going to bed and getting in (well, you can hope).

Bedtime ritual

Remember that babies can get hooked on the back pat or rub, the soothing music, the dummy, mum or dad lying down with them, or a breastfeed or bottle. This could be fine with you, or it might pose difficulties now or later.

A bedtime routine for an older baby can include a story, a catchphrase – 'Sleep tight, I love you', 'Sweet dreams, my little farter' (maybe not) – and a firm but loving exit (yours).

Products

Many baby-gear shops and hire places have a full range of bassinets, cots and baby hammocks, as well as other bouncy things for settling a baby, although not necessarily settling them to sleep (Chapter 31, Kid Equipment, has all the info). Remember that a baby who's used to sleeping only in a bouncy bed will be unsettled for a few nights when adjusting to a motionless cot.

Sleepy music

Some say any old drifty classical music will do; others insist the magical ingredient is a beat that's like the human heartbeat. Some babies like the white noise of an electric fan or other machine, but that's an expensive fix. A clock radio on low between radio stations might work, or an app. If your baby gets to associate sleep with only this noise, and they wake up and don't hear it, they'll cry. So you could be making a problem for yourself in the future – but sometimes feeling desperate means desperate action.

Night lighting

Here are some lighting hints:

⭐ Get a blackout blind that blocks sunlight and streetlights. Some parents add curtains and a pelmet to stop light coming in around the blind.

⭐ A very dim night-light in their bedroom can reassure some kids. It should be very diffuse light that isn't near their head or eye line. Plugged into a low power point can work but not if a baby or toddler wants to investigate and see if any parts are edible, or pull it out and stick a fork in the power point.

⭐ The 'old' incandescent, more orangey lightglobes signalled a moonlit atmosphere. LED lights tend to signal 'daylight' to the brain. A warmer colour – less blue in the light's spectrum – can help to indicate night-time. Fancy light globes, marketed as 'alert' or 'night-time', can be more expensive but are certainly worth a try if they add up to a successful nap or bedtime.

⭐ Any lit phone or device screen in the room also says 'daytime' to our lizard brains (that's why the night-time screen on some devices looks orangey – it still says 'light', but not as brightly). Start now with screen rules and you'll set good habits for your kid's whole childhood. No looking at lit screens two hours before bedtime is the recommendation for kids and adults.

making a safe sleeping place

See the Anti-SIDS Checklist in Chapter 1, Your New Baby. Subject to safety considerations, your baby's bed in the early days can be a bassinet, a specially designed carrycot that snaps out of a pram, or a cot.

Okay, let's get the stern, rulesy bits out of the way: babies must never be left alone in a car, even if they're sleeping peacefully, in case of overheating or theft. Babies in a locked car can overheat and die in a matter of minutes even on a seemingly mild day (more on this in Chapter 32, Safety & Injuries). Apart from this, a baby in a car seat can droop their head too far forward – for most babies this won't matter, but a very few can cut off their air supply and will not be able to revive.

Always put the baby somewhere safe for naps, such as their own cot or bassinet: it will be familiar and they can resettle themselves if they wake up, rather than be startled, and if you fall asleep or are somewhere else you won't have to worry about them being at risk.

In case they wriggle into a suffocating position, babies should never be put to sleep and then left alone out of sight in a pram, a stroller, a baby capsule or a baby seat (either in the car outside or brought inside), or on a couch or a chair. Never fall asleep with a baby on a couch or other surface as this is known to increase the risk of SIDS (see the 'Co-sleeping or sleeping "apart"' section coming up).

It's dangerous to leave a baby sleeping unsupervised in an adult-sized bed: they can become tangled in adult bedding, wedged between the bed and the wall, or caught under a pillow, and they can also roll out and fall at a very early age.

All makeshift sleeping arrangements are dangerous. Don't make adjustments to or use prams, beds or devices not designed for babies to actually sleep the night in. Follow construction and operating instructions exactly.

Mattresses for babies

Many pillows and mattresses now have underlays or toppers that mould with pressure and body heat to the shape of the user, usually called 'memory foam'. These are dangerous for babies as they can restrict breathing – a baby must *never* sleep on one. Keep this in mind for naps at friends' houses, or when travelling. Any mattress for a baby should be custom-designed to exactly fit its safety-rated crib or cot. Most new mattresses have been treated with chemicals or insecticides: they should be taken out of delivery plastic and other coverings and aired in a safe place before use until any odours and 'outgassings' have disappeared. Outside in the sun is ideal if you can manage it. Wash any removable covers and dry them in sunshine if you can.

Cot safety requirements

It's best to buy a cot to the Australian standard (see Chapter 31, Kid Equipment, for more). A cot needs to have the bars spaced at the right intervals – not so far apart that a baby can be trapped between them. It should have a tight-fitting mattress. If possible get a new mattress made from cotton or another material that 'breathes', rather than hard foam. Advice from SIDS researchers is that a cot should only have a fitted cotton bottom sheet, and no doona. For the latest on safe baby wrapping and sleeping-bag suits see 'More info on a safe sleeping place' coming up.

- ⭐ It's better to heat the room a little bit in winter if you can afford it, rather than have extra bedding in with the baby.
- ⭐ Cot 'bumpers' restrict the flow of air in and around a cot, and babies can get their heads stuck underneath them and suffocate.
- ⭐ Any waterproof undersheet should be a plastic-backed fitted cotton one so the baby doesn't get too hot.
- ⭐ Babies don't need pillows and they're not recommended until the child is at least 2 years old. If you use pillows and other foofery to 'dress' the cot and make it look nice, take it all out before a small baby goes down to sleep.
- ⭐ Fluffy and stuffed toys should be out of the cot at sleep times.

～～～ more info on a safe sleeping place ～～～

rednose.com.au
The national website of Red Nose (formerly SIDS and Kids) will take you to your local branch of this charity that has used research and awareness to bring down the rate of sudden infant deaths. Find apps and other info on safe sleeping positions and sleepwear, and lots of answers to FAQs.

co-sleeping or sleeping 'apart'

In an effort to snatch as much sleep as possible, parents often choose to sleep with their baby in their bed so they don't have to get up to crying or for breastfeeding (unless they have to change nappies). For many years this has been recommended as part of the 'attachment parenting' philosophy. Unfortunately, new evidence has shown that this is not the safest choice for your baby. To significantly lower the risk of sudden infant death syndrome, it's better to have your baby in the same room, but in their own bed right next to yours.

The latest advice from the premier research and advice organisation Red Nose is that room-sharing with a baby is good for the first 6 to 12 months (say, in a cot next to your bed), but recommends against sleeping in the same bed with any baby, even after the first year. (For more on SIDS, see the index.)

Red Nose especially recommends against co-sleeping ('sharing a sleep surface', as they put it) if your bub is a premmie or very small for its age, and if a co-sleeper is a smoker, or is above a 'recommended' weight, or has used alcohol or drugs before falling asleep. The organisation warns that sleeping with a baby on a couch carries a very high risk of 'infant death' (suffocation) and sleeping accidents (such as falls).

Despite these new recommendations, several websites and co-sleeping advocates will still recommend co-sleeping, some because they haven't caught up with the latest research, others because they won't be swayed from what they think is best.

~~~~~~~~~~ **more info** on co-sleeping ~~~~~~~~~~

rednose.com.au
This is always the go-to source for the latest research and evidence-based info on baby sleeping and related issues such as co-sleeping.

sleeping solutions

Training bub to sleep longer

Some babies, especially ones who sleep next to their mum, can train themselves to take little bits of milk, often, at the all-night milk bar lying next to them, which means that instead of feeding every few hours, the mum has to wake up every hour or so for snack time. And some babies are picked up whenever they make a little cry or snuffle during the night, which is quite normal behaviour for babies. Instead, wait and see if they settle themselves, and always try to soothe them back to Dreamland with a soft word or ritual pat. Of course if it's the usual time for a feed, they probably won't settle.

Even with their baby in the next room, some parents have to wear earplugs to cut out the little snuffles, grunts, sighs and snorky noises in the night. If the baby is really awake and needing attention, the noise is quite different – and louder. And even through the earplugs most mums hear the sounds first and are out the door before the dad is aware of the slightest noise. Here's a brilliant suggestion I heard: reverse the baby monitor, if you have one, so the baby can hear their parents snoring or chatting (but perhaps not doing erotic folk-dancing practice). Or put the baby monitor in the bottom of a wheelie bin, put rubbish on top, take your rubbish to the kerb, and wave bye-bye, as one mum suggests. No electronic surveillance means you can't hear the little grunts and snuffles, but you'll hear them yell out if they really want you.

Working out a pattern for night & day

Help your baby understand daytime and night-time. Night-time feeds should be a sleepy, quiet, darkened affair, with no play and straight back to sleep. Daytime feeds can be animated and chatty, wherever you fancy, with a play afterwards. See Chapter 12, Baby Routines, if you want to try starting a routine for you and your baby that builds in sleep times.

When to wake a sleeping baby

Generally it's a good rule not to wake a sleeping bub. If the baby's asleep, they probably want to be. Certainly never wake a sleeping baby at 2 a.m. for their usual feed – this could be the night they drop it! Yes, but what if it's the 11 p.m. feed they sleep through? Then baby may wake you at 12.30 a.m. for a feed. So I reckon if the baby is asleep for the 11 p.m. feed, wake them gently just enough to be able to feed them, so you can get a few hours' unbroken sleep. But I'll deny I ever wrote that, if it all goes wrong.

What if the baby is asleep in the car and you have to go inside? Take the baby. Never, ever leave the baby asleep in the car.

What if you need to move your baby from pram or baby car seat to cot so they can keep sleeping and you can get on with something somewhere else? Put the baby in the cot every time, but try to be so gentle that their sleep isn't much disturbed. Good luck.

Getting more sleep yourself

Sleep when the baby does: if you need sleep, forget housework and turn your phone off and disconnect any landlines. Make a sign to put on your front door. Of course you need sleep. You have a baby. (Unless you have a 24-hour live-in nanny and a weekend-nanny and go to the hairdresser every day, in which case you won't be reading this book because you'll be getting your 24-hour live-in nanny to read it while you have Tumultuous Mauve painted on your fingernails by someone whose name you don't know.)

You may find yourself getting hysterical when your baby is just a few days old, and sobbing that there's no point going to sleep if you only have to wake up in two to three hours for another feed.

If you have a partner or flatmate, get them to do half, or some, of the night feeds (using expressed breastmilk or formula). Also get them to settle the baby to sleep sometimes so the baby doesn't demand you every time.

I know it seems obvious, but there are some things you can do or not do to get a better sleep. If you sleep better with your baby right next to the bed, do that; if you sleep more deeply with them elsewhere, do that. Avoid stimulants such as coffee, tea and cigarettes. Drink warm milk with honey in it, have your own rituals such as a warm bath, make your room dark, make rules about other people being quiet if you need to, wear earplugs. Taking sleeping tablets is *not* a good idea for the same reason that you must not sleep with your baby if you're drunk or high, and because drugs will go through to your milk if you're breastfeeding.

You could find you need to readjust to sleeping through the night once your baby decides to!

Scheduling daytime naps

Some people say day sleep times shouldn't be unduly quiet so the baby learns to sleep through any noise. Really it depends on the baby. At certain times in their sleep babies can sleep through anything loud, but a sudden noise such as a slammed door will always wake them at other times. As mentioned, you can put a sign on the front door asking people not to ring the doorbell or knock.

Make people call beforehand to get the go-ahead for a visit. The result will be that the baby sleeps as long as possible, and so do you.

'sleeping through'

Say the baby finally drops a feed between 12 a.m. and dawn so they sleep through from an hour or so before midnight to 6 or so in the morning, to take a random example. Be aware that they might do this once and then not again for days or weeks, and they might do it earlier or later than other babies. The first sleep-through is often a big surprise to the parents, especially a breastfeeding mum with explodey-feeling bosoms. If the baby is old enough to be getting all the milk they need during the day, sleeping through can be encouraged by having a non-lactating person go in to the baby to try to settle them without a feed. If the baby goes back to sleep without minding, it can herald the start of sleeping through. Your child & family health nurse can help you with advice, and see Chapter 12, Baby Routines.

helping a baby to go to sleep alone

Your baby will adjust to whatever bedtime or naptime ritual you decide to use. Many people develop one accidentally, although this might not end up being the most useful one for them; for example, exhausted mum breastfeeds, then baby and mum flake out and so baby only learns to go to sleep when mum is there.

When babies are little – before the age of 6 months – you always need to go in to comfort them if they cry or call out, but it is good to be able to comfort a baby back to sleep without picking them up (of course, they might have done a particularly irritating poo and need to be changed).

See Chapter 12, Baby Routines, for how to build in a pattern to the days so babies start to understand when it's sleep time – after a feed and a play, the familiar bedroom is darkened, and the baby 'goes down' when they're tired.

The usually recommended way to help a baby get to sleep on their own is some sort of variation on the following.

- ★ Have some wind-down time.
- ★ Wrap your baby firmly, but not too tightly.
- ★ Place your baby to sleep on their back.
- ★ Give them a dummy if you want to.
- ★ Pat their tum gently, with a slow rhythm, a few times until they're sleepy.
- ★ Leave the room before they actually fall asleep.

You can train your baby over time to understand that they are being put to sleep by themselves (a book read together in their bed; a darkened, familiar room; a comforting back rub or gentle pat; and the same catchphrase, such as 'Nightie-night, possum') but that you'll return reassuringly if they need you, so that they understand they're not being abandoned. The idea is to get the baby to realise that it's safe and fine to go to sleep by themselves in their own bed, without you rocking the side of the cot forever or always breastfeeding them to sleep – or worse, putting them in the car and driving aimlessly because they're rocked to sleep. It will go a long way to setting up good habits that you'll be grateful for later.

The key is that after comforting rituals, the baby is left in the room calm, happy, safe, hopefully sleepy, but still awake, and learns how to go to sleep independently without your obvious presence so that when they wake during the night, which is totally normal, and don't need a feed, they can go to sleep again without your help.

Yes, I know it sounds like an impossible dream when you're in the mad, sleep-deprived early weeks. It isn't, but I fully admit I was in a tizz and to get the hang of it had to go to a day-visit sleep school when my baby was 4 months old, and then we needed to refer to a book to practise. After we learnt some patting and settling techniques, our baby could go to sleep herself, knowing that if there was anything wrong she could yell and someone would respond to her.

Think of it as you and your baby learning together. And if another way suits you, then for heaven's sake use that. It's just that most people eventually don't want to have to rock their baby to sleep or breastfeed every time, or lie down with their toddler until they're asleep and then again if they wake up during the night.

Sleep school

If you feel you need one, ask your child & family health nurse, doctor or maternity hospital about sleep schools, which are run as daily classes or live-in programs at hospitals and independent health centres. Find out if you need a referral from your doctor, if your options include public and private medical services, and what your out-of-pocket expenses might be. You can also call one of the parent services, which run classes or can give phone advice. For parent helplines and services see Chapter 2, Your Help Team.

Baby snoring & odd breathing

A little gentle snore during sleep is normal if a baby has a blocked nose or the sniffles. But if you notice odd snoring or sounds during your baby's sleep that worry you, see your doctor.

Some babies have 'periodic breathing', where they don't breathe in or out for a few seconds. That's normal and nothing to worry about. It is very rare, but if your baby stops breathing for more than twenty seconds, asleep or awake, this is *not* normal. After twenty seconds a baby's tongue and lips will take on a bluish tinge. Gently try to wake your baby. If they don't revive, start CPR and ring the ambulance on 000 (in NZ it's 111) and they'll tell you what to do.

Even if your baby starts breathing again after such an episode, go straight to the emergency department of your nearest hospital or call an ambulance.

'controlled crying', 'controlled comforting', 'learning to sleep', or 'sleep training'

Most babies will cry when you're trying to get them to go to sleep by themselves, or be used to having a dummy or being fed to sleep or rocked. There are various names for a structured way of training a baby more than 6 months old to go to sleep, and also how to calmly get back to sleep on their own during the night without being upset: controlled crying, controlled comforting, learning to sleep and sleep training.

Despite the various names, these techniques are the same thing, only 'controlled crying' sounds a bit scary, and 'controlled comforting' is what you want it to feel like, and 'learning to sleep' sounds even better. Sometimes people call it 'baby self-settling' or 'independent sleeping'. These techniques are no good until your baby is more than 6 months old: talk about it with your child & family health nurse if you're unsure when or how to begin. Before 6 months old, babies wake up because they need a feed. Not all babies at 6 months old can sleep six to eight hours straight and learn to resettle themselves.

With this technique, some time is spent letting the baby cry (but not become very distressed) and some is spent comforting them. It is *not* 'letting your baby cry itself to sleep'. It's a program of repeated visits and reassurances, with strategic withdrawal times. The aim is to slowly change the sleeping habits of your baby if they are disrupting family life or driving you bonkers.

The approach is to reassure the child that it's time to go to sleep, institute the ritual and then retire to the other end of the house while they 'grizzle' or even yell at you. You don't go back for little whimpers. For crying – depending on whose method you follow – you wait, say, 30 seconds, then go in and reassure your bub again and resettle them. You wait a minute, or until the baby is settled (not asleep). The next time you stay out for one minute, then progressively make the margin wider – but never longer than five to ten minutes. A baby left to cry for a long time will wind up being really upset, and of course nobody wants that.

While practising this routine, parents will often sit in the hall, feeling mean and stressed that they're not immediately going to their baby, looking at their watch, crying themselves, and taking turns not to let the other one in until the right number of minutes has elapsed. Anyone trying it needs a few clear nights of normal family life in which to do it, with a baby who's not sick. And maybe a friend who isn't as sleep deprived and addled as you, to stay for the first hours on the first nights to be a reassuring presence for you, and help strengthen your resolve.

Often the attitude of the baby is 'Well, all right, I can see the way this is going. I might as well go to sleep.'

In five to seven days the controlled comforting technique works for almost every-one (about 80 per cent) who can tough it out. For some, it's just two or three nights. For the first few nights the going-in-and-out and sporadic crying can last two hours. It's short-term pain for long-term gain, though it doesn't feel short-term when you're in it. Some parents need a method that suits their baby's personality more, and this can include being in the room as a comforting presence but not picking the baby up for seven nights. Some babies think this is reassuring, and others get very cross indeed. (See the 'camping out' method, coming up.)

BLAST FROM THE PAST

'Until they are two, children are required to sleep the whole of the night.
And also several hours in the morning and again in the afternoon . . .
until aged 4 or 5 the full half of its existence should be allotted to sleep.
The best mattress for a baby should be stuffed with hair or chaff . . .
the bed should be midway between ceiling and floor for the best air.'
– *The Handbook for Wives and Mothers of the Working Classes*,
Christian Women's Association, 1873

Sleep training

Baby sleep researchers report no rise in stress hormones in the baby and mother during the technique or a year later. A big majority of mothers in a large study reported a better relationship, or the same relationship, with their baby afterwards. None reported a worse outcome. But of course that doesn't mean it appeals to everyone, or will immediately work for everyone.

If controlled comforting doesn't work for you, or you don't fancy the idea but are going demented, then talk to your child & family health nurse. Many people go through controlled comforting and achieve the results they need when they are desperately sleep deprived, and attend a sleep school or parenting centre as a last resort so they have trained nursing staff made of sterner stuff, and who can do the settling techniques while the parent isn't in the room.

Some people prefer the attachment-parenting ways – always picking up your baby if they are crying, and perhaps sleeping in the same room. That is fine as a matter of preference, but it isn't true, as some say, that controlled comforting causes harm or mental health problems in your baby. For many people, their lack of sleep is causing them to be dangerously stressed, which is far more likely to cause parents to react in ways that are stressful for a baby and for a family in general.

~~~~~ **more info** on 'controlled crying', ~~~~~
'controlled comforting', 'learning to sleep'
or 'sleep training'

raisingchildren.net.au
Search 'controlled comforting' for a how-to guide with lots of tips.

'If we had not done controlled crying – it took three nights and then we all slept through after that – I truly believe I would have lost my mind.' CARRIE

'camping out' method

This is the halfway method, in which instead of leaving the darkened bedroom, you 'camp out', sitting on a chair or on a camp bed next your baby's bed so you can pat them to sleep. Soothing voice, and no eye contact. You stay there until your baby falls asleep this way, for three nights, then move your spot a bit further away, and stay still (you can listen to music or a podcast in headphones!) until your baby goes to sleep. Three nights of that then move a little further away, and so on. If your baby wakes in the night, you stay in the spot you're up to until they fall asleep again. Within one to two weeks you can remove yourself from the room.

No method works for everyone. So if this doesn't work for you, see your child & family health nurse.

~~~~~~~~~~~~~~~ **more info** on 'camping out' ~~~~~~~~~~~~~~~

raisingchildren.net.au
For instructions search 'camping out' on the home page of this government Health Department-backed site.

~~~~~~

'Make sure they're full and if not settled after having a dry nappy pat them on the bottom until their eyes start to droop, and repeat if they stir.'   ANITA

'For me a baby's sleep routine was when they wanted sleep. The old tired signs of rubbing eyes, yawning and generally getting grumpy work if you can catch them at the right time. But if all else fails be a sucker mum like I was and rock your baby to sleep: you never know, you might like it . . . if your child needs a cuddle or a story or just someone to be there then so be it. Enjoy that. They will only be little for a small amount of time.'   CHERRIE

more info on baby sleep

raisingchildren.net.au
On this federal Health Department–backed website, click on 'Babies' then 'Sleep' for your buffet of choices.

The Tresillian Sleep Book
by the NSW Tresillian parent support organisation, ABC Books.
A comprehensive and kind book by specialist child & family nurses. Covers the first 5 years, providing tested methods for routines, recognising sleep "cues", settling techniques, & tips on how to re-establishing good habits. With real parent stories.

www.mcri.edu.au/infant sleep
Infant Sleep eLearning Program
A program based on years of expert research on how to get kids more than 6 months old to settle for sleep. It's the same online training as child & family health nurses and doctors do as part of their training to be accredited with an Infant Sleep Certificate by the Murdoch Children's Research Institute.

'Attachment'-based books & websites
Some attachment-parenting advice advocates co-sleeping in the same bed, which is not recommended by Red Nose, the charity with the best medical info on sleeping advice to avoid sudden infant death syndrome. See **rednose.com.au**

Sleeping Like a Baby
by Pinky McKay (Penguin, Australia)
Kindly tips and ideas for all things sleep related, up to the toddler years.

'Giving anyone a cuddle helps to calm them . . . if cuddling your baby to sleep makes you feel better and less distressed go ahead – cuddle away without feeling guilty about the future.'   SUSIE

9

CRYING

The baby is not crying because you are a bad mother, or an incompetent dad, or a lousy babysitter.

The baby is crying because the baby is a baby.

the truth about crying

I think one of the biggest shocks I ever had in my life was finding out it's totally normal for newborn babies to cry for two to three hours a day for the first weeks and months. In other words: a baby will cry several times – adding up to hours a day – no matter who its parent is, or what the parent does.

Newborn babies have only a few ways to communicate: the most useful one for them is crying. You might like to regard this as a design fault. Babies are used to being in the womb, minding their own business and hanging out at the Umbilical Cord Cafe, when suddenly they're thrust into a world full of touch, taste, smell, sound and light, with a digestive system that has never had to work this way before. No wonder they burst into tears every now and then, especially at the end of the day (I mean, who doesn't?).

If a physical problem is ruled out, and your baby's getting enough to eat and its nappy changed when it's wet, then your baby's temperament – the personality they came with – is the biggest factor affecting whether they cry a lot. Doesn't mean your kid is a sook, or weak, or 'naughty'. It just means they're reacting to all the new feelings of being a baby. Many parents say their baby cried a lot but grew into a really happy kid. It has nothing to do with your skills or aptitude as a parent. You can learn tricks that will help. Do everything you can, but treat yourself with special kindness. Don't try to do it alone: traditionally babies have been brought up in gigantic extended family situations, with lots of help and a collective approach. Besides, when you're sleep deprived, you sometimes can't see solutions, and that isn't your fault. Above all, take it day by day. This hard time will end.

BLAST FROM THE PAST
'A young baby should cry from a quarter to half an hour a day . . .
it's good for the lungs.' – *Nestlé's Book for Mothers*, 1917

'My doc had a helpful tip when we were sleep training:
"No baby has ever died from crying".' LURLEEN

things a baby's cry might mean

You'll get to know each other over time. Don't get stressed out trying to interpret your baby's cries. It isn't a secret language. Paediatricians don't always know why a baby is crying. Very experienced child & family health nurses can be at a loss. In the first few weeks and months, a baby's cry can sound the same, yet mean:

⭐ I'm hungry
⭐ I'm too hot
⭐ there's a weird feeling in my nappy
⭐ I'm all floppy and I used to be snug
⭐ that was a scary noise
⭐ I'm grizzly and a bit cranky
⭐ I am bloody furious
⭐ is everything okay?
⭐ stop waking me and poking me and picking me up
⭐ if that's my grandmother, let me out of here
⭐ my sister stood on me when you were out of the room
⭐ I'm tired but I don't know what tired means
⭐ I'm tired and I don't know how to go to sleep
⭐ I'm not used to doing this so I don't like it
⭐ I'm scared in the bath because it's floaty but I'm not scrunched up
⭐ something squishy is coming out of my bottom
⭐ I need a cuddle
⭐ I was just checking one of my people was nearby
⭐ I'm tired, don't pick me up
⭐ pick me up!
⭐ I don't know why I'm crying.

Recognising different cries

Baby development expert Lise Eliot says a hungry cry is likely to be 'rhythmic and repetitive', an angry cry is 'loud and prolonged' and a cry of pain is 'sudden in onset, punctuated by breaks of breath holding'. A parenting expert once told me: 'Most cries sound the same, but the behaviour gets more predictable.'

Crying peaks

'They' say there's a crying peak at about 6 weeks old, and some of these 'theys' say there's another one at 8 weeks. If your baby suddenly seems to cry a lot, and you've ruled out a hidden illness, it's quite possibly just a phase, like a mysterious growth spurt that makes them need more milk more often than usual. Being with a baby is about constant little shuffle readjustments.

Babies who cry a lot usually cry even more towards the end of the day, and even some otherwise placid babies do too. This is what's known as 'arsenic hour'. It can really bring everyone to the end of their tether and often coincides with the partner who works outside the home coming back to scenes of utter despair. I sometimes wonder if it's babies just being fed up with all this new world business by late in the day: a sensory and neurological overload. I think I'd cry too.

Come to think of it, I did cry every day during arsenic hour for the first couple of weeks: big, tired tears – not hysterical, just quiet, exhausted ones.

Things that might help stop a baby crying

There are lots of things you can try.

* **Food:** is a feed due? Or could the baby be needing extra? (Careful: they might not be hungry, in which case only time and comforting will help! I don't know how you tell the difference either – unfortunately it's trial and error, which takes time.) If crying is because of tummy pain, then a feed won't help.

* **Sleep:** is the baby overtired and needing help to go to sleep?

* **A nappy change:** the baby might have a wet or pooey bot.

* **Security:** the baby, if under 4 months, might like to be wrapped up snugly to remind them of womb living.

* **Soothing:** the baby might just need a pat, a cuddle or a dummy.

* **Closeness:** the baby might want to be carried around so that they can hear a heartbeat like the one that ticked away near the womb – a strap-on baby carrier, or older children, can save your arms.

* **A quiet time:** the baby might be in sensory overload and need to be away from visitors and busy places.

* **Quiet music:** Lullaby compilations are available wherever you buy or stream music.

* **Someone else:** everything may have gone into a vicious circle, with you being tense and the baby being tense – after you've tried for hours, a baby can be quite suddenly comforted by someone else (don't feel too demoralised by this, it happens to us all!).

* **A big burp:** this can relieve a feeling of tummy pressure. Hold the baby upright and gently pat or rub their back. Prevent the baby from swallowing air when they feed, which is especially likely if you're bottle-feeding: hold the bottle so the milk, not air, covers the inside of the teat as the baby sucks.

* **A medical check:** the baby could have a medical problem – have them checked out by your local doctor or a paediatrician.

* **A gentle massage with an edible oil:** most people avoid nut oils in case of allergy (look up 'baby massage' in the index).

* **A lullaby:** your voice, no matter how untuneful, is very soothing to your baby. You can even read an adult book aloud.

More things that might help stop a baby crying

* **A warm bath:** babies often enjoy a deep one with a hands-on adult.
* **Rocking:** this can take the form of a trip in the car, jiggling the cot, or wheeling the pram back and forth.
* **A comfy temperature:** a room somewhere between 18 and 20 degrees Celsius will be fine. This doesn't mean you need to strictly maintain a 'perfect' temperature in your place. After all, millions of babies are brought up in the tropics and the Arctic Circle. (Actually I don't know how many babies live in the Arctic Circle. Possibly I mean moose.)
* **Time in a pram:** this might even just be being wheeled back and forth, although fresh air is a bonus for both of you.
* **Fewer clothes:** a lot of Australian babies are overdressed. For little babies a general rule is one more layer of clothes than you need yourself as you move about.
* **A daily routine:** after the first weeks, naps at customary times can prevent a baby from being regularly overtired (see Chapter 12, Baby Routines).
* **Strategies:** you will build up some that work for you. It's a matter of trial and error.

pick up or put down?

Some people reckon babies should be picked up straight away if they cry because otherwise they get distressed, and then it's harder to settle them again. Others say to leave babies to cry for a minute or two. One thing to keep in mind is to try soothing methods other than picking up every time (singing, rocking, a comforting voice, a rhythmic pat), as your baby may just need to know you're there so they can go to sleep happily. If you pick them up every time, they can get very irritable because they're not getting a chance to sleep or lie about. Most young babies will be happy being in a baby carrier close to one of their people.

Newborn babies need to sleep a lot. Respect this, and don't try to keep them up all day entertaining visitors, no matter what the visitors want. You're the one who'll end up with the overtired, blubbering flummery bub at the end of the day.

crying & sleeping

Crying problems and sleeping problems are almost always tightly linked, so have a look at Chapter 8, Baby Sleep, and don't hesitate to get professional help to set up a sleep routine or learn settling techniques.

You aren't what you eat

If you're breastfeeding, people might tell you to take note of any foods you've eaten that seem to cause windy problems that lead to more crying, but studies show no evidence of this for usual suspects, such as garlic and onions. All babies fart independently of what makes their mother fart. Cutting out foods suddenly, either for yourself when breastfeeding, or for an older baby starting to eat solid food, isn't likely to do any good unless there is a medical diagnosis of an intolerance or allergy, and it could do some harm (see more in the allergies section in Chapter 30, Family Food).

babies who cry for hours ('colic')

'Colic', 'reflux', 'fussy' and even 'difficult' used to be common diagnoses or 'labels' for a crying baby. Once a physical problem such as a feeding difficulty has been ruled out by a doctor, best results are now believed to come from settling techniques for the bub and more rest and baby-care help for you.

In the past, 'colic' was usually blamed on a digestive problem – a pain in the tummy that causes a baby to be upset and cry. 'Colic' is a less common diagnosis these days and crying babies are more likely to be labelled 'unsettled': many babies cry for more than an hour a day in the first weeks and months and it isn't because of digestion, it's because they're a baby. Which doesn't make it any easier to live with, I know.

Diagnosing 'reflux' (a crying baby who vomits) is now also less common. There's more on this in Chapter 7, Throwing Up.

Pharmacy formulas or anti-wind 'treatments' are unhelpful to most crying babies, and similar herbal preparations are not safe for babies.

Whatever it's called, a constantly crying baby is hard to cope with and can make you feel demented, so get help.

cuddle me!

leave me alone
(no, don't)
(oh, I don't know)

I'm cross

shall I cry?

I'm not tired

feed me!

ouch!

I can't remember
why I'm crying

I couldn't be
more shocked

where's my teddy?

...Sounds like...

I saw a great
big DOG

'fussy' babies

If you've checked out all the possible causes and your baby still cries, keep in mind that you've done everything you can – everything a good parent could do. Your baby might just be a 'crier', also known as a 'difficult' baby. This doesn't mean that your baby is naughty or trying to be difficult. A 'difficult' baby is not a sook: they very often turn into happy kids and robust adults. You'll need some longer-term strategies to cope in the next weeks or months – the most important being to rustle up as much help and babysitting as possible to give yourself breaks.

Getting some help with a crying baby

I used to ring up for professional help quite a bit when I felt bamboozled – no doubt I would have been less bamboozled if I could have had more sleep. I'm sure sometimes I sounded completely mad: luckily they're used to it, and nobody ever minded a bit. And there's no such thing as a silly question when you're learning to be a parent. Others have found their mothers group or playgroup very useful for sharing stories and strategies (and providing babysitting swapsies).

If you can afford it or wangle it, get some childcare, either from a professional or a friend or relative, so you know there's respite coming. Even if someone calls in every evening or afternoon for a while and holds the baby so that you get some things done or go for a walk or even get some sleep (try a roster system!), it can be crucial time out. See Chapter 11, Getting Through Tough Times, for more suggestions.

If you need help now, because you feel angry or despairing or potentially out of control, call one of the 24-hour parent helplines listed in Chapter 2, Your Help Team. That's also where you'll find contacts for parent services that provide counselling, classes in settling and sleeping, and residential stays. You can also contact your child & family health nurse or your GP.

BLAST FROM THE PAST

'There is a mistaken idea that crying for three or four hours is good for a baby . . . under the mistaken idea that you are strengthening your baby's lungs.'
– *Yackandandah Times*, Victoria, 1920

Which babies cry?

* All babies cry.
* Babies in stressful homes cry.
* Babies in calm homes cry.
* Babies with good mums cry.
* Babies with good dads cry.
* Lonely babies cry.
* Babies who are never left alone cry.
* Smart babies cry.
* Sick babies cry.
* Healthy babies cry.
* Normal babies can cry for more than an hour a day in the first few months.

* Babies who are carried around by their mothers in slings all day in small African communities cry.
* First babies cry.
* Second and subsequent babies cry.
* Safe babies cry.
* Babies who grow up to be delightful children cry.
* Babies of self-assured parents cry.
* Babies of nervous parents cry.
* Babies of childcare experts cry.

more info on crying

raisingchildren.net.au
Search 'Cry Baby program', 'how to settle a crying baby' and just 'crying' on this Health Department–approved site for lots more info and ideas.

purplecrying.info
Canadian paediatrician Ron Barr says a 'purple period' of crying lasts from about 2 weeks to 3 or 4 months. PURPLE stands for Peak of crying, Unexpected, Resists soothing, Pain-like face, Long-lasting and Evening, and Barr addresses all these 'normal' aspects. His website is a hub for useful info on preventing and managing crying and sleep problems, and it has a section for dads.

Attachment-parenting books on crying
***100 Ways to Calm the Crying* by Pinky McKay (Penguin, Australia)**
A range of suggested solutions from the philosophy of calm and kindness.

***The Discontented Little Baby Book* by Pamela Douglas (University of Queensland Press)**
By a Queensland doctor who specialises in crying, sleep and breastfeeding advice.

10

LOVING YOUR BABY

We hear so much about the wonderful joy of having a baby. If we don't feel attached to our baby straight away we think there's something wrong with us. But the 'slow bond' is okay, too. Some things take practice and experience. Here are some ways to help you love your baby.

ways some people respond to a new baby

It's different for everyone:

- ★ Immediately you see your baby for the first time you feel a rush of protective love and never want to be parted.
- ★ You look at the baby and wonder what all the fuss is about and feel nothing. Gradually you learn to love them.
- ★ As a partner, when you see your baby being born you realise you want to protect and love them and their mother every way you can.
- ★ The first time you put your baby to your breast you feel that it's all perfect and natural.
- ★ The first time you hug your baby to your breast you remember you're a man and feel a bit useless.
- ★ When the caesarean drugs or the shock of labour wear off, you slowly begin to marvel at and feel connected to your baby, whether you breastfeed or bottle-feed.
- ★ As time goes by, you feel more and more loving and confident in your relationship with your baby.
- ★ After a period of confused thoughts, you get help from counsellors, a doctor, maybe a residential-care centre that specialises in postnatal depression, or some prescribed medication perhaps, and you begin to learn how to look after your baby and you begin to care. You understand that this feeling will build, and doesn't come immediately or without effort for everyone.
- ★ The thought of anyone affronting, let alone hurting, your baby makes you instinctively furious.

With almost every other relationship in life, love develops over time. And yet we are expected, through miraculous hormones or somehow automatically, to love and bond with our children. This can make us feel terribly guilty if we don't experience great surges of love and bonding straight away, or even in the first weeks.

The process of birth is such a huge thing that we've been concentrating on for so long, we can forget the need to deal with our own exhaustion and healing, afterwards. It is very common to feel quite disconnected or helpless when the baby is born, just as it's common to feel a great rush of relief and love. Because as first-time parents we are often not experienced with babies, we are quite overcome and shocked by how tiny and defenceless our babies look, and this can make us feel frightened to cuddle, scared of responsibility.

For many of us the birth of a baby (especially the first) can mean giving up and grieving for the permanent or temporary loss of a whole lot of really good things, such as independence, cocktails on a whim, an income, and our former kept-to-itself body. All these legitimate thoughts and conditions can give us pause, and get in the way of feeling joy and attachment.

Every parent can get help to move on from feeling empty or frightened to gradually falling in love with their baby and having a happy future together. Feelings of anxiety and depression can arise in mums, dads and partners before or at any time after the birth. See Chapter 11, Getting Through Tough Times, for how to manage your feelings, and how to get advice and help.

Common reactions to the birth

* Oh, my GOD. Did it really come out of me?
* I've never felt such a strong love.
* I'm scared to touch him.
* Give her to me!
* I can't wait to try breastfeeding!
* They're not expecting me to actually feed that, are they?
* Don't take my baby out of my sight.
* I really need to sleep: can you look after her for a while?
* I won't know what to do because I'm a bloke.
* I don't have any 'mother's instinct'.

Common feelings in the first weeks

* bewilderment
* pride
* blank exhaustion
* exultation – a high
* fear of Doing the Wrong Thing
* calm bliss
* anxiety about the baby's health and safety
* inadequacy at the thought of being a parent
* a maelstrom of different thoughts and emotions
* shock
* relief
* strong desire to have staff

help with your feelings

You don't have to be perfect. You just need to try. Your child & family health nurse will help you learn the new skills needed. That's why they have tissues in their office – they're used to tears. They'll be able to help you, or refer you to somebody who can help. Also see your doctor, as an underlying physical problem or a low-grade infection might be making things harder for you.

BLAST FROM THE PAST

'Once or twice every day baby requires a short "mothering" time, when he is picked up, played with judiciously and nursed by his mother or father. This period must not be overdone.'
– Bad advice from *The Australian Woman's Complete Household Guide*, early 1950s

---

Stressful parenting

Babies know when you're stressed, and when you're stressed your reactions to a baby's behaviour can be different. It's much harder for babies to attach to their mums or dads when they're unsure of how you might react to them. And it's harder for parents to feel confident, sensitive and attuned when they feel like a walking zombie. The old cliché 'Happy mum, happy life' has truth in it. If you are unhappy and finding it hard to cope, do whatever is necessary for you to feel in a better mood: maybe fresh air and exercise will help. Get someone else to stay and do a few night feeds with expressed or bottled milk. Strap the baby to you, or strap the baby to someone else for a while so you can have a break or a sleep. Babies are learning from you to read emotions, and how to react in good times and bad.

'If your maternal instinct doesn't kick in (mine never did), then read books or seek help from family services.'
CRYSTAL

ways to increase 'bonding'

Don't forget to spend time flaked out on the couch just looking at your baby and having as many calm moments as you can. The newborn time feels endless now, but when you look back it really will seem to have gone in a flash. The only way to get to know baby cries and baby body language is to spend relaxed time together. Here are your instructions.

- ⭐ Sit quietly and inspect your baby from top to toe.
- ⭐ Chat to your baby face to face up close.
- ⭐ Name your baby and start using the name a lot, or use lots of special nicknames.
- ⭐ Sing to your baby: anything will do.
- ⭐ Watch your baby's expressions and try to guess what they mean.
- ⭐ Think about what you'd do if someone tried to hurt your baby.
- ⭐ Tell your baby you're going to get to know each other over time.
- ⭐ Have lots of skin-to-skin contact.
- ⭐ Be very still and listen to your baby breathing.
- ⭐ Feel your baby's heartbeat.
- ⭐ Look at your baby's feet, hands, back of the neck.
- ⭐ Hold the baby to your chest when standing or lying down.
- ⭐ Gently massage your baby (see 'Baby massage' below).
- ⭐ Watch your baby sleeping.

Loving your baby and feeling in a good place is the most important thing in your life right now – ask friends, family and workmates to help you by taking other things off your plate. Forget the clock, forget other commitments, forget looking glamorous, or even presentable: this is what it's all about, for now.

Baby massage

Gentle, stroking motions will probably soothe your baby. For centuries people have been touching and massaging babies without having to take lessons on baby massage, so don't feel you have to do anything special. Baby massage classes can be fun, though, and a way to meet other mums or dads, and are often especially recommended as a way to help bond with your baby. Skin-to-skin contact between baby and carers, like cuddles and chat, is known to improve baby happiness and health, and can help you fall in love with your baby.

Tell your baby when you're going to touch them. Lay your bub on their back on a towel on the floor (they can't fall if they're already on the floor), then sit down and lean forward to stroke them. Make sure your core is strong, your tummy is held in and your back is braced. (This is no good in the first weeks after a caesarean, obviously, because it will be too painful.) If your baby is on a raised surface, remember midwife consultant Cath Curtin's motto: 'If your eyes are on the baby you can take your hand off; if your eyes are off the baby, your hands must be on!' Talk to your baby and make funny faces.

This isn't a job you have to do vigorously or with fancy, brilliant technique, or diarise – it's all about time connecting with your baby that you and your baby both enjoy.

There are many baby massage lessons or sessions available, some online. Some are run by organisations that have been investigated due to dodgy financial and other practices. Others are run by qualified physiotherapists or massage practitioners and are just pay-as-you-go, more community-based local classes. Beware any baby massage courses that charge large fees or claim that it makes babies smarter or prevents postnatal depression. Babies do not need treatments from chiropractors, and medical doctors know that these 'treatments' can be dangerous and cause harm to a baby's spine or neck.

more info on baby massage

babyinmind.org.au
This non-profit program provides national accreditation and training for therapists and parents in a massage program called First Touch that teaches you how to recognise communication 'cues' from your bub. There is a list of facilitators who have done an Australian Skills Quality Authority government-accredited, evidence-based course.

Cuddle karaoke

Music, singing, voice, body language, facial expressions, lullabies and stories, and repeating words and rhymes all help you and your baby to love each other and your baby to learn. Babies want to make a connection with you. You don't need fancy toys or flip cards or technology or apps. You just need to be with your baby, and react to and enjoy them. You don't have words together yet, but your baby is already trying to talk to you with feelings and body movements, and you can join in. From the moment you and your baby hold a gaze together, from the first time you present your finger and your baby curls their hand around it, you've started communicating.

You time

Mums and dads who have some time to themselves once a week, say, for their hobby or to see friends or see a movie and have a coffee, are less at risk for depression and anxiety.

BLAST FROM THE PAST

'Mothers who are too fond of Baby. There is nothing so beneficial to a baby as a judicious amount of letting it alone . . . continual nervous strain wrecks babies. Dress the baby properly, feed it at regular intervals and prevent it from being disturbed by enthusiastic friends.' – The *Albury Banner and Wodonga Express* finds a way to get it all wrong AND blame mothers, 1906

~~~~~~~~ more info on learning to love your baby ~~~~~~~~

For extra help, see the next chapter, Getting Through Tough Times.

raisingchildren.net.au
Here you will find fact sheets and a video about behaviours and movements of babies that can send you a message. On the home page, search 'baby cues', 'connecting' and 'communicating' for lots of info and videos.

'What Do Babies Think?' talk
Search the name of author Alison Gopnik on ted.com to find a great talk from her called 'What do babies think?' She explains that when babies play they're also doing 'research and development'. Check out her books on how parent caring naturally makes babies learn.

~~~~~~

11

getting THROUGH tough times

Sometimes the good feelings of being a parent get pushed to the background or swamped completely.

Everyone needs help to get through tough days and tough times. Me, you, people living in hunter-gather tribal societies and all the fancypants celebrities with professional photographers to help pretend their lives are perfect.

a perfectly sane response

Parenthood isn't always wonderful: the first weeks will be tiring and stressful, too. It isn't madness or weakness or failure to feel overwhelmed when a new baby arrives – in lots of ways it's a perfectly sane response.

As well as being fascinating – 'Look at those darling starfish hands!' – your baby will scream and poo and not explain themselves at all. This is probably your training ground in unconditional love and devotion, and sometimes it's a pain in the arse at best and absolutely maddening and exhausting at worst. The hard aspects can be balanced by the pride and joy of keeping your little one alive and well, and the thrill of getting to know your baby.

In sensible cultures, new parents aren't made to feel alone, and they can reach out for lots of support and human contact while going through it. Our 'modern' way could do with a lot more of the tribal in it.

To be honest I can't quite work out why anyone *wouldn't* come crashing down after the ultra-stress of birth, the lack of sleep, the realisation that this isn't for the weekend but for life, the sore aching bits of your body at the same time as it feels your body is not your own any more, the carry-on or early pain and worry of first-time breast-feeding and the anxiety about whether you're doing ANYTHING right, the pictures on social media that look like another planet away from your life. How come you feel like a worn-out old couch instead of a supermodel holding a stunt-baby?

And that's if everything's going fine. If you're also dealing with outside relationship problems, a sick baby or unhelpful relatives, it can all seem a bit of a disaster. I think parents at this stage can sometimes feel terribly alone, especially sole or single parents, and parents whose partners go back to work leaving them – aarrgh, surely some mistake – in CHARGE. And the house looks terrible a day after getting home from hospital and how are you supposed to eat fresh, healthy food when you can't even get out of your PJs by 5 p.m. and I can't cope, and shut up.

Which often leaves partners and dads not knowing how to be helpful and supportive (see Chapter 28, Dads).

All this is not helped by the amazingly intense attention that newborn babies need – feeds every two to four hours, nappy changes, comforting – while you're trying to snatch bits of sleep here and there. Honestly, I think if you weren't feeling a bit demented at least once a day there'd be something wrong with you.

One of the contradictions I remember feeling through the newborn days was wishing that somebody would turn up and say, 'There's been a terrible mistake, this isn't your baby and we're going to take her away and have her looked after by more competent folk', while simultaneously knowing that if someone did actually try to take my baby away from me I would try to kill them with a fork. Or some dental floss. (I wasn't thinking very clearly.)

It's not a failure to struggle as a new parent. It's normal. Reach out for help. We all need to help each other stumble through, instead of pretending to be superparents who know everything. It's especially hard in our society if we don't have family help, or the support we need, and we're all isolated in our own little flats and houses not realising there's an army of us who feel, or have felt, the same.

'I wish other mums would stop putting up walls and saying that everything is okay and life is wonderful. Because that is garbage. Having children, a husband and a household is plain hard work.' TESSA

'I was desperate for a baby, and I think I couldn't see past that, and saw the life through rose-coloured glasses. I was quite shocked by how hard it can be and also by how mundane it can be at times.' LOUISE

'I think that some people just need to be allowed to feel overwhelmed. I think that we should all be taught that childbirth is a real effort for a lot of women and may not come easily to you.' CATHY

Talking blue

People use different terms to describe low feelings associated with being a new parent. Feelings of anxiety and depression can happen before the birth or right after, or start up when your first kid's a toddler and a new baby arrives.

* **Perinatal** means during pregnancy and the first year of a baby's life.
* **Antenatal** means before the birth.
* **Postnatal** means after the birth.

Terms used to describe negative feelings of new parenthood can include any of the words above (perinatal or postnatal, for example) plus depression, blues, anxiety, and mood swings. Depression can manifest itself in feeling blank, sad, unmotivated. Anxiety can present as worry, obsession, strict rules-making or rules-keeping, panic and anger.

Finding out you can't delegate the baby

Mums are smart women who have taken time out from school or work to have a baby. Before we got pregnant we were striding about being independent, spending our own money and demanding that unfairnesses be corrected and equality enforced, and if there was a problem we'd nail it down and fix it, or get somebody else to fix it. But being a mother, especially in those first weeks, can't be delegated. You can't go somewhere else outside work hours. No amount of scheduling meetings, ringing up dispatch, rational thought or rope ladders will solve the problems. In most cases, like the *We're Going on a Bear Hunt* kids' book says, 'We can't go over it, we can't go under it, we've got to go through it.'

Make important decisions when you haven't had more than three hours' sleep in a row for nine days? Can't just pick up your keys and go out for a while? Can't send the crying baby back to the shop for an adjustment? A problem without some sort of immediate solution? We're so not used to that. We'd never start a job and expect that we won't receive any training – yet we expect to somehow be great as parents straight away, even though we haven't trained for the job, or spent weeks and months getting up to speed. Not to mention most new jobs are not 24 hours a day, with no deep sleep for weeks. Call the union!

the early days blues

All those lovely, floaty, hippy pregnancy hormones and brain chemicals shut off like a tap just about day three or four after the birth as your prolactin hormone levels gear up for milk delivery (progesterone, oestrogen, cortisol and beta-endorphins fall away). This is often what's called the 'baby blues' or the three-day weep.

Recovering from a difficult birth

Maybe the labour or the caesarean didn't go the way it was 'supposed to'. Traumatic or disappointing births often cause feelings of sadness, shock or distress that are played out in the open, or suppressed, in the first few weeks of a baby's life. Recovering from a particularly exhausting, complicated forceps or surgical birth, or perineum tearing, is a factor often overlooked by people who simply assume you're fine once the baby comes out. Some new mums are also dealing with ongoing pelvic pain or prolapse problems.

It's normal to feel traumatised after something scary happens. It's how the brain works. Some women even end up with post-traumatic symptoms they need help with. It's important to acknowledge the trauma, but also to realise you didn't do anything 'wrong' to 'cause' a non-natural birth. That, my friend, truly is random luck-of-the-draw stuff. It is a myth that everyone who wants a 'natural' birth can have one safely. Some people who eat organic food and do yoga and who are 24-year-old gymnasts have difficult births. In the past you or your baby might have died. If everyone had a 'natural' birth, we would lose thousands more babies and mums in childbirth.

Unfortunately, we have had to trade off the idea of a natural birth for everyone against higher survival rates of babies and mothers. Natural births are much rarer than they used to be because, quite simply, natural births without any available medical intervention kill a lot of babies and a lot of mothers. And rates of 'intervention' – help – have gone up because Australian babies now tend to be larger, as do their mothers, and their mothers tend to be older.

Giving birth is still the riskiest medical event in a woman's life. And it is a medical event, even though we'd all like it not to be. If you had an elective caesarean section, not an emergency one, for medical, safety or other reasons, there's no need to feel guilty or a failure over that, either.

Sometimes many tears need to be shed, and a birth story told or considered in counselling or with friends and family, before you feel able to move on.

Writing the birth story

Many mums find it useful to write down their birth story for themselves, or to share in a website forum or in a parents group.

Mums matter

You need to be patient with yourself about recovering, and be careful of the idea that 'having a healthy baby is really all that matters now'. *You matter, too.* You're not just a baby delivery system. It is wonderful if medical intervention helped you have a healthy baby, or maximised your baby's chances. But you and your feelings are important, too.

Ask your obstetrician, hospital staff, child & family health nurse or family doctor to refer you to a specialist counsellor if you need extra help to work through your feelings. You can also speak to a counsellor from one of the services in 'More info on postnatal depression & anxiety' coming up, and see 'Ways to move on from a difficult birth' in Chapter 3, Looking After Yourself.

A health problem with the baby

Sometimes babies are born with minor or serious health problems, which can trigger depression and anxiety in parents. In the intensity of focusing on your child, it's good to pay attention to the mental health of the rest of the family, including yourself. Don't be afraid to ask for help. See Chapter 35, Special Needs, for more.

Coping at home

Let the housework go, say ta-ta to your hairdo and just make sure some food goes into everyone and sleep is grabbed whenever possible. In the early weeks that's all you can and should do.

Another thing that helps is getting outside into the fresh air and seeing the sun in the sky: otherwise, you live in a twilight world ruled by feeds every few hours, regardless of day or night, experiencing something like endless jet lag.

'Sometimes you have to have a good cry and try and remember that the bad days will end.' JILLIAN

Support from a partner (if you have one), family or friends is crucial. For every mum who told me they were so grateful for their mum's help, there was another whose mum was bossy, or had forgotten what it was like to have a baby, or gave old-fashioned advice and came over all offended when it wasn't followed. A lot of people had difficulty with their mother-in-law. And sometimes the child's grandparents can be more of a burden than a help. You can look elsewhere for supportive help – see Chapter 2, Your Help Team, for ideas and contacts.

I realise now that I should have had more visitors to help and chat and normalise things, but I was so tired and felt so inexperienced and down that I didn't want anyone to see me. It's a big mistake to think you have to put on a show of any kind for visitors. If we all pretend, everyone will continue to be shocked by the reality. Believe me, anyone who's been through it understands.

Although routines can make your life easier at this stage, if part of your routine is 'Thursday afternoon: clean the toilet' maybe instead just go out and have a cup of tea and talk to some adults for a while.

'I'm an A type personality and it was hard not having the control over my life that I used to have.' GARDA

'If you are tempted to look at the stay-home full-time mums of yesteryear and wish for their capabilities, remember that they often had four generations of helpers. Don't compare yourself to a situation that bears no resemblance to your own.' MICHAEL

'Ignore housework TOTALLY, ask friends and rellies to do the washing, cook the casserole or have the other kids. Nobody shows up to help these days, we're so busy: you have to ask, and make sure you show your appreciation later when you are on your feet: bake them a cake or buy them a scratchie. Don't read too many books by "experts".' ANONYMOUS MUM

'I felt like a cross between a milking machine and a washing machine.' LESLEY

Things that can help head off the blues

* Know that the tiredness and stress of a new baby are likely to get better with time.

* All new babies cry for hours. It's not caused by bad parenting, and this period will end (see Chapter 9, Crying).

* It's okay to be bored, impatient or annoyed by aspects of parenting, as long as you don't take it out on the baby.

* Get out into the open air as much as possible – a half-hour walk a day with the baby in the pram will make you feel better. It doesn't matter what you look like. Put sunnies on and repel all paparazzi.

* Talk to parents who've been through it and come out the other side.

* Tell people how you're feeling.

* Get away as much as you can: maybe to a local cinema that takes you into another world even briefly.

* Understand that if you feel alone, there are thousands just like you going through it, and thousands who have come out the other side.

* If a friend came to you with your problems, what would you advise them? Why be harder than that on yourself?

* Avoid people who are critical and negative without helping: you don't need them, even if they're related to you.

* Go to a mothers group, parents group or playgroup, even if your baby is too young to really play.

* Learn yoga or another relaxation technique. Look into a special postnatal class, or do baby massage (see 'Baby massage' in Chapter 10, Loving Your Baby).

exhaustion & not feeling yourself

After the first few weeks, you still might be feeling isolated, or too exhausted, or 'not quite right'. A friend who thought she had postnatal depression turned out to have a low-level infection from parts of the placenta left behind. Another turned out to have a thyroid condition that was making her hormones misbehave. Reach out to your child & family health nurse and your family doctor, and ask for a referral or another doctor if you're still not where you want to be, emotionally or physically.

Once a physical reason is ruled out or treated and managed, you can think about other strategies that will help with getting more sleep (see Chapter 8, Baby Sleep) or reducing stress caused by having an unsettled baby (see Chapter 9, Crying). Ask a partner or relative or friends to step up and get amongst it with you, making you go for more walks, getting help with work or housework, or making sure you don't feel isolated.

the ongoing low-level blues

A more specific level of ongoing blues is a form of low-level depression that usually comes in small doses, such as a few days or a week or so at a time. Symptoms include mood swings, crying, crankiness and tiredness.

> 'Having worked as a private maternity nurse and nanny, I really thought that motherhood would pose no problems for me. How wrong I was. In those first few weeks, with both my children, I had serious doubts as to whether I was really cut out to be a mum. When I finally expressed my concerns I discovered that 99 per cent of the mothers I knew had experienced the same physical and emotional problems.'   TARRYN

'Aaargghh! I ended up in a mother/baby care unit for a week after the first month – thank God for them.'   ZOE

feeling angry

It's common to feel angry, in general or with a baby, particularly a baby who won't stop crying, even when you know how irrational that is – babies can't be 'naughty', because they have no idea what they're doing. What's important is that when you feel angry you do something about it that doesn't involve blaming – or harming – the baby.

If your frustration with your baby rises to boiling point and you think you might shake, hit or otherwise harm them:

★ put the baby in a safe place – a cot is best – and walk out of the house (into the garden, if you have one) to calm down, and

★ call one of the parent services or, if it's late, a 24-hour parent helpline (see Chapter 2, Your Help Team), or

★ take the baby, crying or not, and go straight to your child & family health nurse or doctor, or

★ go and sit in the park with the pram. The baby might still cry, but you'll be outside and in public and less likely to do something awful. Ring somebody – a relative or friend – who can come and be with you.

In general, fresh air, sunshine and personal connections with neighbourhood folk, family, friends or a mums group can really help. A very experienced person in the field of distraught mums tells me a good quickie soother is to stand with your hands palm down in a basin of warm water and breathe slowly. Of course, sleep is what you really need. What you're feeling is probably at least partly related to sleep deprivation: don't be hard on yourself. If anger is your usual default position when you're tired or frustrated, though, this needs to change for your child's sake. Talk to your doctor or a parent advice line about getting help to change it.

If you have got to the stage of feeling at the end of your tether you will probably feel that way again, and it may get worse, so it's a good idea to get help at this point. I think many, many parents have shouted rather uncontrollably at a baby who has 'refused' to go to sleep or to stop crying. This can frighten both of you and make everyone cry even more.

postnatal depression and/or anxiety

Postnatal depression and anxiety can turn up straight after the birth or unexpectedly sometime in the first couple of years, and often comes on gradually. 'Postnatal depression and anxiety' is the catch-all term often used, as the experience can seem to be one or the other, or a mixture. Even though many people don't talk about it, these feelings affect tens of thousands of Australian women each year, and thousands of men too. The feelings can be hormonally caused, psychological or even a recurrence of depression from another time. Any parent can find themselves dealing with it, including adoptive parents and parents who have conceived with IVF or other help. In some cases depression and/or anxiety can recur with the arrival of each child. This is the black hole from which you can't see a way out: you think it's never going to get better. But it can – you just need to put your hand up.

Postnatal depression or anxiety can seem utterly unrelenting to those in it: you don't have any good days, or you have more bad days than good days, and you feel no optimism or enthusiasm for anything. The feelings are intense or constant, and you can't 'shake yourself out of it' or 'pull yourself together'.

This, my friend, is completely treatable, and so many mums (and dads) have been through it; you must tell your partner or someone you're close to, and see a professional about your feelings now. If you need it, somewhere near you there's a special residential-care centre for new mums where you can go for as long as you need with your baby, get treated, be with other women with the same problem, and learn how to get your life back.

Common symptoms of baby-related depression

* Feeling tired
* Feeling cranky
* Crying – quietly or sobbing
* Not getting hungry or 'emotional' eating
* Black moods
* Feeling worthless
* No sense of self
* Despair or pessimism
* Feeling numb or blank
* Thoughts of self-harm, guilt or shame
* Thoughts about harming your baby
* Memory blanks
* Exhaustion
* No interest in affection

Common symptoms of postnatal anxiety

* Obsession and repeated actions or checking
* Strict rules-making or rules-keeping
* Panicked feelings
* Insomnia
* Anger
* Fear
* Catastrophising (seeing small problems as huge ones)
* Indecision as the 'right' decision seems elusive – from a brand of pram to naming the baby

Risk factors for postnatal depression & anxiety

* Low self-esteem
* Feeling inadequate as a parent
* Having little or no support or help
* Unrealistic expectations or requirements from yourself or others
* Being isolated
* Feeling trapped
* Looking at social media all the time
* Depression or anxiety during pregnancy, or with a previous baby
* Problems with a partner
* Being a sole parent
* A difficult labour or emergency caesarean
* Having a baby who cries a lot
* Wanting things to be 'perfect'
* Being a pessimist
* Having a depressed or anxious partner
* Having a history of family unhappiness
* Being poor
* Having a history with violence and/or emotional abuse
* Stressful events all happening at once (childbirth plus a house move, or a family crisis)

'Don't let pride get in your way of getting help for PND. I felt like a zombie with lipstick and despite family trying to get me to the doctor I never went. I still regret it, years later.' MELISSA

Mistaken identity: postpartum thyroiditis

Sometimes women are diagnosed with exhaustion or postnatal depression when they actually have postpartum thyroiditis, which affects almost one in a hundred new mums. It's an inflammation of the thyroid gland that causes confusing symptoms because hormone levels are depressed, elevated or fluctuating. Problems can begin at any time from a couple of months to a year after your baby is born.

★ Symptoms of an **underactive thyroid** include feeling tired, cold or depressed; a perplexing weight gain; dry, coarse or thinning skin or hair; constipation; and heavy periods. Treatment includes medication that boosts the hormone levels, and it can take six months to a year to get back to completely 'normal'.

★ Symptoms of an **overactive thyroid**, a condition that usually sorts itself out without treatment, can include feeling tired, anxious, panicky, hot or cross; a perplexing weight loss; thinning skin or hair; diarrhoea; insomnia; and sweating. It can be diagnosed with a simple blood test by your doctor.

'Make new friends, even if you never would have liked that type of person. Invite them for morning tea. You will have to get out of your pyjamas and so will she. Go to the local mothers groups . . . get the baby outside even if he screams for the entire walk.' SOPHIE

'Get a diagnosis because thyroid condition can also cause milk supply problems, you can sort it all out at the same time.' RUBY

'What a nightmare those first 6 weeks were. I tried to take everyone's advice, which was contradictory in most cases, and ended up tying myself in knots. Luckily my family ignored my breezy, confident "I'm fine!"s and were wonderfully supportive.' KELLIE

Partners of people having difficulties

Partners can be terribly stressed and worried about you and need to get away some-times too. You can end up with two depressed or anxious parents in the house, which needless to say is really bad for babies and children. For their sake as well as yours you need to get professional help from someone trained specifically. See 'More info on post-natal depression & anxiety' coming up.

Treatment for postnatal depression & anxiety

Treatment can be a combination of any or all of the following:

★ counselling – on your own or with your partner
★ group support or therapy
★ antidepressant medicine, which should always be used with other treatments such as getting practical help at home and counselling
★ hormone-balancing medication
★ getting help to make a plan for improving your life and routine
★ a residential stay in a mother–baby unit of a parenting service
★ talking to mums who have been through it and are fine now.

Medication doesn't always mean an end to breastfeeding: ask your doctor for safe medications for breastfeeding, and see Chapter 4, Breastfeeding, for more on that.

BLAST FROM THE PAST

'I am afraid of myself at times. Sometimes . . . I have to go right out of the house away from the children for fear of what could happen'
– Letter from a mother to the women's page of *The Daily Standard*, Brisbane, 1918.
The columnist wrote that such cases of 'deranged nerves' were common:
'To speak of the trouble partly puts it behind one; to be afraid to speak helps it to grow . . . cure lies in a removal of causes.'

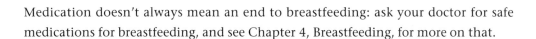

'Wear your tracksuit to bed, and then if you don't have time to dress/shower in the morning, you still look like you have!'   ANN

∼∼∼ more info on postnatal depression & anxiety ∼∼

Your child & family health nurse or family doctor will be able to help you, and refer you for extra help if you want it.

panda.org.au
Helpline: 1300 726 306
The Perinatal Anxiety & Depression Australia (PANDA) website has advice, a referral service, fact sheets, links, and recovery strategies for parents who are feeling overwhelmed, blank or unable to cope, or who are otherwise struggling. Their site for dads is **howisdadgoing.org.au**

beyondblue.org.au
Australia's depression organisation beyondblue has specific info on PND: on the home page choose 'Pregnancy and early parenthood' for info.

gidgetfoundation.com.au
Infoline: 1300 851 758
Non-profit provides video counselling by specialist psychologists and resources for women and medical professionals.

Mensline: 1300 78 99 78
Lifeline: 13 11 14
Both of these helplines have 24-hour counselling services.

'Get your husband/partner involved from day one. Teach him the ins and outs or you are setting yourself up to be the only one that settles, feeds, etc. Maintain contact with the outside world and delegate, delegate. Have one day a week that is yours.'   ANNIE

'I thought my postnatal depression only affected me. My other half has his struggles and down-times, too. Encouraging him to talk was so helpful!'   CHANTEL

postnatal psychosis

This is a mental illness that affects just a couple of mothers in every thousand, and in a small number of those cases can be life-threatening to a baby and a mother. It's completely treatable and usually involves a temporary situation that's resolved as quickly as possible. Postnatal psychosis isn't something people can just snap out of by free will. Urgent medical attention is essential.

It tends to come on in the first month or two after the birth, or even almost immediately, and can be characterised by a very severe depression as well as feeling very 'up' and having a very 'busy' mind, or mood swings between those two extremes, manic spending, delusions of grandeur or claims of special knowledge, hallucinations, talking or activities, annoyance with others, and other scary business such as wanting to harm the baby or yourself, or thinking this is a good idea. There might be confusion about what's real, or delusions about somebody telling you things.

There could be a known or unknown genetic predisposition, or a family or personal history of bipolar disorder (meaning the wild high and low feelings formerly called manic depression) or schizophrenia. But if you know you have a family history of bipolar disorder or schizophrenia, you're at an advantage: you know that having a baby is a risk factor for the onset of an episode. Cannabis use is also a well-recognised trigger point for psychosis in some people.

So be aware of possible symptoms and let your medical supporters and close family members help look out for you: in the vast majority of cases, you won't need intervention, but if you do, it can all kick in earlier and the problem can be resolved more quickly.

When recognised and treated properly, it can take only weeks to recover. Treatments include coming off any medication that may be making things worse, and finding the right medication that helps; counselling and practical advice; intensive personal nursing; and a baby-and-mum stay in a residential hospital unit. The aim of all treatment is always to reunite mum and baby as soon as possible, with lots of support.

Some people who develop postnatal psychosis have no history of warning signs at all. Some recover quickly; others need ongoing medication to control the condition. Postnatal psychosis is very successfully treated with medication to help restore a balanced brain chemistry – this can take some time to get exactly right.

What to do if you suspect postnatal psychosis

Perhaps you recognise these symptoms in somebody else: you must act quickly to get them medical help. If you are having dark days of depression yourself all the time, or serious thoughts about harming yourself or your baby, or are hearing voices or experiencing unusual urges, or you haven't slept for days, get someone to be with you *right now*, and tell them why. Have someone with you to help you with the baby and get you to a doctor's office, if it's daytime. Tell the staff there's a baby involved and you need help straight away.

If it's night-time, you may need to call an ambulance so you can be assessed by a mental health team, as somebody with temporary psychosis can't be helped by an appeal to logic, or by telephone counselling.

It's very important that the focus is on treating the mental illness. If you don't have a partner or close relative to help with or care for your baby, doctors will help you to find someone to take care of your baby while you're in hospital. Custody of your baby will not be taken from you. Breastfeeding may go by the wayside if the medication is likely to affect the baby, but that's not the most important thing at a time like this.

If you feel you can wait a day, you can make an appointment with your doctor to talk about the best way forward, and who to be referred to. You will need to be referred to a specialist psychiatrist, so don't be fobbed off with antidepressant drugs without knowing the exact nature of your illness.

Mums with a mental illness can maintain normal and loving lives, but they must have an understanding that they are sick, and an insight into their disease that means they keep taking their medication – indefinitely, if necessary. They also need understanding and support from family and friends. Uncontrolled and untreated mental illness can be one of the most lonely and terrifying things for both parent and child.

Like any other mental illnesses it is made worse, never better, by alcohol and all non-prescribed drugs.

'I'm living proof that recovery is possible and that a breakdown can be a breakthrough.' KERYN

more info on postnatal psychosis

If you think you or your baby are in danger, get help immediately by going to your local doctor's office and telling the staff it's an emergency, or going straight to the nearest hospital emergency department. Tell a trusted friend or relative you need help.

Ambulance: 000 in Australia; 111 in New Zealand

sane.org.au
Helpline: 1800 18 7263 (weekday business hours)
Counsellors at SANE Australia will talk with you about depression, psychosis, manic episodes or anything you'd like help with. They can refer you to services offering practical help.

panda.org.au
Search 'postnatal psychosis recovery stories' on the home page of this premier mental health service to read honest, inspiring accounts from real mums.

'I always thought it only affected mothers who felt no bond with their baby or who had a "high maintenance" baby. I found out it had nothing to do with any of that. I went from being a fearless and capable professional to an anxious, fearful, blubbering heap of misery in a matter of months. When I yelled at my baby because I couldn't hear the TV, I called my child & family health nurse (the nicer one) and she did a depression questionnaire on me. Two days later I was in a parent–infant unit. I spent five weeks there and got all the help I needed. It was the best thing I ever did, reaching out to the nurse.'   ALEX

12

BABY ROUTINES

A routine is a daily schedule for when to feed, play,
sleep, have a shower, tidy your undies drawer, that
sort of caper. (You'll have time to tidy your undies
drawer in about eight years.) A newborn baby's idea
of a routine is to wake up whenever they get hungry
and cry, but you can gradually make a pattern for
your days to help you through the first year.

customising your routine

Babies are not necessarily going to take to a pattern, and even those who do may not like it all the time. Babies going through growth spurts can wake earlier for feeds, and any baby can do unpredictable things, such as suddenly change their sleep habits for no obvious reason.

After the first weeks you might be able to work out a bit of a pattern that brings some order to your days, but be prepared to abandon it when necessary. Little babies can't be fed on a strict schedule that follows the clock, or in between precisely-timed meetings. Sometimes they will be extra-hungry earlier than usual, or they'll be in a transition period from, say, three big sleeps a day to two.

A routine isn't a set of 24-hour rules. It's a flexible plan with a bit of structure, to make a baby feel secure, and to make more sense of the day for you.

Later on, a strict routine can make it hard for you to go out – some babies are too interested in the world to be able to sleep away from their own bedroom, but most will sleep in a soothingly mobile car. Some people really need to stick to their routine because they know that otherwise they'll pay for it with an overtired, grumpy child later that afternoon or even in the night. Others can fiddle around the edges of their routine and miss bits of it quite happily. And others hate the whole idea of a routine (in which case skip this chapter!).

arsenic hour

Arsenic hour is an alarming term for the early-evening time when everyone's overtired and cranky and the baby reaches a peak of crying – anywhere from 4 to 7 p.m. rather than for a strict hour. By anticipating it in your day and having some strategies to deal with it, crabbiness might be kept to a minimum. Strategies can include getting the baby down for a late-afternoon catnap; enlisting help with the baby, a sibling or the cooking; and drinking vast quantities of gin. I beg your pardon, that's not a strategy – it's a typographical error.

'Strict routines don't work for all families but you may find a pattern in the organised chaos of your own family life. Stick with what works for you.'   NADIA, a family doctor

feed, play, sleep

This is the tried-and-true method used by many sleep schools and parenting advisers. Feed (breastfeed or bottle-feed), then a play and a cuddle, then a sleep, then repeat, for chunks of the day.

In the case of a newborn, 'play' means a chat and a bit of a kick on a rug. 'Play' for a young baby over 6 weeks old means chatting, being sung to, being taken out for a walk and looking at things they can focus on, a baby massage or a visitor. This is designed to let the baby have a feed, enjoy a social or interesting time and then get enough rest to be able to do it all over again.

The aim is to separate the feed and the sleep, as many babies get so used to a breastfeed or bottle-feed being part of their sleep ritual that they reach a point where they can't nap or go to sleep without it. There is an exception: it's fine to give a young baby a big feed immediately before the big night-time sleep, say about 7 p.m. This feed is often a deliciously comforting wind-down ritual for both baby and carer. Talk to your child & family health nurse about changing this if you want to.

possible newborn routine

Baby wakes up:
- ★ **Feed**: breastmilk or formula.
- ★ **Play**: nappy change; chat, fresh air, cuddle,
     pre-sleep ritual pat, rock or words.
- ★ **Sleep**: as long as the baby wants to.

This feed–play–sleep block can be repeated six or more times in a 24-hour period. In the first few weeks the awake part of the feed–play–sleep routine will probably last only about an hour or an hour and a quarter, but watch for your baby's tired signs rather than the clock. When a baby shows classic tired signs, pop them down to sleep. (There's a list of classic baby tired signals coming up.) In the very early weeks babies often nod right off wherever and whenever they feel like it, and if a baby takes a laid-back 50 minutes to feed that will eat into their 'playtime' as well.

Many newborn babies tend to want to stay awake for two hours in the late afternoon or at the end of the day, contributing to arsenic hour when everyone's fed up to pussy's bow. If your baby is showing tired signs at this time, try to get them off to sleep. If they're alert and seem to need the extra time awake, try using a baby carrier or having a relaxing sing, bath or massage routinely at this time. Not easy if you've dinner to prepare and others such as a toddler to attend to.

The feed–play–sleep routine can be repeated as needed into the night, but remember that night-time feeds in dim light need to be followed directly by everyone going back to sleep, instead of playing, to get the baby used to the most excellent idea that there are no playtimes at night.

Sleep if you can when the baby does or, if you can't nod off, just rest all the times your new baby sleeps at night and some of the times during the day too.

Let them sleep when they want to, instead of keeping them awake to amuse you or your Aunty Agatha, who's due to visit at 3.15. Aunty Agatha will have to wait or come back later. Try to keep visitors flexible: make sure they ring before they come so that you can adjust their arrival time with them if need be, or make sure visitors and other kids understand the baby must be allowed to fall asleep and not be disturbed. And watch babies for those tired signs. If the baby is tired, even if it isn't sleep time in your 'schedule', be guided by the baby, and fiddle your schedule to match.

Baby tired signals

A newborn baby's 'I'm tired' signals can include droopy eyelids, slow blinks, stiff and jerky movements, frowning, blank stares, whinginess and irritability, and yawns; and in an older baby, rubbing their eyes, pulling their earlobes or hair, sudden tears or aggression, happy one moment furious the next (oh wait, that's also just being a baby), and looking fed up with toys.

'I found putting the newborn into the older siblings' routine to be the best way, especially for afternoon naps and bath time.'   TRACE

possible baby routine from 3 months

Continue the feed–play–sleep routine and again watch for your baby's sleepy signs, not the clock. As time goes on, though, the daytime awake periods will get longer – say, one to two hours – and there will probably be three big sleeps during the day.

⭐ Baby wakes up. **Feed:** breakfast (breastmilk or formula). **Play. Sleep.**

⭐ **Feed:** morning tea (breastmilk or formula). **Play. Sleep.**

⭐ **Feed:** lunch (breastmilk or formula). **Play. Sleep.**

⭐ **Feed:** afternoon tea (breastmilk or formula). **Play.**

⭐ Arsenic hour: introduce a restful activity if the baby is cranky or overtired.

⭐ **Sleep:** possibly short or the baby might want to stay awake, but watch for tired signs.

⭐ Bath, wind-down.

⭐ **Feed:** dinner (breastmilk or formula). **Sleep:** bedtime about 7 p.m.

⭐ Adult dinner and relaxation or sleep.

⭐ **Feed:** late supper at 10.30 or so (breastmilk or formula). **Sleep:** through the night (hey, it's a plan!).

Playtime sessions can involve outings, walks, visitors, reading a board book, looking at cars swishing past outside the window, singing, chatting and cuddling. Remember that when a baby wakes for a night-time feed there's no playtime and the light is kept dim.

Put your baby down to sleep at about 7 at night, then wake them gently for a non-stimulating, business-only feed in the dark room at about 10.30 or 11 p.m. This should see you through for a longer period of sleep, until 5, 6, even 7 a.m. If you're not getting a longer night-time sleep of five or six hours by the time your baby is 6 months old, ask your child & family health nurse or doctor for help with adjusting your routine.

'Kids love consistency, consistency, consistency. My baby actually sighs with delight and relief when she is tucked in and usually lets us know (loudly) when we are running behind time.' HAYLEY

possible baby routine from 6 months

The feed–play–sleep routine continues, with the baby moving towards two big sleeps during the day – a big morning and afternoon nap – and probably a catnap at about 4.30. Catnaps usually last 20 or 40 minutes.

By 6 months a baby will need four or five milk drinks during the day, and tastes of solids (see Chapter 14, First Food). By 1 year old the emphasis is on solid food and about 600 ml of milk throughout the day or the equivalent in dairy products, such as yoghurt and cheese.

⭐ Baby wakes up. **Feed**: breakfast (breastmilk or formula and a taste of solids, such as rice cereal or a bit of fruit to suck, 'gum' or nibble on).
Play. Possible sleep for a baby closer to 6 months than 1 year.

⭐ **Feed**: morning tea (breastmilk or formula and maybe a taste of solids). **Play. Sleep.**

⭐ **Feed**: lunch (breastmilk or formula and a taste of solids). **Play. Sleep.**

⭐ **Feed**: afternoon tea (breastmilk or formula and maybe a taste of solids).
Play. Possible catnap if there are tired signs.

⭐ Arsenic hour: a restful activity.

⭐ **Feed**: dinner (a taste of solids and a drink of water). **Play** (longer than usual, but watch for tired signs). Bath. Drink: breastmilk or formula. Night-time ritual.
Sleep: bedtime about 7 p.m.

⭐ Adult dinner and relaxation.
Possible feed: supper (breastmilk or formula) or start phasing it out. **Sleep.**

Put your baby down to sleep at 7 or 7.30 at night. After the bub is 6 months old you can experiment with the late-evening feed. Drop it and see what happens. If your baby wakes up at 3 a.m. starving, then it isn't time to drop that feed yet. But maybe the baby will sleep through until 6 or even 7 a.m. It's not unusual for babies to sleep ten or twelve hours before morning. The solid food introduced at this age helps babies stay full through the night. By about 9 months the late-evening feed should be gone and you should be getting a big sleep yourself at night: if you can't quite seem to manage it, talk to your child & family health nurse or doctor.

'Everyone wanted us to have a routine except me and my baby.'
ALANA

possible baby routine from 9 months

The same sort of pattern is followed but the late-afternoon catnap is usually dropped, leaving just a morning and afternoon sleep; and you can move to getting a longer sleep at night if you haven't already.

- ⭐ Baby wakes up. **Feed:** breakfast (solids and breastmilk or formula). **Play.**
- ⭐ **Feed:** morning tea (a snack and a drink in a cup). **Play. Sleep.**
- ⭐ **Feed:** lunch (solids and breastmilk or formula). **Play. Sleep.**
- ⭐ **Feed:** afternoon tea (a snack and a drink in a cup).
   Play (watch for tired signs but a very late afternoon sleep could interfere with bedtime). Arsenic hour: a restful activity. Bath.
- ⭐ **Feed:** dinner (food and a drink in a cup). Night-time ritual.
   Drink: breastmilk or formula. **Sleep:** bedtime about 7 p.m.
- ⭐ Adult dinner and free time for exciting housework.
   Sleep: everyone until the morning (fingers crossed).

dropping a daytime nap

At around 1 year old (maybe earlier, maybe later) your baby might start showing no interest in the second, afternoon sleep, and want to just faff around. This probably means they're ready to go to one sleep a day, which traditionally is an afternoon sleep. You'll need a transition period, which will probably last about three weeks, while you slowly winch the morning sleep later until they're having one daytime nap that eventually starts at midday or 1 or 2 p.m. As they're making the transition you might find them getting crankier at the end of the day; if so put them to bed an hour or half an hour early. (Splendid news: in most cases this makes absolutely no difference to the morning wake-up time.)

By 18 months most kids are down to one sleep a day, and this can last right through until your baby starts school. Others drop the afternoon sleep somewhere along the way, although it's always useful to pick it up again briefly during those stressful or exciting times when they're sick, they're overtired in the first days or weeks of day care or kindergarten, or they've been to see the circus.

Baby sleep & daylight saving

Spend a few days before each daylight-saving changeover gradually altering your routine so that by the time you get there it's a fifteen-minute adjustment rather than a whole hour. Or you can start the day an hour later by the clock in summer.

more info on baby routines

raisingchildren.net.au
Search 'newborn baby routine' for a rudimentary chart, or 'routine' for lots of options for babies and sleep rituals.

BLAST FROM THE PAST

'Regularity enters largely into good mothering. The whole universe works in rhyme and mother and baby are no exceptions to the great law of order.'
– A rather pompous *Telegraph*, Brisbane, 1936

'Be flexible! Accept from the start there is no such thing as a baby routine . . . Baby Number 1 slept from 6 p.m. to 5 a.m. from 6 weeks and still needs 10 hours' sleep at age 6. But he refused to sleep during the day for more than 20 minutes: no time to get anything done. Baby Number 2 used to sleep all afternoon and stayed up until 11 p.m. Baby Number 3 woke at 11 p.m., 2 a.m., 4 a.m., 6 a.m., for 5 minutes at a time. All three now go to bed on their own.'   ANONYMOUS

BABY WASHING

Babies weren't traditionally washed every day until the 1950s scientific cleanliness mania, when mothers were told to wash their tiny tots in alcohol and antiseptic solutions. This, along with soap, meant lots of kids got dry skin. Bathing your baby once every couple of days, or few days, is plenty. Unless there has been something a bit volcanic from either end.

newborns & baths

Here's my big tip: if your newborn baby doesn't like the bath, just put them on a couple of layers of towel and give them a going-over with warm, wet, soapy cottonwool balls or throw-away gauze pads, then rinse them with non-soapy warm, wet cottonwool balls and dry them well by patting them with a towel or let the air dry them.

Newborn babies, used to being curled up in the womb, get all stretched out for a bath so it can be strange for them the first few times. It always helps to explain to your baby what you're up to as you bath them. If your baby still doesn't like it, don't continue but reintroduce the bath now and then: most babies eventually love it – at least when they can start splashing about.

Bath safety

Keep a hand and eyes on your baby *at all times* in the bath. All water, however shallow, is dangerous. Empty a baby bath or sink immediately; don't wait until later. Get a non-slip rubber mat for the big bath as soon as your baby is ready to go into it.

bathing your baby

Many people use a plastic baby bath but, as long as it's in a warm-enough room, a laundry trough or even a cleared kitchen sink is fine. Baby baths can be so heavy to lift and empty and a pain to fill from kettle and jug, especially as you'll have to put the baby down safely somewhere else if you're dickering about with kettles and hot water. Make sure any taps are out of the way, turned off tight or swivelled away.

Assemble everything you need on the bench next to the filled baby bath or sink:
- ⭐ cottonwool balls, or a face washer (if you use them on your baby's bot, wash them in antibacterial powder)
- ⭐ a liquid soap substitute – this helps avoid dry skin (ask your pharmacist for a good one for babies)
- ⭐ a soft towel (some fancy ones come with a baby hood)
- ⭐ a new nappy, and nappy-rash cream if necessary, plus a clean outfit
- ⭐ no talcum powder – it's a health risk (there's more on this in Chapter 6, Nappies).

The bathwater should be a temperature that feels pleasantly warm, but not hot, on your elbow. Don't let the baby get too cold as the water cools: you want to replicate the relaxing amniotic-fluid feeling rather than plunge them into a bracing trough.

Make sure you have one arm under your baby, supporting the neck and head, during a bath, and use the other one for washing.

A two-person team bath can be had by one adult sitting in the big bath with the baby bath on the bottom of it. The baby is bathed in the smaller receptacle by Person One, then removed by Person Two, who is also instructed to present Person One with a pineapple daiquiri.

Newborns don't need any bath toys: wait until your baby is reaching for and grabbing things before you introduce a rubber ducky or a floaty plastic anything.

Washing eyes & ears

If they look mucky, eyes should be washed separately with a cool sterile saline solution: don't hold eyes open to wash them.

Don't poke anything smaller than your elbow into a child's ear. This means you can wash any bits you can see (the outside), but *not* inside in case you damage the eardrum or introduce infection.

Washing willies & girly bits

Babies and toddlers with penises don't need to be washed under their foreskin. Between the ages of 3 and 5 the foreskin will usually become moveable, and you can teach your boy to clean underneath it himself, and eventually to understand the importance of doing so for the rest of his life. Until then, don't try to roll back the foreskin. It's tight when he's little because it's there for protection against grit and infection. Just clean the outside of the penis with a cottonwool ball when he's a bub, and normal soap and a face washer will do in the bath as he gets older.

The folds of a girl's vulva also need to be washed carefully and gently, and this skill passed on to her.

Your child & family health nurse can demonstrate good washing methods for willies and all the nooks and crannies.

bath toys

Cheap baby toys that last into toddlerhood and beyond include safe, colourful, soft plastic shell and sea creature shapes; old shampoo bottles that become squirters; sieves; plastic cups and other containers for pouring water into; all manner of plastic dollies and boats; and towelling glove puppets.

Every few weeks you can give all the plastic bath toys a good jooshing with a washing-up brush in a bucket of water to which a cup of white vinegar has been added, and then dry them in the sun to make sure there are no germy bits. On the other hand you might figure they get washed every night so get a grip. Regularly squeeze out all the old water that splooshes around in the squirty toys because otherwise it becomes a mouldy, bacterial swamp in there. If in doubt, chuck out.

BLAST FROM THE PAST
'Remember to put the cold water in the bath first and then to add the hot water to the temperature required. Test the water: if it is warm to your elbow it will be right for the baby.' – Advice from *The Weekly Times*, 1936, that still holds up.

'Bath time can be fun for everyone and a lovely way to wind down each day. I loved bathing my babies. Allow yourself plenty of time for water play, singing, cooing and tummy blurting!' MEL

first food

I couldn't bring myself to call this chapter 'Solids', as that sounds quite industrial and disgusting – especially since in the beginning 'solids' should be called 'mashes' anyway. This chapter's about when your baby first starts to eat (and throw, and try to spoon into their ear) some squished-up stuff. They'll still need breastmilk or formula milk, too.

when to start 'solid' food

'They' used to say always start giving your baby solid foods at 4 months, then 'they' said after 6 months, and now the recommendation is to start introducing a wide range of solid food after 4 months but before 6 months. This is when babies begin to need more iron and other nutrients – more than just breastmilk or formula can give them. But they still need the milk, too.

At this age babies need to start training their brain to accept new tastes and learn which foods are familiar and therefore safe, which also trains their immune system to accept safe foods so they don't develop sudden allergies. (See the 'Allergies & intolerances' section in Chapter 30, Family Food).

When you first start feeding solids, you can get stressed thinking you have to shovel it in or give babies special, rare organic foods to keep them healthy. 'Piffle!' I hear my inner nanna snorting. Just have fun throwing some nosh about – and don't forget to duck. Here's what you need to know.

baby food is about experiments

While babies are still being mainly fed on breastmilk or formula, any beginner's-food business is just rehearsals. You don't suddenly start cutting down on milk feeds. In the beginning eating is just part of life's big adventure for your baby, and you get to be there to see amazing facial expressions the first time they try strawberry ice cream (wooooow!) or something they hate (they make their mouth like a cat's bum).

In those first weeks of trying mushes, don't think of the food as sustenance or keeping your child alive. It doesn't matter if they spit it ALL out, it just means you should put 'solids' away until your baby's interested. They're not ready, and it will just make you miserable if you push it. Some kids, especially breastfeeders, could try to hold out longer than 6 months, but you do need to start offering food by then.

As long as they're getting lots of breastmilk or proper formula milk, you are hereby instructed not to panic about food. Up to 1 year old, babies should still be getting about 600 ml of breastmilk or formula milk each day. I know you can't measure your breastmilk if it's coming straight out of your nipples, but if your bub is putting on weight and pooing and weeing as usual, the amount is fine. If you're worried about quantities, talk to your child & family health nurse or doctor.

Try one new food at a time in case of an allergic reaction – then you'll be able to pick the culprit straight away. And babies will enjoy learning the individual tastes.

To mash or not to mash

Some baby folk say you don't have to mash or squish baby's first foods, and they talk about 'baby-led weaning' and how babies should go on to whole pieces of foods. Do be aware of little babies' inability to properly chew yet, so grate raw carrot to start with, for example.

Food choking hazards for babies

Things that can cut off a baby's little airway, and get stuck halfway down, include both soft and hard foods. There is no 'safe' food.

Avoid obvious dangers, such as long stringy bits of stuff (like bacon rind), and squishy-expanding foods like small pieces of sausage or hot dog, marshmallows, popcorn, cherry tomatoes and large plump grapes (cut them in half longways), hard or soft lollies, lozenges, mints and breath fresheners, raw bits of apple, meat, whole nuts, raw carrot, uncooked peas, fruit pips and pits, mini Easter eggs, corn chips and other hard chips.

Always be with your baby and watching as they eat. Choking can be utterly silent. Look up 'choking, first aid for' in the index for what to do if a kid is choking. It's in Chapter 33, Health. There's a list of non-food choking hazards in Chapter 32, Safety & Injuries.

Trying new foods

The theory goes that the more varied a diet you give your baby and toddler, the more they will experiment with new foods. It's worth a try and makes nutritional sense, but some babies have other ideas. Another evolutionary theory is that when kids start to walk they get more conservative about foods so they don't do the equivalent of wandering into the bush and eating poisonous berries. This means you don't have to take rejection of your spoon personally and can't blame the kid or yourself, because they're just exercising their in-built survival instincts.

The following things will mysteriously get food on or in them as your baby spits, flings, squeezes and pats some mash: your hair, the baby's hair, the baby's nostrils, your back pocket, the letterbox, the front of what you're wearing, the back of what you're wearing, and the pillowcase in the laundry basket. All I can say is stock up on bibs, kitchen sponges and tea towels. And tarpaulins. Eating outside is always good.

Learning to drink from a cup

A lot of babies start using a 'sippy cup', which avoids spills, after 7 months to 1 year or so. Sippy cups can collect mould or 'off' milk hidden inside their sealed and 'leak-proof' tops, valves and mouthpieces. That goes also for bottles with non-disposable straws and some push-up tops on squirty drink bottles.

Make sure you can dismantle cups and kid bottles entirely to wash and occasionally sterilise them or put them through the dishwasher. Easier still is to teach a baby or toddler to drink from a proper cup or a reusable drink bottle. You can carry a water bottle and put a little of it in a plastic cup for drinking, then throw out the leftover water when you pack up to come home.

Sippy cups are so convenient that they usually result in kids using them for long after their development means they don't need them. Sippy cups and bottles are also associated with more holes in children's teeth. Remember, kids don't need juice, cordial, flavoured milk, fizzy drink or drinks with sugar, and shouldn't drink cow's or other milk before the age of 1 year, so water should be your go-to drink on the go.

Organic & 'natural' baby food

'Natural' could mean anything. Everything – even water – is made of chemicals, so beware of meaningless marketing. Organic products should be certified with the approved logo (check it out at Australian Certified Organic: aco.net.au). Independent studies of organic foods suggest they are not necessarily more nutritious than 'normal' foods.

Organic products do, however, contribute to a healthier planet by encouraging the reduction of pesticides where their use is unnecessary. And chefs and other food gurus encourage the availability of local, diverse and 'heritage' fruits and vegies. Let your own philosophy, and what you can afford, be your guide.

some foods to start on

Put the bub in a highchair, or somewhere else wipe-cleanable or hoseable such as the backyard, and try a teaspoon or two of one of the following:

⭐ iron-fortified rice cereal for babies (homemade recipes
   can be found in baby cookbooks but will be low in iron) –
   this is usually given first because of the iron and because you
   mix it up with breastmilk or formula milk so it's not too wildly
   different a taste for the baby, and because it's runny and easy
   to swallow

⭐ cooked, pureed fruit flesh – raw fruits can be hard to digest

⭐ mashed ripe, raw banana or avocado (although some bubs hate
   the 'slimy' texture)

⭐ pureed cooked pumpkin or sweet potato

⭐ full-fat yoghurts, with live cultures

⭐ tiny pinches of totally squished-up bits of chicken, fish, beef,
   lamb or tofu

⭐ rusks – homemade or from the supermarket baby aisle;
   these are good for a teething bub when the baby teeth are
   breaking through the gums.

Your baby could become more enthusiastic about a taste they haven't liked if you leave it for a couple of weeks and then try again. Or they might need a new food to be offered up to ten or more times to accept the idea of eating it. And if you don't introduce a food at all during the baby stage, toddlers are likely to be very suspicious of it later: you'll have to offer it many more times. I forgot to introduce tomatoes early, and they were treated as if they were small ticking bombs for months.

> 'The food most often offered to babies in a Western diet is fortified rice cereal, a far cry from fatty nuk-tuk.'
> SBS.COM.AU

'I never want to hear the word "puree" again, even if it is French.'   CLEO

babies' nutritional needs

'Listen' to your child and be guided by their interest in food or rejection of it. As long as they aren't offered solids straight after a big breastfeed or bottle-feed, and as long as they're not sick, they'll probably eat enough to keep them going. In the first few weeks the 'eating' is just experimenting, and up to the age of 1 year the real nutrition is still coming from the breastmilk or formula milk. Gradually you can build up the amount from a few teaspoons: ask your child & family health nurse what's right for your baby's size, weight and interest in food, if you're concerned.

Food for babies older than 1 year

Babies won't eat exactly the same amount at each meal on each day, or the same amount each day. Most parents recognise an erratic lurching-about rather than a pattern. The cup referred to in the list of serving sizes coming up is a standard metric measuring cup, but the amount suggested doesn't have to be exact – it's just a guide. These are minimum requirements: to have more is also fine, but offer more variety rather than more of one thing.

There's no need, once you get the hang of portion sizes, to weigh and measure food. Life doesn't work like that. Feeding kids isn't a perfectly calibrated science, and besides it will send you screamy la la bonkers. As long as you have fresh and varied food on offer from the groups listed and your kid is putting on weight, you're doing fine.

Things to avoid until after 1 year

Current guidelines from child dieticians say you should delay giving some foods to children. Until 1 year old, they suggest holding back on:

★ straight cow's milk (but not formula based on cow's milk) because there is not enough nutritional value in it

★ honey because it could have bacteria in it that babies are more vulnerable to

★ whole nuts or big chunks – use nut spreads instead.

Daily needs for babies 1 year old & over

1½ serves of cereal-type things   A serve is 1 cup of pasta, rice noodles or porridge; or 2 slices of bread.

1 serve of fruit   A serve is a bit of fruit or bits of different fruit adding up to the size of 1 apple; or 1 cup of tinned fruit.

1 serve of vegies   A serve is ½ a cup of cooked vegies; or 2 large scoops of mashed vegies; or 1 potato; or 1 cup of salad vegies.

⅔ of a serve of proteiny things   ⅔ of a serve is 1 large chop; or ⅓ of a cup of cooked mince; or 60 grams of any other meat (a thin slice about the size of an adult palm); or 1½ eggs; or ⅓ of a cup (100 grams) of beans.

2½ serves of dairy stuff   A serve is 1 cup of milk or custard; or 2 slices of cheese; or 1 small (200-gram) tub of yoghurt.

If you think your child needs a vitamin boost, talk about it with your child & family health nurse or your doctor.

~~~~~~~~~~ **more info** on learning to eat ~~~~~~~~~~

Most parenting websites have advice, suggestions and recipes for first foods, but on commercial websites, suggestions may be influenced by advertisers.

raisingchildren.net.au
This comprehensive site has great info on good baby food and how to prepare it. On the main page, choose 'babies', then 'Nutrition', and away you go.

cyh.com
The South Australian Child and Youth Health website has fact sheets on food for babies. Choose 'Parenting and Child Health' on the home page, then 'Nutrition' from the alphabetical list.

Avoiding allergies

Breastfeeding does not cause or prevent allergies. Special baby formulas don't cause or prevent allergies. Giving babies common allergens won't cause a food allergy unless they were already 'programmed' to get one. Feeding a baby little bits of all foods regularly before the age of 1 is now thought to protect them against allergy by 'training' their immune system a little bit at a time.

Allergy specialists recommend you feed babies from the start with all sorts of different foods (in small amounts to start with) so you can check for any rare, allergic reaction), including dairy, wheat, fish, cooked egg, and nut pastes. Restricting babies and kids to soy, rice or goat's formulas and milks, or nut juices (often called 'milks'), won't prevent an allergy or intolerance. There's more stuff on allergies and intolerances in Chapter 30, Family Food.

BLAST FROM THE PAST

'Wean a baby at 9 months old, or when four or five teeth appear. Introduce meat such as mutton at 18 months old . . . a draught of water may be given between meals till the child is 5 or 6 and after that a piece of bread will be sufficient to prevent exhaustion, which is all that is required.' – *The Handbook for Wives and Mothers of the Working Classes*, 1873. It's a wonder anybody survived, really.

'Unless you're advised otherwise by a medical specialist, all babies can be given foods that are "common" food allergens, including products with butter, thoroughly cooked egg, dairy, smooth peanut butter and other nut butters (with no added sugar), and wheat. Offer them regularly, starting before 1 year.' KATE, **expert paediatric dietician**

15 MULTIPLES

The news that you're going to have more than one baby has hardly sunk in when suddenly you have a much bigger family than you expected. And are being bombarded with clichés. Twins and triplets, you'll be told, are 'double trouble' or 'three times the joy'. Pay yourself a dollar into a jar each time you hear this, because eventually you'll be able to buy yourself a yacht. Here are hints about having multiples, from feelings to feedings – and some snappy comebacks for those annoying comments.

feelings & fears about multiples

There are special considerations around having more than one baby at once, just as there are fears about having one. A pregnancy with multiples is likely to involve more tiredness, more hormones running around your system, often a greater weight gain. Babies might come early because they feel like it, or to ensure a safer delivery, so your bubs might be underweight or need special medical care.

Because you'll have an extra dose of pregnancy hormones that 'turn off' after the birth, and you face the possibly daunting task of being mum to twins or more, you might go through a period of feeling depressed or freaked out (see Chapter 11, Getting Through Tough Times, if that's how you feel). You'd be mad if you didn't feel at least a bit apprehensive about how you'll manage everything.

Handy multiples facts

* Forget 'perfect'. It is dead to you.
* Lots of people have had twins or more and managed it really well.
* None of them tried to do it without help: don't try to be a martyr and go it alone. There are people you can talk to and places you can go, from phone counsellors to residential-care centres. (As well as 'More info on multiples' coming up, see the parent helplines and services listed in Chapter 2, Your Help Team.)
* If you're loving and kind to your babies, it doesn't matter if the washing isn't done – but ask a friend to do it anyway.
* The first six months are likely to be really intensive. Apart from finding time for feeding, changing and washing (and that's just the grown-ups), you'll be getting to know some new people with different personalities. This is the hardest part; then it gets easier.

a support team for multiples

If possible, get a 'project manager' for when the babies arrive: a sister, mum, close friend or partner who can ideally take some time off work, but in any case can help coordinate rosters for helpers and food bringers, and do other sensible things such as answer the telephone, organise meals, and keep visitors away unless they're actually assisting the process of settling the newies into the home.

People often don't offer to help because they don't know what to do: assign tasks based on capability and ability to learn, rather than waiting for people to work out what to do. This makes them feel needed and wanted instead of all at sea.

Ask for help from strangers as well as family and friends. 'Here, feed this baby with a bottle while I do the other one,' said a mother of twins to my partner once, in a public place: he was thrilled. People are almost always happy to help with prams and hold doors open as long as you need them. Always ask.

If it's at all possible, get someone to pay for a cleaner for at least a while. If it isn't, try a roster of friends and family.

See the contacts in 'More info on multiples' coming up for support and help. (If you come across the term 'super twins' online it means a multiple birth with more than two babies.) For more on toilet training, when the time comes, see 'Twins & the loo' in Chapter 22, Toilet Training.

Reasons to be cheerful about multiples

⁕ The idea of dressing identical twins in exactly the same clothes has mostly long gone, though some parents swear by its simplicity and say the kids want it that way.

⁕ Fingers crossed, down the track, your multiples will play together while you lie on the couch wearing a bejewelled turban.

⁕ You've produced a whole family all at once, like an efficiency expert. Do pretend you did it on purpose.

⁕ You have a ready-made excuse not to do anything else, such as 'bring a plate' to a family do, until, I would suggest, the babies leave home.

⁕ You're not alone. There are parents like you and support groups everywhere.

⁕ Each child will gradually have their own special interests, ideas and possessions, but in the meantime they can share equipment and toys: one mum informed me this honeymoon period ended at 6 weeks.

⁕ Most people will be cluey enough to refer to your children by their individual names rather than 'the twins' each time.

multiple babies & sleep

Most parents of multiple babies need help to establish a sleep routine to avoid the sanity-challenging situation where one baby sleeps but the other stays awake, then they swap and the parent never gets any rest. See the 'More info' sections in Chapter 8, Baby Sleep, for books and other help, or ask your GP or child & family health nurse to refer you to a sleep 'clinic' or parenting centre where you can get sensible 'training'.

feeding the multitudes

Bosoms, bottles or a mix of both? The most important thing is to change if and when you need to. And use all the help with feeding you can get. Feeding one baby while the other cries can be very stressful and emotional for you, but there will be no harm done to the bubs. Some mums can breastfeed two babies at the same time, given support, practice, the right seat and pillow arrangement, and bribes of up to $300 a bosom. Some mums use expressed breastmilk in bottles for one bub during the day and breastfeed that twin at night. Others say this is too difficult and requires too much time expressing when you might as well be feeding.

For ideas on how to stay on track feeding two as a routine, see your child & family health nurse or get in touch with the Australian Breastfeeding Association. Or hire a private lactation consultant with multiples experience. (See Chapter 4, Breastfeeding, and Chapter 5, Bottle-feeding, for more in general.)

> 'They're just people and it takes a while to get to know them.'
> A MUM OF TWINS

∿∿∿∿∿ more info on breastfeeding multiples ∿∿∿

breastfeeding.asn.au
Advice line: 1800 686 268 (or 1800 MUM 2 MUM) (24-hour)
The Australian Breastfeeding Association can help on the spot or put you in touch with mums who have breastfed or are breastfeeding twins. On the home page, search 'twins', 'triplets' and 'premature baby' for fact sheets. You can also check out recommended breast pumps (under 'Services').

how people react to multiple babies & kids

When you have multiple babies some people say extremely stupid things to you. It's like there's no filter between their brain and their mouth. Here are some comments you'll hear, probably more than once, and some handy replies.

'Oh, my God! Twins!'

'I suppose you could be right.'

'You'll go mad.'

'Well, I've had lots of practice.'

'Are there twins in the family?'

'Yes, these are the twins in our family.'

'Were you on IVF?'

'Why do you ask?'

'Are they natural?'

'No, they're completely made of plastic.'

'They must be a handful.'

'Must they?'

'Are they identical?'

'I'm not sure. I've never looked.'

(or)

'Are they twins?'

'Oh no, they're not even related.'

The all-purpose 'Wow', 'Really?' or 'Did you just say that out loud?' accompanied by a level stare is a good response to any intrusive question.

BLAST FROM THE PAST

'Six babies in 27 months. The babies are those of Mrs James Campbell, West Brunswick, and comprised triplets, twins and a single child. The babies' names are Jean, triplets Florence, William and Alfred, then twins Colville and George. Her eldest baby, Herbert, died aged 8 months.'
– Explanation of special prize awarded at the Baby Show at Caulfield, *The Argus*, 1931. (Not one of several news reports at the time records poor Mrs Campbell's own first name.)

~~~~~~~~ more info on multiples ~~~~~~~~

amba.org.au
The not-for-profit Australian Multiple Birth Association (AMBA) provides support and info, from the happy and funny side of things to acknowledgement and help, to knowing that parents of multiples are at higher risk of anxiety and depression.

raisingchildren.net.au
Search 'twins' on this government-funded parenting website to find out the difference between fraternal, identical and other sorts of twins, and refer busy-bodies or friends to it so you don't have to tell a grizillion people the same things.

twins.org.au
Twins Research Australia is a hub for twins, twin researchers, people who can help with studies on twins – you get the picture.

***Twins* by Katrina Bowman and Louise Ryan (Allen & Unwin)**
By two Australian mums of twins who give honest assessments of feelings, fears and practicalities.

multiples.org.nz
The website of Multiples New Zealand.

BLAST FROM THE PAST
'Triplets are exceedingly rare . . . in 1923 (the latest available statistics) there were only six cases of triplets in the whole of the Commonwealth.'
– *Warwick Daily News*, Queensland, 1925

'I kept telling myself "humans are learning animals" when I was trying to get the twins to coordinate their daytime naps. I put them in separate rooms.'   NICI

'It amazes me how many times this happens: Random stranger: "Ooh, twins. Are they IVF?" Me: "No, they're S.E.X." Then I quickly walk away.'   FREMANTLE GIRL

16

BABY DEVELOPMENT

Babies are social. For the first few months they need
to hang out with their people. Babies develop their
social and other skills at different rates. Think of the age
ranges given in this chapter for 'milestones' as a kind of
average. Your baby might roll over very early, but take
a little longer than most kids to walk. No drama.

how babies change & learn

All kids learn social and physical skills by interacting with their parents, siblings or carers. Much of what seems like straightforward development, such as being able to grasp a toy, helps kids learn other skills as well, such as hand-eye coordination. Every time your baby topples over they are learning what not to do in order to stay upright. So 'mistakes' or everyday events and movements are very important for kids learning how to use and enjoy their bodies.

Learning by doing

Baby skills don't come pre-wrapped inside your bub. A baby doesn't know how to try to sing a song or roll a ball until somebody shows them and practises with them as a fun game. Just spending time with your baby doing simple things will help them develop in their own way.

Your baby could develop at about the pace outlined in the lists that follow or get to 'milestones' a bit sooner, or later. This doesn't mean they're 'advanced' or 'backward'. It means they're in the normal range. Some babies miss 'stages' altogether: there are plenty of kids who turn up their nose at crawling, one minute doing a funky bum-shuffle or that commando tummy crawling, and the next standing up and wobbling about.

How your child develops and which milestones are reached when depend on a complex interaction between their genes, their prior development and their environment: a kid in a sporty family of nine who live on a beach in Queensland might develop some skills more quickly and some more slowly than an only child in a family of oboe players who live where it snows most of the year and whose home is full of books.

Babies need to mature naturally to certain levels before they can acquire more skills. Giving lots of encouragement, praise and cuddles goes for every stage of your child's life and development.

There are also ideas in this chapter on fun activities that help development. The point is for the child to enjoy them and then move on when they feel like it. You're not 'training' them. You're just playing, and that's how they learn.

For premmie babies it's important to adjust the milestones range to the age they'd be if they'd been born on their due date – that is, if your 3-month-old bub was one month premature, check out the development range for a 2-month-old baby in the list below. In some cases their abilities could be a little curtailed by the fact they have so much catching up to do. See a paediatrician about when they'll catch up.

Beware of articles and forum comments on parenting blogs and websites: the advice could be helpful or it might be outdated, incorrect, judgemental and shouty, or just plain bonkers. Just because it's on a fancy website or said by a celebrity or someone who really believes what they're saying doesn't make it right.

When to see a doctor about development worries

Any time is a good time to ask questions, especially if you're worried or have a niggling feeling. All babies can stop being interested in eye contact now and then, especially when they're tired. It's the pattern of your baby's behaviour over time that's important, so talk to your child & family health nurse, who will have much more of a grasp on babies in general – you will always be the expert on yours. See your doctor if you're concerned about your child's progress. If your baby performs some deliberate physical movements or becomes chatty, but then seems to go 'backwards', see your doctor. It's always worth raising a worry: it will either result in reassurance, or an assessment that leads to getting some help. There are a few other specific 'See your doctor if' suggestions in the development lists below.

BLAST FROM THE PAST

'The child does not hear until the third or fourth day . . . by the end of the first year the child begins to express itself in sounds . . . the development depends on the intellectual powers.' – Absolute nonsense told to mothers by *The Mercury and Weekly Courier*, Victoria, 1896

Babies & screens

Babies should not be watching any TV, game, tablet or phone screen. An age-appropriate toy or a book is a much better distraction for your baby's development as it engages their brain in important social learning.

Parents should spend lots of time interacting with their babies and speak to them, sing to them, and have 'conversations' in different singsong tones. 'Baby talk' helps your baby to learn and develop their vocabulary, speech and social areas of their brains, even if it will be months before they say their first word.

It doesn't matter if your conversations are nonsensical or the songs unlikely to win you a recording contract. This is how babies learn to identify and understand emotions, facial expressions and voice tones, and develop other vital social and speech skills.

When a parent is constantly or often on the phone or looking at a screen while with a baby, the baby is learning the wrong 'cues' and responses for conversations, and for processing and expressing feelings.

baby development milestones

These milestone times are averages, and will vary among babies – even babies in the same family.

newborn baby (first 6 weeks)

Physical development

Your newborn:

★ knows its mother's voice as soon as it's born
★ responds to a higher-pitched, baby-talk voice
★ sees faces that are close up – about the distance between a mother's and a baby's face when breastfeeding
★ makes random and jerky movements
★ needs their neck supported

⭐ will stay in the position you put them in to sleep

⭐ sees the world first in strong contrasts of light and dark

⭐ will look towards a light if they can't focus on an object

⭐ can smell breastmilk and see the darker areola on the breast, and will turn their head and home in on it

⭐ loves skin-to-skin-in-the-nuddy contact

⭐ is just starting to touch, smell, taste, hear their new world

⭐ has a curly-up body and hands – they'll unfurl in their own time

⭐ tends to need quiet, especially if they're preterm, while their hearing develops to cope with louder sounds.

Reflexes

Reflexes are involuntary movements; the newborn's reflexes are unique to babies and disappear over time.

✳ Stepping: for about the first 2 months when you hold a baby vertically and their legs touch the floor or another surface, they'll look as if they're trying to walk.

✳ Rooting (obviously not named by an Australian): a tickle of a finger, a breast or a nipple on a baby's cheek will make their mouth automatically open for a feed.

✳ Startling (also known as the Moro reflex): a baby throws out their arms and legs automatically when they are startled or feel lost in space.

✳ Sucking: for months everything available goes in the mouth because it's the baby's means of checking things out.

✳ Grasping: a baby curls their fingers around an adult finger, but otherwise keeps them in a fist.

✳ Survival: a baby should turn their head if their mouth and nose are accidentally covered, to try to get more air.

'Babies want to be enthusiastically enjoyed by other people from the beginning of life. When that happens they feel good about themselves, with a healthy pride and good self-esteem and secure attachment.'   FRANCES, a child psychotherapist

Emotional & mental development

Your newborn:

- ⭐ is learning to love you
- ⭐ can't quite get their brain to tell the rest of their body what to do
- ⭐ is easily startled and needs a soothing environment
- ⭐ is learning to trust you and know 'their people' (family and carers)
- ⭐ likes relaxing music (think classical or reggae, not thrash metal)
- ⭐ likes listening to baby-talk with exaggerated vowels
- ⭐ can recognise the face of their mother, father and other carers if they have a lot of contact, and prefers expressive faces, but not wildly changing ones
- ⭐ will have some unconscious and some experimental facial expressions
- ⭐ learns how to fit expressions to feelings and mimic faces
- ⭐ can recognise their mother's voice and then their dad's
- ⭐ has their own feelings
- ⭐ needs to feel your loving touch and kindness
- ⭐ is also learning eating, digesting, sleeping, breathing, moving, seeing, hearing and other stuff
- ⭐ has dreams – it's now believed that babies probably dream even before they leave the womb.

Communication development

Your newborn:

- ⭐ communicates mainly by crying
- ⭐ can also let you know how they are feeling by being suddenly still and wary, or shaping themselves to your body, or relaxing with skin-to-skin contact and breastfeeding; or even by staring hard when trying to understand or make a connection with you
- ⭐ still has the equivalent of an on-off switch from comfy/happy to hungry or wet/crying.

What can you do to help a developing newborn baby?

Try lots of baby-talk, lots of cuddling, songs and baby massage. Massage is believed to be calming, especially in their first 3 months, and also helps a baby become aware of their body and feelings of touch and movement. Baby massage is good.

Don't think you have to do anything special to entertain your newborn: sitting still in a chair having a cuddle and a chat for a while before a sleep is good for them and doesn't cost a cent. If you're out walking the pram, don't spend all your time on your mobile: talk to your baby – they love it!

When you're talking to your baby, pause for responses: pretend they've answered. This is more entertaining for you, and the baby has time to develop reactions, even facial expressions, that will show you they're trying to keep up and communicate. Bubs can be very good at compensating when they can't hear, so for your own peace of mind ask your doctor or your child & family health nurse to do or arrange a hearing test. Sadly, these are not done automatically for each child.

If you have had a grumpy or stressful day, try to start afresh the next hour, after a nap, or at least the next day so your baby is reassured.

Let them spend time unwrapped, with little spurts of 'tummy time' so they learn to hold their head up independently so they can kick and wave, even if they're not quite sure what they're doing. You can start at one to two minutes a few times a day, and then build up to ten or fifteen minutes a time in a few weeks. There will be face planting, so make it a soft surface. See 'Tummy time for newborns' in Chapter 1, Your New Baby, for instructions.

6-week-old baby

Physical development

An awful lot seems to go on at 6 weeks. One day researchers will probably work out why. Some people say it's also a peak time for crying for many babies. Your baby:
- will probably cry real tears
- probably smiles at things
- stares, fixated, at things – maybe a person, maybe an object. Sometimes this is because their eyes aren't yet used to doing what the brain wants them to do, and they just get kind of stuck. You can move the whole baby so their gaze is broken
- is less floppy, and can hold their head up independently – there's more head and neck control now
- responds to faces and other things up close, but also notices things further away and more to the side rather than right in front or above.

Emotional & mental development

At 6 weeks your baby has fleeting 'emotions', shown by gurgling happily or crying inconsolably, although these episodes are over and forgotten practically immediately. But if the same thing makes the baby cry each time – a particularly loud and bumptious relative, for example – the baby will learn to cry when that person picks them up and speaks to them in a shouty voice, and will 'remember' the nice smells and feelings of being rescued by their mum or dad.

Communication development

At 6 weeks your baby is steadily practising all those newborn ways of communicating with you.

At 6 weeks, what can you do to help development?

Give your baby more of those cuddles, chats and songs, but also lots of 'tummy time' to develop their arm, leg and abdominal action. This is also a counterbalance to babies being put to sleep on their backs – one of the recommendations to help avoid SIDS (sudden infant death syndrome). If your baby doesn't like tummy time, try it on your chest instead of the floor, giving them the 'reward' of seeing your smiling, encouraging face if they lift up their head.

Let your baby uncurl and straighten out at their own pace, but feel free to move and bend their arms and legs gently if they enjoy it. Put a rattle in their hand and let them learn what it's for (there could be some preliminary accidental eye-whacking, so make it a lightweight plastic rattle).

2-month-old baby

Physical development

At 2 months your baby:

- ⭐ still usually has closed fists most of the time – although they will curl them around a finger or other object
- ⭐ is following an object with their eyes more smoothly, with fewer jerks
- ⭐ can focus more easily on things to the side, front and centre
- ⭐ waves their arms around trying to get control of them
- ⭐ is starting to distinguish colours as well as light and dark.

Emotional & mental development

At 2 months your baby:

- ⭐ is trying to make sense of so many things at once that they get tired
- ⭐ is learning emotional responses, taking their cues from you.

Communication development

At 2 months your baby:

- ⭐ wants to make contact and talk with you
- ⭐ smiles more in response
- ⭐ makes extended, babbly vowel sounds and has totally incomprehensible chats. Excellent 'conversations' can be had. Actual words start to come out much later (usually at about 9 to 12 months or just after).

At 2 months, what can you do to help development?

Your baby is learning conversational tone from you so be amazed, serious, thrilled at what they're telling you, and tell them lots of stuff too. They'll be riveted. Be lively but not frightening (that'll be when they cry or look freaked out). Sing to them. Repeat the sounds your baby makes so they can practise the sounds with you.

Babies communicate with you even before they can talk. They need to experience changes in your facial expression, mouth position and voice tone to develop their brain, feel loved, socialise and (eventually) learn to talk. If you talk to others on the phone for extended periods while with your baby, or talk to your baby while you look at a screen, this can confuse their communication and social development.

3-month-old baby

Physical development

At 3 months your baby:
- ⭐ may have a growth spurt that requires feeds more often for a day or so
- ⭐ definitely seems to have worked out that their hands are attached
- ⭐ continues using their mouth to explore the world
- ⭐ lifts their head to look around while lying on their tummy – maybe with a slight 'push-up' action of the arms
- ⭐ sits when propped up and held
- ⭐ continues to watch things intently now and again
- ⭐ grasps something put in their hand.

Emotional & mental development

At 3 months your baby:
- ⭐ can suddenly laugh or giggle
- ⭐ recognises familiar people.

Communication development

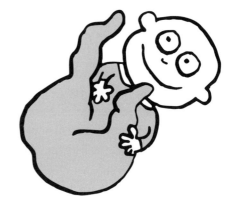

At 3 months your baby:
- ⭐ is more sociable
- ⭐ smiles at voices, faces and things
- ⭐ has funny little noises that are attempts to make a connection.

At 3 months, what can you do to help development?

Most babies are social and, when feeling secure, love to have new experiences and see new people, places and objects. Keep it simple and don't introduce too many things: learn your baby's tired signs (look up 'tired signs' in the index) so you'll know when there's been a little too much stimulation and it's time for a nap. Put your baby on the floor a lot, continuing 'tummy time'.

Give your baby shakers and rattles, safe plastic toys in bright colours, and soft toys with furry or silky sensuous textures to play with. Dangle things for them to whack and eventually grab.

Keep up the chat and songs and show them simple board books you borrow or buy. Colourful, dangly, musical, revolving mobiles are a hit at this age.

Babies, kids & eyes

* Babies are born near-sighted, because for the first little while they only really need to see faces, bosoms or bottles, and the difference between light and dark.

* By about 4 months they're getting better at noticing different colours and watching things that move or are further away. By about 8 months they should have it pretty together and be able to see things in the distance. But you still need to help them protect their eyes and develop their eyesight skills.

* Have fun with your babies and toddlers by pointing out things in the middle distance, far away and up high, so they're used to using their eyes in different ways. Babies don't need to look at fancy toys or screen 'games or tests to have good eyesight. They need plenty of time in the outdoors to help develop their eyesight (see 'Toddler eyes' in Chapter 25, Toddler Development). Babies under 3 months can't use sunscreen, so be extra careful with protective hats, clothing and shade (see 'Sun protection' in Chapter 33, Health).

* It's better to have a pram or stroller umbrella, or a shade screen with mesh sides, that can be repositioned to keep bub in the shade than to cover the baby's area with a bunny rug or muslin wrap, which restricts light and airflow.

* Get your doctor to check your baby's eyes if one seems to move or behave differently from the other, or they appear to be crossed most of the time, or are otherwise a bit unusual. Most eye problems can be corrected with time, glasses or, in the longer run, simple surgery.

4- to 5-month-old baby

Physical development

At 4–5 months your baby:
- ⭐ is able to see colours, not just black-and-white shapes
- ⭐ may roll from their tummy onto their back
- ⭐ holds up and moves their head independently
- ⭐ can grab something dangled within reach
- ⭐ may start to try to get toys that are out of reach
- ⭐ is becoming stronger and pushes harder with their legs and arms
- ⭐ is feeling some things with their hands
- ⭐ is still exploring most things with their mouth
- ⭐ often drools a lot – bring on the bibs.

Emotional & mental development

At 4–5 months your baby:
- ⭐ laughs when you pull funny faces
- ⭐ likes looking in a mirror
- ⭐ shows their enjoyment of, for example, music, and delight at leaves blowing in the wind
- ⭐ expresses concern at stressful or shouty situations.

Communication development

At 4–5 months your baby:
- ⭐ is learning how to interact with people more
- ⭐ is working out how to communicate using their face, body language and babble
- ⭐ shows feelings in their facial expressions. Can't fake them.

At 4–5 months, what can you do to help development?

You can help your baby to stand and 'walk' by holding their hands if they enjoy it – but 'baby walker' contraptions won't help them walk any earlier, and are dangerous. Let your baby have a clear view of their own feet, and take their shoes and socks off as much as possible so they can feel things with their toes – this applies to babies of all ages.

Play with your baby's hands and feet so they work out that those bits belong to them and can be manipulated. Try 'tummy time' in front of a mirror so that when they lift their head up they can see their reflection (although they might not yet recognise themselves).

Keep showing your baby simple board books. This will be the start of all sorts of language and understanding development. Kids love stories and pictures even at this age. And don't worry, they all chew the corners.

Play peekaboo, make funny noises, blow raspberries on their tum. Play different kinds of music and dance with your bub – but not spooky, scary classical or frenetic hard rock: babies and kids are very sensitive to the mood music creates. Try some boppy songs or songs especially for babies or kids.

Find time to do some things you like by yourself or with a partner or friends. A trip out of Babyland is a helpful break and you can come back refreshed.

6-month-old baby

Physical development

At 6 months your baby:
- ⭐ reaches for and grabs things
- ⭐ still uses their mouth more than their fingers to feel objects
- ⭐ can stick their toes in their mouth
- ⭐ checks things out solemnly
- ⭐ can maybe pass an item from one hand to the other
- ⭐ usually can't hold things in two hands at once
- ⭐ may find peekaboo a big hit
- ⭐ is starting to enjoy having an effect by whacking, throwing and picking up
- ⭐ recognises their own name and perhaps other names
- ⭐ hears high-frequency sounds better than low-frequency ones, but is still not hearing softer noises as well as an adult does. By this age a hearing test should have been done by your child & family health nurse or doctor if the hearing wasn't tested in hospital
- ⭐ can sit unsupported for a few minutes

⭐ is ready to experiment with 'solid' food, and to learn lots of new tastes

⭐ may have their first teeth starting to come through just as they get interested in food (see Chapter 36, Teeth)

⭐ may put their arms out as if to say 'Lift me up'.

Emotional & mental development

At 6 months your baby:

⭐ is simply much more engaged with the world around them

⭐ will develop emotionally much more between 6 months and 1 year

⭐ will become aware of more sophisticated feelings (outrage, surprise, amusement)

⭐ recognises themselves in the mirror and finds it fascinating

⭐ may start getting clingy in the next 6 months, maybe peaking at around 18 months. They show a clear preference for the close family circle. (They are hardwired not to wander away, but don't let that fool you: some develop into escapees.)

Communication development

At 6 months your baby:

⭐ mimics facial expressions and sounds

⭐ probably has a funny baby chat, often to themselves

⭐ matches sounds and actions to events – waving bye-bye; ducky goes quack

⭐ responds to chat from others with facial expressions, body movements and sounds

⭐ has a crack at saying a word or sound here and there, or even a babble-sentence.

At 6 months, what can you do to help development?

Over the next few months your baby will enjoy doing things they seem to have control over: batting at things that make a noise or that pop up, or fiddling with objects.

Songs and nursery rhymes help babies learn tone, rhythm and words. Play together with simple musical instruments – a lot of these, like most things, can be homemade. Try a saucepan-and-wooden-spoon drum, and a plastic jar with lentils (and a tight lid!) to shake.

Flop down on a rug in the shade in the garden or a nearby park and just relax: look at butterflies and blades of grass, talk about the clouds and people going by.

Showing your baby photos of special friends, carers and relatives and talking about these people can help to widen their circle when the immediate family are not around for a while.

Encourage and praise independence in your baby, while making them also feel secure. (Yes, sorry – in other words, be perfect while doing two opposite things at once.)

See your doctor if by 6 months your baby never smiles or if your baby hasn't rolled over by themselves.

BLAST FROM THE PAST
'At six months, baby has become a lively, rowdy little person.'
– *South Western Advertiser*, WA, 1938

7-month-old baby

Physical development

At 7 months your baby:
- can sit up without being propped
- continues to hone their reaching and grabbing
- will try to see the source of sounds
- tries to move to see something or be nearer something (so re-babyproof the house!)
- will stretch out or angle their head to see better or be part of the action
- still throws up if they cough or cry a lot or something gets caught in their throat or is put well into their mouth. This is the gag-reflex survival instinct that babies have from birth, which may last for years
- may be an early starter for crawling or bum-shuffling (some babies miss out on the crawling stage – it's usually not a problem).

Emotional & mental development

At 7 months your baby:
- ★ remembers what certain toys are built to do
- ★ points at things to indicate 'I want that'
- ★ plays swapsies with you (you take it – now give it back)
- ★ has worked out how to get your attention.

Communication development

At 7 months your baby:
- ★ is becoming more and more social
- ★ takes increasing interest in their world and understands more of conversations and atmospheres
- ★ loves a chat.

At 7 months, what can you do to help development?

Keep making things available for your baby to grasp and listen to.

Don't be alarmed if you see your baby adopt strange sleeping positions, even curled up on their tum with bum in the air and head to the side. If your baby can roll onto their tum to sleep they should be able to roll back if they want to: the tum position is more of a worry for younger babies who can't move themselves. This new mobility is a sign of your needing to worry less – not more!

Make baby sounds such as 'bub bub bub' for your baby to copy, and listen to their attempts to communicate, responding as if in conversation. Repeat the names for things and put them in sentences, so that 'hat' is associated with that thing that goes on the head, and 'drink' is the wet yummy stuff referred to in 'What would you like to drink? Milk? Okay then.' Repetition is the key to building a vocabulary of understood words. Explain to the baby what's going on around them. Read simple storybooks to them and explain the pictures. Babies this age love animated conversation: play with facial expressions and body language. Let them watch you dance, and 'dance' them in your arms.

Over the next month or so, introduce paper and big crayons and pencils, things with wheels such as large plastic trucks, and building blocks (knocking down might come before building up, so get in there and help).

Roll a ball to your baby and encourage them to roll it back. Keep giving them toys they can have an influence on – especially those where something pops out or makes a noise when they press a lever. Also introduce them to shape-sorting 'put in the slot' toys or other toys that provide putting-in and taking-out opportunities, and to a sturdy cart or toy to push along.

Give them careful swings and slides at the park, where they can also watch other kids playing.

8-month-old baby

Physical development

At 8 months your baby:

- ★ may start to crawl from now on
- ★ can look for and find a toy you have hidden
- ★ likes to fill things up and empty them
- ★ loves any game of 'now you see it, now you don't'
- ★ can sit alone but might fall over once in a while
- ★ should turn their head to locate the source of a noise.

Emotional & mental development

At 8 months your baby:

- ★ knows who their primary carer or 'attachment' figures are (usually mums and/or dads)
- ★ may start to develop separation anxiety and attachment to other people and things
- ★ starts to understand the idea that something or someone who disappears will come back again
- ★ can discern your mood by your tone and body language.

Communication development

At 8 months your baby:

- ★ is developing more control over the babble, and their 'words' sound more like real conversation
- ★ in the next month or so will develop greater powers of concentration and learning from what they've seen. This means if they've always had milk in a green cup they could be dubious about a yellow one.

At 8 months, what can you do to help development?

Gently broaden your child's circle of carers. Help your baby with the idea of something going away and coming back – hide a toy under a tea towel and let them reveal it. Lift-the-flap board books are still perfect for this age.

Use toys that they can have an effect on: blocks to build up and knock down, banging and shaking things such as musical instruments, and toys that can be pushed or pulled or that go on wheels.

Walks with lots of pointing-out of things and chats with neighbours and shop-keepers can be fun: remember, what's mundane to you is new and perfectly thrilling to a baby. (Which is why you can be infected with the delight, but need to have time off to do adult things! You can only go gaga over a dandelion so many times when you're a grown-up.)

9-month-old to 1-year-old baby

Physical development

At 9 months to 1 year your baby is:
- crawling or shuffling
- climbing over or going around things (but they usually prefer to go right through them!)
- pulling themselves up to a standing position
- then looking confused and plonking down on their bot
- 'walking' when an adult holds their hand, or alone, tottering
- dropping things for you to pick up
- passing things from hand to hand
- throwing things
- clapping their hands
- waving bye-bye
- using a spoon or a fork, holding a cup, clutching food
- picking up small things; by about 1 year they've mastered the true 'pincer movement', using their thumb and first finger
- not putting everything in their mouth (but still doing it often, until 2 years old or so).

Emotional & mental development

At 9 months to 1 year your baby:

⭐ will probably show more of their 'personality', and quirks will become recognisable

⭐ will probably become an alert observer

⭐ even though they can't see an object, will probably know it still exists ('object permanence' – a friend of mine says this never works with her ex-boyfriends)

⭐ will probably know where things 'belong' on a shelf and which way up they should be

⭐ will probably grasp simple concepts and explanations

⭐ will probably enjoy familiar songs and rhymes, or sets of words

⭐ may become more clingy as they gear up for crawling and walking – this is evolution's way of keeping babies safely close to home instead of pootling off into the bush

⭐ might show a preference for a fluffy toy.

Communication development

At 9 months to 1 year your baby can probably:

⭐ interact by making eye contact, copying facial expressions

⭐ follow simple instructions and sentences ('Find Nanna', Give me the book, please')

⭐ respond to their name or familiar words

⭐ happily babble away

⭐ recognise familiar voices and copy sounds and words

⭐ make sounds that are definitely more like words, some with several syllables

⭐ make sounds that start with a consonant and end in a vowel, such as 'dada' and 'fa', building up new words as the months go by.

'Read with your child every day! Even if it's the same book for weeks on end. Keep pretending you don't know where the damn green sheep is!'   TARNI

At 9 months to 1 year, what can you do to help development?

Allow a crawler to crawl as much as they like, but make sure you babyproof their environment first. Help them to 'dance', whether standing, sitting or lying down. As with any new skill, the more they have the opportunity to do something, the better they will get at it, so they can move on to the next step. Provide an opportunity for them to do their stuff but don't prod a baby to do something or 'teach' them to crawl or walk. It doesn't happen that way.

Hand your baby things to hold in their shopping-trolley seat, and help them to reach for some things on the shelves.

You can respond to their 'Barbufdubbadubpaddca' with 'Oh well, yes, I shouldn't be at all surprised'. It helps to teach the art of conversation and is a more amusing way for you to pass the time.

See your doctor if by 1 year your baby hasn't begun to crawl.

Ditch the baby walker or 'jumper'

What doesn't count as healthy, learning activity is anything done in a 'baby walker' or 'baby jumper': they are recognised as dangerous and a big cause of accidents and injuries. They also hold kids back from proper development – being able to walk and move well on their own, and developing necessary skills. See Chapter 31, Kid Equipment, for more.

BLAST FROM THE PAST
'Wonder baby of America! She is three-feet tall . . . she has 16 teeth,
says "mama" and "papa"; the impressive dimensions of Baby McClung.'
– *Newcastle Sun*, 1923

1-year-old baby

Physical development

standing

At 1 year your baby:
- ⭐ seems ready to move on from crawling, bum-shuffling or commando-style moving across the floor
- ⭐ is standing up and holding on to knees or coffee tables
- ⭐ may be toddling
- ⭐ is learning to drink from a cup
- ⭐ can put things into a bag or box and take them out again
- ⭐ will try to fit the noise to the item, such as an animal or a car.

Emotional & mental development

At 1 year your baby:
- ⭐ is fascinated by and enjoys other kids but is not into sharing toys with them
- ⭐ may be clingy
- ⭐ enjoys interacting with you – passing objects and looks.

Communication development

At 1 year your baby:
- ⭐ understands many more words
- ⭐ is building on their vocabulary every day, but at this stage uses far fewer words than they actually understand.

At 1 year, what can you do to help development?

Help your baby to do things for themselves: pass them objects to hold and experiment with. Continue to roll balls to them and have some soft ones they're allowed to throw.

Make jokes by using funny voices or doing odd things such as putting a shoe on your head. Enjoy favourite songs and books together, and introduce new ones. Keep playing disappear-and-reappear games with toys and your face.

Use new words and practise familiar ones. Give them room to reply or react in conversation.

You might like to take your 1-year-old to a playgroup: they'll probably enjoy the play and watching other children, and it's also a chance for you to see kids at different stages of development, regardless of precise age.

See your doctor if by 1 year your baby seems to dislike eye contact or communicating with you and others.

~~~~~~ more info on baby development ~~~~~~

raisingchildren.net.au
On the home page click on the appropriate age tab ('newborns', 'babies' or 'toddlers'), then 'Development'.

playgroupaustralia.com.au
Playgroup Australia will help you find or start a playgroup with parents and kids getting together.

17

BaBy toys & games

Toys and play are fun for babies, and as an extra bonus, they're an essential part of their development and learning.

toy & game ideas from parents

You'll see from the lists of suggestions below – based on info from parents – that I've edited out the merchandising or brand-name favourites. I figure they don't need the advertising, and they tend to be fads, not stayers. These suggestions are low-budget options that stimulate babies' social interaction and learning. All kids will have different favourites: some never get turned on by dollies, others never really like cars. Offer 'non-gendered' toys – dollies to boys and trucks to girls. If you have a boy, look in the 'pink' aisles to see if there's anything there they fancy. If you have a girl, offer her traditional 'boy' toys as well. Ignore any friends or relatives with outdated ideas on this.

Keep a small swag of toys – say, enough to fit in a bucket or a plastic box on wheels – in the cupboard and bring one out every few days or weeks while the others go away so that your baby always has a fresh lot. (Obviously real favourites such as special comfort or sleepytime toys can't be whisked away.) A huge selection of toys leads to a jaded baby.

Always check the safety and age-appropriate labels on new toys. Make sure toys that are safe for one age group don't get used by younger babies. Look out for damaged or elderly toys, with bits coming off. Anything that would fit into a small prescription-pill bottle can be a choking hazard for kids up to about the age of 3.

Button battery warning

Button and other batteries in toys and other items, when swallowed, can cause permanent disability and even the death of babies and toddlers. See the 'Button batteries' box in Chapter 32, Safety & Injuries, for more on this and other good things to know to avoid injuries.

'My daughter formed such an attachment to "Cheeky Monkey", I was terrified of losing him. The first was a gift; I bought a second to keep in reserve, just in case.'   MAYA

Good toys for babies

★ dangly toys to hang on the pram or above the baby to swat at – if they make noises so much the better ★ small things that are easily grabbed, such as cars or blocks ★ floor mats with interesting patterns, for tummy play ★ 'touch and feel' books ★ balls too big to swallow, easy to grasp with two hands and not too hard or full ★ rice in a tightly sealed plastic jar to rattle ★ a teething rattle or teething ring that plays music ★ crackly packaging for grasping (but be careful: it will be eaten if possible) ★ a baby photo album with photos of family and friends for you to look at and 'talk' about together ★ a safety-standard bouncing harness ★ little toys with wheels, which they can pull or push, or a small trolley or doll's pram to push along if they're toddling already ★ stacking cups ★ a ball with a bell inside ★ a low toy shelf rather than a box so that they can see things better and learn to take them off and then, you hope, put them back ★ plastic chains or rings ★ soft toys with long ears or tails for sucking ★ plasticware and cooking utensils ★ net bags used for oranges, filled with scrunched-up paper ★ broken or toy phones (the battery must be removed from old mobiles) for pretend calls and button pushing ★ a soft stubbie holder for holding, biting, pretending to drink, rolling or putting things into (but not soft enough to bite off bits – that is, not polystyrene) ★ blocks ★ board books ★ a musical mobile ★ an activity play centre ★ teddies and fluffy toys (some babies and kids never really get into fluffy things, although they're often given heaps) ★ books that have little flaps to open and look under ★ unbreakable plastic spoons ★ a xylophone ★ a hammering game (pegs or balls are pushed or whacked through holes with a hammer) ★ cloth books ★ a cloth dolly with a rattle inside ★ a key ring with lots of keys ★ piano-style keyboard

★ a cardboard carton to be sat in, to put things into, and to be pulled along in down the corridor at warp speed ★ cardboard tubes (not toilet ones – sturdier ones that used to have foil or cling wrap on them) ★ an inflatable ball ★ sticky tape half-stuck on something for the baby to pull off and put on (but don't let them eat it) ★ a babyproofed kitchen drawer or cupboard for unpacking and packing contents such as wooden spoons and plastic containers and lids ★ foam jigsaw mats with numbers or letters that pop in and out ★ a napkin or tea towel for playing peekaboo with ★ a cardboard tissue box with the plastic bits removed, and bits of ribbon, material and different-textured things to put in and take out ★ large plastic animals ★ a small squirting plastic animal ★ pegs either by themselves or pegged onto something ★ a baby-sized plastic watering can for bath time ★ empty plastic yoghurt containers to experiment with (babies love to stick their hands in, roll them, put other things in and rattle, and tip things out of) ★ a toy wagon ★ a stuffed caterpillar ★ a safe mirror ★ a large rubber bathplug ★ a tambourine and anything else musical ★ a broken calculator (remove and safely dispose of the batteries) or a cheap, safe toy with buttons to press ★ a sturdy plastic potato masher ★ a squeaky duck ★ old paperbacks or magazines with pictures of kids and animals ★ finger puppets (big ones can be scary)

Good games for babies

Childcare workers (and maybe some relatives) will know lots of baby games and rhymes: ask them to teach you some for your baby's age. Most good bookshops have compilations of nursery rhymes.

★ peekaboo ★ hide something and make it reappear ★ the baby throws and you catch (they won't be able to catch yet) ★ 'What noise does a duck, cat, truck (or whatever) make?' ★ rhyming games or songs ★ pat-a-cake ★ blow bubbles for them to look at and try to catch ★ flap a cot sheet or coloured fabric gently above the baby, cover them with it and remove immediately ★ 'round and round the garden' rhyme with actions

Books for babies

Ask the resident children's book expert staff member at your local bookstore, or the local public librarian, to show you the best local, classic and new books known to get babies interested.

~~~~~~~ more info on books for babies ~~~~~~~

Your local library or bookshop may have regular storytimes for parents and wee ones.

BLAST FROM THE PAST
'Toys should stimulate imagination and beautiful thoughts . . .
toy animals should not be travesties of nature or a grotesque impossibility.
The teddy bear, for example, is generally a good toy.'
– *The Examiner*, Tasmania, 1926

'Celluloid toys . . . are also highly inflammable. Toys should not be made of lead. First toys: unpainted cotton reels or large wooden beads on a string, not a circle he may be able to get his head through. Bone or ivory rings, wooden clothes pegs, wooden blocks . . . a large rubber ball.'
– *The Advocate*, Burnie, 1948

'I have never seen my baby happier than crawling in and out of a cardboard box to play peekaboo.'   ALYA

PART 2

YOUR TODDLER

wobble

wobble

18

YOUR TODDLER

Your bubba is now a toddler, still with their baby face.
But they're growing into their own little person,
balancing how much they still need you with how
much they want to feel in control. VERY IN CONTROL,
I think you'll find. So here's the full bottle on toddlers,
including developments to expect, and how to
deal with their behaviour and emotions.

what's a toddler?

The toddler years are about ages 1 to 3, depending on when your cherub first takes to their tootsies. Although 'toddler' refers to the physical act of walking, it's also a time for lots of mental and emotional action.

Toddlers are growing into little people who, depending on their personality traits, will observe the world keenly, adore a chat, explore objects and places, and make and take a joke, although be careful with that one. Kids under 5 (and older) are not able to fully understand sarcasm – it's just confusing or hurtful. But they often love some elementary contradictions or slapstick: putting an umbrella in the fridge, spilling a cup of water into the bath or pretending to eat their gumboot.

In the first years after they get mobile, kids are most at risk of accidents. Reorganise your house along toddler-safe lines (see Chapter 32, Safety & Injuries) and be extra careful about pools, ponds, baths, ladders, button batteries, and other dangers at your place and elsewhere. Kids are programmed to be curious, so it's safer to remove anything dangerous, or corral the kid, than to expect them to stay away.

Your new (eventually) all-talking, all-walking kid will soak up as many experiences as they can from social interaction, physical play, books, art and music. They'll probably have firm ideas about what they want to eat, do and perhaps even wear, and be more interested in playing with other kids their own age than they were before. Toddlers are building their communication skills and will 'talk' to you in words, behaviour and body language. Varying the way you explain things will help you work out which ways your child most enjoys learning and communicating – by using facial expressions, drawing a picture, acting out the physical effects of a feeling, or letting the kid thoroughly examine something new with their fingers, even if it's gloopy or disgusting (jelly, not dog poo). Their curiosity and capacity for mimicking and copying are almost without limit.

Your toddler's personality is developing and they're experimenting with how to get what they want. This can turn into an ongoing fight between a little person and a big person over who gets total control of which bits of life, or into

'Cleaning your house with toddlers is like cleaning your teeth with a mouth full of biscuits.'
JANE

continual push-me, pull-you negotiation. You'll need to show them (sadly by example, mostly) how to react to frustrating situations. For instance, I like to lie on the floor, kick my legs and swear in a shouty sort of way.

Give your toddler as much control and as many options as possible when the outcome doesn't matter ('Do you want pineapple or mango?', 'You be the boss: shall we go to the beach or the park?'). This will allow you to get away with other negatives and absolutes ('You can't touch that because it will burn your hand and hurt a lot', 'We are tidying the room now, but after that you can choose whether to go to the park or the shop'). If you give in to tantrums, the toddler learns that tantrums are a good way to get what they want.

Hints on how to avoid these and other potential battlegrounds (move to another country) can be found in Chapter 24, Toddler Behaviour. And nope, it's never too late to change your expectations and your kid's behaviour as long as you explain the change, help them to make the transition and then consistently stick to your approach. (I know – that's easy for **me** to say!)

Now that your toddler is mobile and exploring the world, you'll need to dress both boys and girls for normal days in ways that allow them to get dirty, fall down and climb things at the adventure playground, and although everyone likes to zhoosh up for a party, a long skirt or things that have to stay clean are not conducive to play. Prepare to face the reality of what happens to the clothes and bodies of normal, healthy kids. Kids get dirty. They need to get dirty so they can learn stuff about themselves and the world around them, and so that their immune system develops properly. Most of the clothes for toddlers in fashion spreads make them look like strange little adults.

Despite the fact that girls and boys often (although not always) show different traits, ask yourself how much is genetic and how much is suggested by the reactions and expectations of grown-ups and by the opportunities that are given to them. Are the boys always first to the construction toys at playgroup so the girls do playdough? Are the boys allowed to have a cry if they hurt themselves, or are they told to be a 'brave little man'? (More on this in Chapter 23, Toddler Emotions.)

> 'Some fairy dust will be lost after washing.'
> **LABEL ON TODDLER UNDERPANTS**

Make allowances for children as individuals: if someone isn't keen to play a contact sport because they're scared of getting hurt, that should be acknowledged as 'normal' – it doesn't matter whether they're a boy or a girl. Everyone deserves some leeway, patience, encouragement and understanding.

Always ask for professional medical advice if you think development in a certain area has stalled. It probably hasn't, as there's a very wide range of kids' capabilities at any age – in almost all cases everyone 'evens up' eventually. You can see what to encourage, and when to talk to a doctor, in Chapter 25, Toddler Development.

These are the bridging years between baby and preschooler, a time when you can make firm friends with your kid, get to know them really well, help them experiment, rejoice that they have a longer attention span and can amuse themselves for – oh – whole minutes on end, and perhaps launch them a little way into the world even though they, and you, know they can run back to you for comfort any time.

For many people this is also the stage when they have a new baby, so you might have to attend to your baby's needs as well as those of your toddler who wonders why they're no longer the single focus of their parents' world. Not to mention parents wondering why *they're* no longer the centre of the universe . . .

Good things about toddlers

* Toddlers are growing out of their baby face and into their own face, and developing their personality.
* Toddlers want to learn to do things for themselves.
* A toddler's laugh makes you smile.
* Toddlers listen to you carefully, even if they don't 'get' it all.
* Toddlers can be much more fun company than babies.
* Toddlers' attention spans vary, but can be surprisingly long or hilariously missing.
* Toddlers can entertain themselves for short periods.
* Toddlers think housework is fun (hee, hee, hee).
* Toddlers are fun to watch when they're determined (to get a sock on, for example).
* Toddlers kiss and cuddle you.
* Toddlers are amazed by things you have come to take for granted.
* Toddlers' emotions are all out there in pure form – sheer joy and terrible misery – so you usually know how they feel. And the joy is catching.
* Toddlers are so adorable when they're asleep (or quiet and not bouncing off the walls).
* Toddlers often bond with their attentive family, friends and carers but warm to others slowly. This is wise and safe behaviour, and not to be criticised as being 'too shy'.
* Toddlers can say 'I love you'.
* Toddlers say unexpected things that make you see the world from a new angle.
* Toddlers get excited and show it, without trying to act cool.
* Toddlers' fatty-nappied bums are cute.
* Toddlers are easier to pick up and carry than when they get older.
* Toddlers usually still have an afternoon sleep so you can too.
* Toddlers love books and the idea of stories.
* Toddlers adore songs.
* Toddlers start to imagine and pretend.
* Toddlers so intensely care about what they're doing that they remind you that little things can be as important as the 'big' stuff in life.
* Toddlers force you to slow down to their pace and concentrate on one thing at a time. (Yes, I know this can be infuriating, but it's probably good for us.)
* Toddlers don't want to borrow the car yet. (Well, they do. But don't let them.)

more info on toddlers

raisingchildren.net.au
Australian government–backed website with the best info on parenting, and on stages of development. Click on the 'toddlers' tab then choose what you want to know about.

betterhealth.vic.gov.au
Search 'toddlers' or a subject keyword on the home page for fact sheets.

19 TODDLER FOOD

Some days your toddler will not be interested in much food, the next they'll be 'on the fang'. Humans are 'hardwired' to be 'fussy' or suspicious eaters who rely on their tribe to teach them which foods are not poisonous. So be patient. Toddlers like to 'graze' – have little snacks here and there.

what toddlers need to eat

Offer lots of different kinds of fresh vegies and fruit, and tastes from different food groups. Simple is fine, but the wider the range of shapes, tastes and foods the better. I don't mean gourmet faffery such as rabbit-flavoured roll-ups and foamed vanilla-pod-and-truffle granita mousse in the shape of a turret on a caviar coulis. Just offer the odd piece of unfamiliar tropical fruit as well as different lettuces as well as muffins. It often helps to get an older kid to try it in front of your toddler – sometimes toddlers are easily led by other children.

Your job is just that: to *offer* different foods. If your kid doesn't eat it, offer an alternative but don't jump through hoops to provide fourteen other options. (See Chapter 30, Family Food, for info on allergies and intolerances, cooking with kids, vegetarians in the family, why it's really important what your baby and toddler drinks, and more.)

Outside advice on toddler eating

When in doubt, talk about your child's eating pattern with your child & family health nurse and have a reassuring weigh and measure so you know your kid is thriving. Weight gain slows right down after the first year. Babies by about 5 months have usually doubled their birth weight and by 1 year have normally tripled it, but after that they only gain 2 kilos or so in the next year.

Don't listen to people who recommend exclusion diets for children, such as wheat-free, dairy-free or low-fat programs, without a relevant medical diagnosis. These diets can be very dangerous, and they are unnecessary. They exclude a range of essential vitamins and minerals for brain and physical development, so do at least please check them with a qualified dietician. Anyone can call themselves a 'nutritionist', or faff away as a celebrity on social media. Dieticians have extensive medical qualifications and experience. (You can look up 'vegetarians' and 'vegans' in the index.)

'Friends ask how I got my kids to eat wholemeal bread; they didn't know there was anything else.' FIONA

'If they don't eat it give it to the dog.' CHRISTOPHER

tips to get toddlers eating

⭐ Eat together as a family, then you don't have to cook for two sessions of dinner (or even three if you have other kids). Also the 'How was your day? What's new?' aspect of the family meal is great for developing children's conversational skills and a comforting family vibe.

⭐ Give toddlers morning and afternoon tea, or snacks between meals. Their tummies are little so they need bits of food more often.

⭐ When your kid seems to be getting too big for the highchair, say at 2, let them use a plastic booster seat, which sits on top of a normal chair – cushions are not stable enough (see Chapter 31, Kid Equipment).

⭐ Let your kid start using toddler's cutlery. Most kids don't learn to use chopsticks until about school age. A spoon is still the easiest implement, especially when they're tired.

⭐ Listen to your toddler: don't be strict about a food 'routine' if they're getting genuinely hungry at different times. If they're eating a wide variety of foods and not filling up on milk before each meal, they should be getting all they need.

⭐ Three serves of dairy or calcium-fortified foods a day is a good aim. It helps kids have growth spurts to build their own teeth and bones, which they need to do while they're a toddler.

> 'Kids tend to be grazers. They eat a little bit, regularly.'
> SHELLEY

M'ungry

> 'Put hundreds and thousands on vegetables.' SALLY
> (This is a bad but funny idea!)

Choking hazards for toddlers

Toddlers under the age of 3 or so need to be protected from choking hazards, so avoid long stringy bits of stuff (like bacon rind), and food bits that are not cut up small enough, including meat, vegies and cheese. It doesn't mean everything has to be mushy. Both soft and hard foods can be choking hazards. There is no 'safe' food.

As already flagged in Chapter 14, First Food, avoid obvious dangers such as marshmallows, popcorn, small pieces of sausage or hot dog and other squishy-expanding foods, large, plump grapes and cherry tomatoes (cut them in half longways), hard or soft lollies, lozenges, mints and breath fresheners, raw bits of apple, meat, whole nuts, raw carrot, uncooked peas, fruit pips and pits, corn chips, other hard chips and mini Easter eggs.

Always be with your toddler as they eat: don't let them wander into another room snacking on something. Choking can be utterly silent. Look up 'choking, first aid for' in the index for what to do if a kid is choking. It's in Chapter 33, Health.

See a list of non-food choking hazards in Chapter 32, Safety & Injuries.

BLAST FROM THE PAST

'Doctor: "I told you to eat only such food as could be easily digested by a three-year-old child. Did you follow my instructions?"
"Yes, Doctor, I ate two handfuls of dirt, a piece of orange peel, a boot button and a couple of cigarette ends!"
From the joke page of the *Sunday Mail*, Brisbane, 1928

things to try if your toddler won't eat

First consider the possibility of a physical problem such as a sore throat, mouth ulcers or an illness coming on. Or that your kid isn't hungry, but will be later. 'Fussy' eating is really evolution at work. Toddlers are hardwired to refuse food until they're really familiar with it – when they've been served it up to ten times, and recognise it as 'safe'. This instinct kicks in about when babies start walking and prevents them from wandering away from the campfire and eating unfamiliar, poisonous berries. So you might have to offer a 'new' food over and over before it passes the test. And some kids just won't like certain foods – just like adults.

Many kids simply feel already 'full' – from a drink – before a meal, so they don't eat enough. Once they're weaned from breastmilk or formula milk after the age of 1, only give three cups of cow's milk a day, and do this after meals, not before. Keep offering stuff on the plate and don't fuss about it or push the issue. When they're hungry, they'll eat. They can survive and thrive on such teeny amounts as to raise the eyebrows on the statue of Venus de Milo. Or even the arms. If in doubt, see your doctor.

Other strategies to try:

⭐ Explain that the bread in their tummy is having a party and the carrots want to come. And the zucchini is all dressed up with its cheese hat on, ready to go too. Give them a choice of a couple of foods they can invite or not invite. In other words, you choose what to offer and they choose which of those foods to eat. This makes toddlers feel as if they're making decisions.

⭐ Try a rejected food prepared another way (cooked or raw) or chopped up or whole, so it won't be recognised the same way each time.

⭐ Offer smaller helpings: it might be that you're expecting a toddler to eat a much larger serving of food than is actually needed – toddlers don't grow as fast as babies do.

⭐ Make a game of eating little bits of different colours – a green snow pea, some grated orange carrot, a grey mushroom, a white potato cube, a red cherry tomato.

'Food doesn't need to be eaten at the table. It can be eaten mid play. Choose a food item – one for each hand.' GILLIAN

⭐ Get a set of cookie cutters in the shape of animals, dinosaurs, or fun objects like cars, and cut out sandwiches or vegie slices in the shapes.

⭐ Don't take it personally. If painstakingly prepared food is chucked around or ignored, skip the painstaking stage. Offer something simple, even raw, instead. That's what fresh fruit and veg – and now and then things that come in packets – are for.

> 'Don't worry. They won't starve.'
> HEAPS OF PARENTS

BLAST FROM THE PAST

'Diet for the one year old . . . one and a half ounces of fat per child per day, one pint of milk . . . and the rest in butter, dripping, and bacon fat.'
– *Daily Bulletin*, Townsville, 1940

---

cooking together

Parents report more success in getting little kids to eat when the kids have helped pick out the food and prepare it (even if they're not really 'helping' to get things done faster, they're 'helping' to get to understand and enjoy food, and spending family time together). Toddlers can cut things up, with their own wee, safe knife, stir things, watch, taste and name foods, and say 'when'. (There's more on this in Chapter 30, Family Food.)

Be a good eating model

Toddlers watch and learn from you, so never talk about you or anyone else being 'too fat' or needing to 'go on a diet'. They're old enough to notice and copy self-image problems and eating-behaviour problems. Talk about 'healthy' foods and 'sometimes' foods – don't give them ideas of 'bad' or 'naughty' foods.

> 'When they decide now is the perfect time to shriek at you that they're hungry . . . half an hour after you fed them lunch . . .' AMY

Drinks

'No sugary drinks' is a great gift you can give your kid. There's more on this in Chapter 30, Family Food, and Chapter 36, Teeth, but in the meantime make sure water and milk are the only stuff your kid drinks. No bottled drinks with sugar in them, no 'diet' drinks, no cordials, no fizzy drinks, no flavoured mineral waters, rare serves of bottled water (there's no fluoride in it), no energy drinks, no colas or other drinks with caffeine, no homemade juice or fruit juice bought from supermarkets or juice bars. You'll save a fortune, and be doing the right thing for your kid's health and teeth.

Toddlers do not need 'toddler formula'. These drinks are marketed as having special properties, but if your toddler is eating healthy food, and drinking milk and water, they will be getting all the nutrients, vitamins and minerals they need. Don't waste your money.

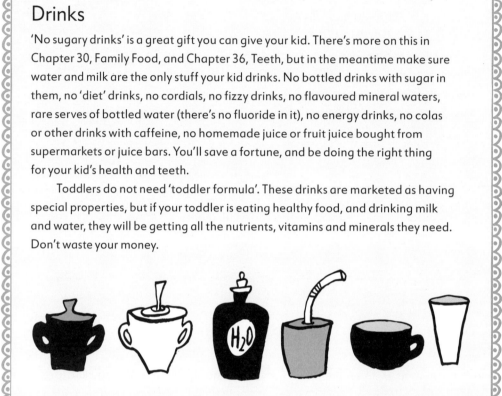

'We realised that she wanted to be independent and feed herself. She was quite happy when given a spoon of her own.' JENNY

'Send them to creche. We have many children who won't eat at home, but put them at a lunch table with five or six others and suddenly the attitude becomes "I'm doing what she's doing!" or "I'd better try this or miss out!"' KAREN

more info on toddlers & eating

See the 'More info' sections in Chapter 30, Family Food.

www.eatforhealth.gov.au
Click on 'Brochures, posters and more' on the left, then scroll down to find a *Healthy Eating for Children* brochure and an *Australian Guide to Healthy Eating* poster.

www.schn.health.nsw.gov.au
On this Sydney Children's Hospital site, choose 'Fact sheets', then 'Food and nutrition', then 'Food – healthy eating for toddlers' for some fast facts.

More Peas Please: Solutions for Feeding Fussy Eaters
by Kate Di Prima and Julie Cichero (Allen & Unwin, Australia)
A print-on-demand book (takes about two weeks) by a specialist dietician and a researcher in feeding and swallowing difficulties, about fussy eaters, solutions and recipes.

20

TODDLER SLEEP

I said,
'Lights
out'

TORCHO

Here's lots of advice and strategies for how to get your
toddler to accept a regular bedtime and sleepytime
ritual. So then you can get some proper sleep, too.
Getting toddlers into a good sleep habit is the aim.
It makes a toddler happier, healthier, able to learn,
able to concentrate better. Sleep problems are strongly
linked to behaviour and learning problems, so if you can
fix some sleep problems you'll be ahead of the game.

how much sleep do toddlers need?

Toddlers need to get ten to twelve hours' sleep overnight. A fairly early bedtime is usually best because sleep-ins are harder to manage. Some parents let their kids stay up until they're 'ready' to go to bed, but a toddler who wakes at 7 a.m. won't get enough sleep if they're going to bed at 10 p.m. Many parents of toddlers go for a bedtime of 7 p.m., with stories until 7.30. If you fancy having a more planned day, see Chapter 21, Toddler Routines, for a suggested timeline that might help.

daytime naps for toddlers

Gradually the morning and afternoon sleeps become one early-afternoon sleep. Most toddlers need an afternoon nap when they're 1 – and most phase it out before they're 3, or 4, or 5 (some time before high school, anyway). Some won't have a nap and are always falling-about-tired before bed; some always have a nap; and some have an afternoon nap occasionally. You'll have to be guided by your child: if they're horribly ratty in the last two hours or so before bedtime at 7 p.m., they could still need to be persuaded to have an hour or so of sleep in the afternoon.

At this age you can explain to them how a nap means they get two sleepytime stories in one day, or that it makes them strong and gives them energy to play or to get ready for that party on the weekend. Keep the afternoon-sleep room dark and have a little bedtime ritual, perhaps just reading a board book and then a phrase like 'Sleep tight, see you soon'.

Even if your toddler doesn't actually sleep, it's almost always a good idea for them to have quiet time in bed because it gives everyone a break. And you never know your luck – if you take the pressure off, the nap might happen anyway.

night-time sleeping

Toddlers, like anyone else, will fall asleep more easily if they're physically tired. Outdoor and active play every day will help sleep habits as well as their development and physical skills. Parents can reassure an anxious toddler: 'I'll check on you while you're asleep to make sure everything is okay.' Tell kids it's normal for everyone to wake up in the night, stay sleepy, feel safe, and go back to sleep.

Regular bedtime every night

Every study that investigates children and sleep suggests that kids with a regular bedtime do better at school, and with their moods, because they get more sleep. You can adjust the bedtime as your kid gets older. See the end of Chapter 21, Toddler Routines, for what to do about daylight-saving changes: you need to change the bedtime gradually over a few nights. Also see 'Night lighting' in Chapter 8, Baby Sleep, for tips on creating a good sleeping environment.

Night-time ritual

Toddlers, like everyone, have hardwired responses to certain stimuli. An association with the same things will help a kid understand it's time to go to sleep. Make the ritual something that can easily happen every night (not an hour-long video).

A ritual can include your toddler:

⭐ fetching a non-spillable drink and putting it next to the bed
⭐ going to the toilet; getting into a pull-up nappy
⭐ brushing their teeth
⭐ getting into jarmies
⭐ putting Mr Whiskers (or a similar toy companion) in the bed
⭐ turning on the night-light
⭐ singing a song with you
⭐ hearing a story
⭐ saying a special or traditional goodnight rhyme, poem, prayer or well-known story with you.

night-drink, night-book, night-light, night-night

Bedtime books

Ask for good bedtime books from your local bookshop's kidlit staff member, or visit an online bookstore and look for recommendations. Bedtime ritual picture books (or audio books) include *The Rabbit Who Wants to Fall Asleep* by Carl-Johann Forssén Ehrlin, *Goodnight Moon* by Margaret Wise Brown, *We All Sleep* by Ezekiel Kwaymullina and Sally Morgan, *Good Night, Sleep Tight* by Mem Fox, *Tell Me Something Happy Before I Go to Sleep* by Joyce Dunbar, *Dr Seuss's Sleep Book*, *Rainforest Lullaby* by Sally Odgers, and many more.

~~~~~~ **more info** on good bedtime books ~~~~~~

thekidsbookshop.com.au
Search 'bedtime' on the home page. You can also search keywords such as 'monster' for reassuring stories on a theme, or 'lullaby'.

toddler sleep refusal, delay & getting-up tactics

Some toddlers get themselves into a habit of refusing to go to bed, or keep getting up after being put to bed or every time they wake during the night. The medical term for this (if you hear it, don't worry!) is 'behavioural insomnia' or 'sleep onset association disorder'. Ask your child & family health nurse for help.

Head off toddler stalling by your counter-strategies being built into the bedtime ritual. Wants a drink? There's already one there. Needs the loo? 'You went just before you got into bed.'

You'll also need a firm, agreed policy by all adults in the house about a 'back to bed' rule. A toddler coming out of their room or into the parents' bedroom will be firmly and kindly taken back to their own bed. You can make exceptions for nightmares, and for individual clingy periods. Many parents insist that a toddler coming into their room who just doesn't want to be alone has to sleep on a mattress on the floor, near the door!

Rewards (aka bribes) for staying in bed after bedtime for a whole week: a new bedtime book, stickers on a chart, high praise, a visit to a favoured friend or destination.

'controlled crying' or 'controlled comforting' or 'learning to sleep' or 'sleep training'

This approach and the 'Camping Out' variation is explained in Chapter 8, Baby Sleep. It is used to end conflict and upset over sleep habits, and bedtimes, and staying in bed. You can do it with a toddler as well as a baby older than 6 months. The problem is that as well as yelling, a toddler is physically able to get up and escape from the bedroom. Calm consistency from all the adults in the house is the only way to achieve a regular bedtime.

The important things to remember about 'controlled comforting' are:

⭐ It means training your kid to go to sleep.

⭐ You don't give in to tears or tantrums – but you don't let a child cry indefinitely. It's a gradual method.

⭐ Children are not psychologically harmed by it.

⭐ It isn't compulsory: you don't have to do it.

⭐ If it doesn't work, ask your child & family health nurse or doctor for help.

Some children will push back hard against controlled comforting. Some will even scream maniacally until they throw up, or hammer on the door. It's tough. But with patient, firm consistency, no cracking and no going back to bad habits, you can sometimes have the problem fixed in literally a couple of days.

Patience and firm consistency are easy to write down but hard to do, especially when you're exhausted and your kid is upset. If you're on your own, please ask someone else to help you to be utterly consistent. To make sure the toddler always feels reassured, and to withstand the barrage of hot, tragic tears, it often takes at least two adults – one sobbing in the corridor and another who stops the sobbing one from going in to the toddler for another few seconds, and then swapping roles the next evening.

Toddlers who can escape from their cot or bed must be gently put back each time, or they'll learn that tantrums and escapology will be rewarded. Some parents use a high-up snib lock on the outside of the door. Others install a toddler gate on the outside of the door – this is sometimes more of a psychological barrier. Reassure your toddler that you will come in if they need you and they call out. Other parents want their kid to be able to get out and come into the parents' room if they have a nightmare.

You'll have to modify or abandon these ideas depending on your kid's personality and what works for you. For example, some toddlers will move a chair or toybox to stand on to try to reach a higher doorknob.

being scared to go to bed

If your toddler says 'I'm frightened', don't dismiss it: talk about why, and deal with those specific fears. Being in a dim or dark room on your own can be a very frightening experience for little kids, although some will use it as a stalling tactic. You'll soon be able to tell if their fears are real.

Make sure there isn't a pile of toys casting a scary shadow on the wall, or an open wardrobe that looks as if it might have monsters in it. Try to distract your toddler with a funny goodnight song, one verse or bits of which they have to make up.

Once a toddler has 'heard' from other kids or books that there are monsters, you'll need to gauge your response and tailor it to your kid. Most kids want to be told there are no monsters; they're not real. Others are happy with funny anti-monster strategies like a labelled 'Monster Spray' spritzed near the bed, or a dolly that is put on guard to tell monsters not to come near. Making monsters seem funny or harmless can help – there are several children's books in this vein.

One mother I know sat her little boy down while she dialled the 'Monster Department' on her phone and told them very sternly they were not to send any more monsters. The trick is to find something that makes your child feel empowered.

> 'We always had to say "We'll come in and check on you while you're asleep" and then it was fine.' GEOFF

bad dreams

Toddlers will need to have dreams explained to them: that dreams are things you see in your sleep, but they're not real, even if sometimes they seem real. Sometimes dreams are happy and sometimes they're just strange, or scary. When a child wakes up and says they've had a bad dream, tell them it's all gone now. Don't tell them it's wrong to be scared. If a kid wants to ask about the nightmare, agree that it can feel bad when they wake up from one, and give short, reassuring responses to any questions. If your kid's unconcerned, that's okay too. Nightmares tend to happen in the early hours of the morning after a toddler has been asleep for a few hours.

Nightmares can be prompted by stressful life or family situations, or be totally unrelated to real life and just part of the imagination. A 'bad dream' can be related to scary things seen by, or told to, the toddler, or a response to an age-inappropriate game or TV show. Make sure 'entertainment' is always rated for the youngest kid, not the oldest kid, in the room.

Some parents like to resettle their toddler in their cot or bed after a nightmare. Others bring the child into their own bed. And some hop into the kid's bed until they are 'dismissed'.

In cases where a bad dream is recurring or prompted by a traumatic event or on-going stress, or something unknown, talk to your doctor about seeing a sleep specialist or child psychologist.

'My daughter is 22 months old and ever since about 3 months old she has had Barry, a small soft toy with a bell (unfortunately), that she goes to bed with. When it's time for her to go to bed or naptime we get her to call Barry and we wander around the house until we find him (surprise!). This works 90 per cent of the time: lately we've had Barry and Elmo waiting for her in bed: she can't wait to get there generally. All of this happened by accident.'   KELLIE

night terrors

A night terror is not a nightmare. It's an occasional episode when a kid stays asleep but looks like they're in a panic. They might cry or yell out or even thrash around or get out of bed. Don't wake your child in one of these, but soothingly lead or carry them back to bed. They won't react to your soothing, but they will come out of the event themselves and stay asleep, and won't remember it later. Night terrors tend to start in the toddler years and can go on until the first year or so after school starts. They tend to happen earlier in the night than nightmares, and are more common in families with a history of kids having night terrors. They're normal developmental events for many kids.

more info on nightmares & night terrors

raisingchildren.net.au
Search 'nightmares' or 'night terrors' for fast facts.

theconversation.com
Search 'nightmares' for an article on the difference between bad dreams and night terrors, and the different solutions, by Australian paediatrician Professor Harriet Hiscock.

BLAST FROM THE PAST

'Bidomak! The tonic of the century. Terrible night terrors ... miraculous results! Brings back speedily to happy, vigorous boyhood! Three shillings.'
– Advertisement to mothers for an iron tonic, 1936, with the heading:
'I was becoming a hopeless hysterical case!'

graduating from cot to bed

Traditionally a kid goes into a lower bed when they've worked out how to climb up and launch themselves out of their cot. Try to anticipate this, and change beds before it happens. Some cots are adjustable and the mattress can go at a lower level once baby can stand up in the cot. Then, when they're ready for a bed, the side rail comes off. Most kids go into their own 'big bed' at about 2 to 2½ years old.

To prevent falls you can buy a bed guard for a single bed at baby equipment or bed shops, or you can put the mattress on the floor for a while.

Give your toddler plenty of warning about the change. Talk about getting a new bed being a fun, big-kid thing to do. Saying that there's a little baby somewhere who needs the cot can be persuasive when swapping it for a 'big girl's' or 'big boy's' bed. But try to get it sorted well before a new baby arrives at your place.

Sleep-disordered breathing

Some toddlers (and adults) who struggle with irritable behaviour, attention problems and learning difficulties could have undiagnosed sleep difficulties. Other warning signs of sleep disorder or sleep apnoea include a pattern of loud snoring (not with a cold), stopped breath or big intakes of breath and gasps while asleep; breathing through the mouth at night; lots of waking moments at night; and falling asleep at odd times in the day. The same symptoms can also be caused by an allergy called rhinitis that causes nasal problems. See more on all of these in Chapter 33, Health. See the family doctor if you suspect any of these conditions.

more info on toddlers & sleeping

raisingchildren.net.au
On the home page of this Australian government–backed site, choose 'toddlers' then 'Sleep' for fact sheets on various problems and solutions. You can also search 'controlled comforting' for a how-to guide.

The Tresillian Sleep Book
by the Tresillian parent support organisation (ABC Books)
A book by specialised baby and child nurses has a section on toddler and preschooler sleep solutions and sample routines.

BLAST FROM THE PAST

'Dr John Collis Browne's Chlorodyne. This invaluable remedy produces quiet, refreshing sleep . . . old and young may take it at all hours and times when required.' – 1860s advertisement for a mixture containing opium, alcohol, cannabis, chloroform and peppermint oil. It was sold in various mixtures, including morphia, into the 1970s.

21

THINGS to DO:

TODDLER ROUTINES

Oh, toddlers do LOVE a routine! And will sometimes inform you of transgressions from it, in no uncertain terms. They know when you change the words of a book even before they can read. They get used to what's supposed to happen next. If it's useful, you can build in times for morning tea (yay), lunch, an after-lunch sleep (yay) and quiet time, general fun, and (hallelujah) bedtime.

getting a toddler routine going

I sometimes wonder if the love toddlers have for a routine and familiar things isn't almost perfectly balanced by the fact that for all their life so far everything has seemed so new. They've been learning new words, new actions and new concepts, and analysing changes in their world and their understanding, every day. The things we see as ordinary are discoveries for them. So, while a new song or phrase will tickle and delight them, you'd better not try to move their bed to face another direction without consultation and lots of chats to prepare them. You don't want a toddler routine? Then sweep majestically past to the next chapter.

Base your routine around your individual lifestyle (and ability to sleep in) while you can: when morning childcare or kinder starts, you'll need a nice early bedtime so your toddler gets ten to twelve hours' sleep a night – most kids tend to wake up at 6.30 to 7.30 a.m. anyway, depending on light. Below are suggested routines you can rearrange to suit yourself.

By age 1 your child might have dropped one of their daytime sleeps or be on the way to doing this, as outlined in Chapter 12, Baby Routines. Of course if your toddler goes to day care, your routine will have to adjust to theirs.

Perfect schmerfect

A consistent routine can make everyone more calm. But if it makes you more anxious, it's not right for you. The routine is not sacred. You don't have to be perfect, you can't control everything, life won't always run to the plan, and having an okay day that everyone made it to the end of is a triumph in itself. Lower the bar. If necessary, dig a trench and leave the bar down there for a while.

Optional toddler routine from 1 year

7 a.m.	Breakfast, chat.
8	Play and usual morning activities.
9	Possible morning sleep.
10	Play.
11	Morning tea or lunch.
12	Play.
1 p.m.	Possible afternoon sleep.
2	Afternoon tea.
2.30	Play, visit or adventure, including some physical activity.
4.30	Possible 20- to 40-minute catnap if two daytime sleeps have dropped to one.
5.30	Dinner.
6	Bath.
6.30	Stories or quiet time.
7 p.m.	Lights out.

It's time for a nap!

ha

Optional toddler routine from 18 months

7 a.m.	Breakfast, chat.
8	Play and usual morning activities.
10	Morning tea.
11	Play.
11	Morning tea or lunch.
12	Lunch.
1 or 2 p.m.	Possible afternoon sleep.
3	Afternoon tea.
3.30	Play, visit or adventure, including physical activity.
5.30	Dinner.
6	Bath.
6.30	Stories or quiet time.
7 p.m.	Lights out.

Kids approaching 3 years old may be dropping a daytime sleep altogether.

toddler sleep & daylight saving

Some parents keep to 'real' time so the day always starts at 7 a.m., which reads as 8 in summer. Or you can take a week or two before daylight saving starts (or ends) to change the bedtime by a quarter of an hour every few days. Or put up with family 'jet lag'.

22

toilet training

Yes, all right. I know 'toilet training' sounds like you're supposed to be wearing a matching tracksuit with a whistle round your neck, training an elite athlete to ... er ... go potty. When they're old enough, and annoyed at the feeling and not-so-grown-uppiness of a wet nappy, and they're able to identify the feeling of an imminent wee or poo, your kid will be interested in learning to use the loo. It hardly ever reliably comes together before the age of 2.

wanting to graduate to the loo

In ye olden grandparenty days children were more often in cloth nappies – smellier, much wetter and more uncomfortable. Kids usually couldn't wait to get out of them. These days disposables, and even the fancy modern reusable nappies, are much easier and drier for many kids and parents – and that means the in-nappies time is extended.

Kids who live where there are real winters tend to graduate from nappies later, as it's too cold to let them run around with a naked bot in the garden or park.

There is absolutely NO POINT (sorry, shouty) in trying to teach your child to use the toilet each time they need to do a wee or a poo if they're not interested. They just humour you for a while and then it turns into a nagfest or a carnival of wet bots. Actual interest is when they ask you questions about it and want to see what's going on when people go to the loo.

By the time they're interested, they'll be able to tell when they're going to wee or poo and be physically able to use the potty or loo: it just takes practice to get it all together.

Teaching them about the toilet can take a while. Every now and then try to spark some interest – a story about where wee goes; 'Look at what Mummy's doing'; 'Here, sit on this toilet seat'; 'Wow, won't it be good when you can wear undies!' Wait until your kid is really interested and wants to do it, then help them – much less stressful for everyone and also much more successful.

Kids love praise and the idea they're progressing, and it helps build their confidence. Praise for trying, and remembering, and giving something a go is just as important as praise for 'succeeding'.

Pull-on nappy-undies for toddlers

These are a kind of final nappy – one that pulls on and off like a pair of undies. They are often used as transitional pants when a child is learning to use the potty or toilet, and at night after a kid is toilet-trained during the day.

Some parents want their kids to go straight from nappies to the potty or toilet, believing that 'pull-ups' extend the time in nappies. But most kids need nappies at night for a while after they've mastered daytime toilet-going.

> 'They do it when they're ready and not before.' JEANETTE

when to start toilet training

A lot of 'parent advice' says kids are ready for toilet-training between the ages of 1 and 3, and the average age is before 2 years old. Out in the real world I've NEVER heard of a kid having sustained interest before about 18 months and hardly anyone before 2, and the average seems to be somewhere between 2 and 3, with plenty saving it for later.

Signs of genuine interest include being interested in reading a book with you about using the toilet; being interested in hearing about where poo and wee goes when you flush; asking about other aspects of the toilet and wee and poo, and watching older or other kids and family members going to the toilet; talking about and looking forward to 'growing-up pants' or 'big-boy pants' or 'big-girl pants'; and being interested in undies generally or a special pair in particular. It's worth investing in horrible movie-merchandising underpants if it helps.

Sometimes interest wanes, or a kid regresses temporarily because a new baby in nappies is getting so much attention, and the toddler associates the attention with being in nappies. Or maybe they're just feeling a bit lazy, as wearing a nappy is damned convenient. Or they have a sore bot from a bout of gastro-wipery.

It's usually easier for a toddler to know when they're going to poo than wee. Wee doesn't herald itself so obviously to a child, and can come too quickly in times of excitement or great interest in something else.

Napping and then night-time control take the longest to get the hang of: usually after age 3. It's very common for kids to still be in night-time pull-ups at age 4, or using a potty next to the bed. It's a long trip down the hall to the loo for a littlie at this age.

Are girls ready earlier for toilet training?

Boys generally start and finish learning to use the loo later than girls, sometimes as late as 4. There's no way of knowing whether this applies to your little individual. Some kids get it all over with very quickly; and some foof along in fits and starts until some time after their third birthday.

how long will toilet-training take?

Learning to go to the toilet regularly can take only weeks, or even just a few days if your kid is really interested. Otherwise months and months. Be prepared for potty and toilet use to go backwards at unexpected times or to take a sudden leap forward. It's normal for most kids to wet the bed occasionally right up until the first couple of years they're at primary school.

preparing for toilet-training

It's always useful to explain to your child:

★ that their body takes all the food and drinks they have and uses these to make them grow and be strong, and anything the body doesn't need comes out as wee and poo

★ that wee and poo can be a bit stinky (though not a big deal, heavens no) so we need to flush them down the toilet

★ that having a poo often makes us feel more comfy.

'It felt like it was never going to happen for us. Try pants during the day and regularly ask them if they need to go. They will eventually get used to this and go themselves. Still working on nights!' BIANCA

equipment for toilet training

You might like to use:

⭐ a plastic potty in the bathroom – and one next to the bed might be a solution if your child finds it hard to get to the toilet in time in the middle of the night

⭐ a smaller-sized toilet seat to fit on yours

⭐ a stool or a step for access to the big loo

⭐ pull-on half-nappy, half-undies things (see info earlier in this chapter)

⭐ a night-time nappy for a while (a toddler before using the toilet will have needed three or four nappies a day)

⭐ a properly fitted waterproof mattress cover – this has waterproof plastic underneath with cotton on the top so they're not nasty, sweaty and uncomfy to lie on. Some parents use this over the bottom sheet so it can be whipped off more quickly. One on the bed and one for emergencies is a good call.

Potty or loo?

Some kids start on the potty and graduate to the loo. Some parents like to start with the potty because a kid doesn't need help to get on; others take their kid straight to the loo or have a smaller, converter toilet seat on the real thing.

Boys & toilet training

⭐ Put a non-flushable floating target in the bowl for boys to aim their weeing willies at: corks and ping-pong balls are popular. Some people swear by teaching boys to wee sitting down; others say the key is getting a bigger boy or man to teach them. A boy starting on a potty will have to graduate to stand-up weeing later.

Girls & toilet training

⭐ Teach girls how to wipe themselves with folded toilet paper, from the front towards the back, so poo is not wiped forward, as this can cause infections.

  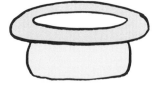

Flushing facts

It's also a good idea to explain what happens to wee and poo after we're finished with it: that they drop down into the water in the toilet, and then we push the button and the water goes whoosh, whoosh, and then the wee and poo disappear down all these pipes, go into other big pipes and finally into a big smelly pond in the ground a long way away, and eventually are spewed into our surf spots by governments that need to be slapped around. Well, maybe not that last bit – it's a little complex. But sometimes explaining the process demystifies the experience for kids; otherwise, it's quite abstract.

If kids are scared about what's in the loo (sharks, monsters, the Unknown), explain that it's like the plughole in the bath: stuff goes down when you flush, but nothing comes up. Explain that kids can't ever be flushed away – and nothing else should be flushed except poo, wee and toilet paper. Explain that anything else that goes into the toilet will break or, because there are germs down there, will have to be thrown away. Watch out for little scientists who want to test this for themselves.

BLAST FROM THE PAST

'From the time baby is a month old, regular training in bowel action should be started . . . at first baby should be held out (over a potty) only after, say the ten a.m. feed. If a motion is not produced within three minutes, it is best to remove [the baby] and try again after the next feed.'
– *The Australian Women's Weekly Household Guide*, early 1950s

'We made the stepping stool together, he painted it and decorated it with his mum and within 2 days had it sussed. [Loo using at 2 years 6 months.]'   JOHN

'All my kids initially trained themselves ("How clever am I!"), then decided to regress to nappies ("That game's not fun any more") before they were properly trained. [Loo using at 2 years 6 months.]'   MELISSA

toilet-training handy hints

Here's a list of practical points about toilet training

⭐ Let your kid watch you on the toilet and have a look in the bowl afterwards to see what happens when you flush (*so* glamorous!).

⭐ Keep talking to your child about why you're asking certain things of them. This will encourage them to explain to you why they're doing what they're doing or why they're afraid.

⭐ Wanting to be like the older kids is often a big motivation. Childcare centres and kinders can be a great help, as can older siblings, cousins or close pals.

⭐ Show kids how to wash their hands afterwards with soap and dry them on a clean towel.

⭐ Don't make a fuss or go on about the disgustingness of poo and wee. It's ordinary and natural and everyone does it, and your kid should know that (of course, the 'everyone does it' can be cause for astonishment and some hilarity).

⭐ Some parents switch to cloth nappies at this stage to encourage a wet-bot feel, in the hope that their toddler will get sick of it.

⭐ Some kids who have had constipation, or who might be a bit worried about sitting on the loo, can get used to it by having a scheduled sit after meals. The full tum can help signal 'down the hatch' to the bowel, which can set up an unconscious association between the body being ready to poo and the brain thinking it's a good idea to go. One day the poo will just happen. Hoorah.

⭐ Speaking of which, do praise a successful loo-going. But don't make it sound so magnificent there should be a parade.

> 'A couple of times he wet the floor and got very upset. I said that if he was going to get so upset when he had an accident it might be better if we left it for a while. He was very appreciative of this. When he did make the transition (3 years 3 months) we were off and running. It was well worth letting him do it under his own steam.' DIANNE

Toilet-training rewards

⭐ A sticker or star chart can be set up to show everyone the marvellous progress.

⭐ Use incentives: undies with pictures of their favourite cartoon character are often a great bribe.

⭐ Don't put a kid in overalls or tights that are hard for them to get out of quickly, by themselves.

⭐ Give your toddler lots of water, fruit and vegies to help a hard poo or constipation problem. Giving fibre without extra water often only makes constipation worse.

⭐ Let a bathroom tap trickle in a wee-like way if your child is having trouble being able to wee; or sing a little rhyme or line that relaxes them such as 'Wee, wee, wee, all the way in the loo'. The only downside of this is that they might still be doing it when they're 38.

Toilet-training accidents

⭐ Always treat an 'accident' matter-of-factly, with a 'Never mind, it's just a wee (ha!) accident!'

⭐ Apologise for being grumpy if you find yourself getting angry or exasperated with 'yet another' wet or pooey accident, or have a laugh with your kid about your grumpiness. Make sure you're consistently nice about the next few.

⭐ If your toddler seems always wet, rather than sometimes dry and sometimes wet, check out with your GP whether it means they have a urinary tract infection or any other physical leaky problem.

⭐ At night have a dim light all the way to and inside the loo, a rug on the floor if it's cold, and the smaller-bot seat and stool in place, or the potty near the bed.

> 'At nearly 3 he is not interested in toilet training. I have tried special jocks, stickers, stamps, cuddles, praise and even chockie bribery but nothing works. This has been the hardest of everything.' REBECCA

Using the toilet away from home

⭐ Always get the kid to go to the loo before you leave home or childcare, or before you leave anywhere for a trip home. Little people's bladders are also very little, and they need as many opportunities to go as possible. (This is especially true when you're using public transport, because it's usually a longer trip than by car. You can carry a pull-on nappy to slip on your toddler just for emergencies.)

⭐ If you're going to be weeing outside on a bush adventure, have them wear something on their lower half that can easily be pulled completely off and then put back on. Tights or shoes wet with wee after a squatting accident are no fun.

⭐ Always carry extra undies, trousers and wipes, and at least two plastic bags for accidents (one bag is for throwaways, another is for the dirty clothes).

⭐ Always stay with your child in a public loo, and use a unisex parents' room where possible.

⭐ Help your child to balance on an unfamiliar grown-up seat.

Toilet training that goes backwards

⭐ A kid who forgets to go to the loo a lot is probably just not interested enough yet. Night-time accidents are normal for toddlers.

⭐ A kid who's been using the potty or toilet for weeks or months and then suddenly isn't any more probably has some kind of easily treated physical reason such as an infection, or a psychological problem caused by ongoing stress or a traumatic event (although it may not have seemed traumatic to you), so see your family doctor.

⭐ A wet bed must never be used as a moment that is shaming, or even as a terrible nuisance. Always be matter-of-fact about it – weeing should never be associated with shame. Just bundle up the sheets and stash them in the laundry, even if you can't wash them until later.

⭐ Likewise, an older toddler or preschooler can be mortified by an occasional or rare accident – reassure them it happens to everyone and is no big deal. Just help them to clean up in private if you're out, and hide any evidence in a plastic bag in your handbag.

> 'Don't put a nappy on at night. While we had a nappy he wet. After I left off the nappy, I only had one or two accidents.' JUDI

Twins & the loo

Most people in the kid business recommend waiting until all the twins (or triplets) are ready to toilet train together – but one twin sometimes forges ahead. Just be careful that the praise given to one doesn't seem like something the other is missing out on because they're not good enough. Perhaps there might be something else to praise them for. Other parents who've been through multiples loo business have good hints: see 'More info on multiples' in Chapter 15, Multiples.

~~~~~~~ **more info** on toilet training ~~~~~~~

raisingchildren.net.au
On the home page of this federal government–backed site, search 'toilet training' for age-based tips.

Picture books about using the loo

The Story of the Little Mole Who Knew It Was None of His Business
by Werner Holzwarth and Wold Erbruch (HarperCollins)
A picture book about a mole who is pooped on and goes in search of the animal culprit. Not a 'how to', but a depiction of different poos.

***Everyone Poops* by Taro Gomi (Kane/Miller)**
A picture book with animals and people.
Who, I think you'll find, poop.

fascinating

23

TODDLER emotions

Toddlers feel all sorts of emotions, but often don't have the words or the maturity to explain them – or to deal with them. Parents can encourage children to feel more confident, and to process their feelings, by helping them to identify, name and communicate their emotions. You can help by describing your own: 'Mummy is very frazzled, and Daddy is completely thrilled. Grandpa is flummoxed!'

making feelings normal

Toddlers already understand they have feelings, and even that other people do, too. You can help them by introducing the idea into conversation:

⭐ 'I am very tired. I think I need to have a little lie-down.'

⭐ 'Ooh, I'm feeling a love wave. I'm going to give you a cuddle.'

⭐ 'I am in a very good mood. Shall we put some music on and dance in the kitchen?'

⭐ 'The man in the other car was very rude and pushed in. I felt quite cross with him. I am very sorry I shouted – that wasn't the right thing to do even though I was annoyed.'

⭐ 'I was happy when we found the yellow block, but I got a fright and then was unhappy that I stood on it and it hurt my foot.'

helping your toddler identify their own emotions

You can help a toddler identify their own emotions by encouraging them to name them, ideally at the time the feeling is happening.

When talking to a toddler about emotions, get close to their level – put them on your knee, or next to you on the couch, or bend down. You might touch their arm, stroke their hand, or if it seems like it would help, give them a cuddle. Ask 'How are you feeling?' in happy as well as difficult times. Some examples:

⭐ 'Are you frightened of the dog? You don't have to go close to it or touch it.'

⭐ 'That was a loud noise! I got a fright, did you?'

⭐ 'I've been giving the baby lots of attention for a while, and I will play with you very soon when they've finished having lunch. Is that a good idea?'

⭐ 'It seems like you might be a bit frustrated. Is that what you're feeling?'

⭐ 'Do you think Nanna was feeling cross?'

⭐ 'Did that make you feel proud?'

⭐ 'Were you upset, or didn't you mind?'

⭐ 'Ché got the presents today because it was his birthday. When it's your birthday, you will have some presents. Sometimes it seems hard to wait!'

Always express empathy before a correction, if you can.

⭐ 'That must have been horrible, to feel very angry, but even when you're angry, it's not okay to bite Mrs Snodgrass on the ankle.'
Be firm about what's required while sympathising with feelings.

⭐ 'I know Frillippa took dolly, and that was not fair and hurt your feelings.'

Helping kids learn empathy

You can explain how others might be feeling, and sometimes ask your child to guess. 'I can see that Finn is crying. Do you think he's angry about something, or just tired?' 'That lady on *Play School* looks very worried, doesn't she? Has she lost something?'

Don't use your own emotions as a bribe

Don't say your child misbehaving will make you angry or unhappy, and don't pretend to cry. In other words, don't try to spark guilt and shame in your child. Speak of their *behaviours* as right and wrong, rather than saying the child is 'bad'. Suggest a better way to behave or respond next time.

Teaching toddlers words for emotions

We need more than 'happy' and 'sad'. We need words that describe a range of distinct feelings. The idea is to identify the emotions, and never say 'don't' feel them, or 'that's silly'. Talk about the emotion, what caused it, and perhaps ways of managing the emotion while you have it, or changing it. You can show that emotions are okay, that things don't always feel happy, and that's okay; the important thing is what we do about the more unhappy emotions.

Sometimes the words are too much for a toddler but you can still sympathise with humiliation ('sad') if a child is teased, or celebration and pride ('pleased') when they achieve a skill they've been working on, like catching a ball. Or Non-specific Irrational Envy (which I made up but it's that thing where they just grab toys from each other for no reason and then get upset when theirs is taken).

As they grow, more nuanced words can be added. Gradual exposure to emotions, and ways of naming and dealing with them, is a great gift you can give a child, who will grow up better able to negotiate difficulties and triumphs.

Name that emotion or feeling

* Angry
* Bored
* Calm
* Cheerful
* Concentrating
* Confident
* Confused
* Cranky
* Cross with myself
* Disappointed
* Embarrassed
* Enjoying
* Excited
* Exhausted (hit the wall)
* Friendly
* Frustrated
* Full of beans/energy

* Guilty/ashamed
* Happy
* Having a love wave
* Hungry
* Hurt feelings (emotional)
* Hurting somewhere (physical)
* Impatient
* In a dancing mood
* Itchy
* Keen to run/skip/ dance
* Laughing
* Lonely
* Missing someone
* Needing quiet time
* Nervous

* Out of sorts
* Patient
* Pleased
* Pushed around
* Sad
* Scared
* Shy
* Sick
* Sleepy
* Sorry
* Surprised
* Tired
* Unsure
* Wanting more attention
* Wanting what someone else has
* Worried

'It's useful for toddlers to experience small doses of rejection in the real world. If a man doesn't say hello back to our toddler daughter on public transport, we can say later, "I don't think he felt like talking to anyone today" as if that's an okay thing, even if it was disappointing. We don't have to say he was naughty, or mean, or try to spare her feelings by pretending he didn't hear her say hello.' JANE, a psychologist

Ways to teach a toddler to manage emotions

⭐ Having a chat – telling somebody

⭐ Having a cuddle

⭐ Telling a pet and having a pat with them

⭐ Having a bath

⭐ Having a moment alone in their room

⭐ Having a nap

⭐ Having a lie-down but not a sleep

⭐ Reading a book

⭐ Listening to some music or a recorded story

⭐ Doing a drawing

⭐ Saying goodbye to the broken toy in the bin

⭐ Having a cry

⭐ Holding their teddy

> 'Tell your kids about your feelings: they understand more than you expect them to.'
> CHANTELLE

See Chapter 24, Toddler Behaviour, for info on tantrums and meltdowns.

Sarcasm

Toddlers can't understand sarcasm. They are learning a lot all the time about communication, so don't confuse them by saying the opposite of what you mean as a 'joke', or as irony. 'Oh great, another drink spilt on the floor' just creates a confusing, negative vibe, and doesn't help anybody. If they hear somebody else's sarcasm, you can help them understand it is confusing, but some people think it's funny to say the opposite of what they mean. Toddlers are amazed by this, as they are in the stage of life when they desperately want to understand things clearly, and be understood.

praise & confidence for kids

Praise doesn't always have to be for an achievement, or for just existing. A kid turning around in a circle knows that 'Awesome job!' is a bit too effusive. Especially if it was delivered by a parent glancing up from their phone screen. Another way to build resilience and determination (and perhaps a more realistic view of life) is to praise characteristics such as trying, participating and being compassionate – not just acknowledge 'results'. See the box called 'Ways to praise kids' in Chapter 24, Toddler Behaviour.

The toddler strut

Do you remember that viral video of a dad doing a live TV interview from his home office and being interrupted by his kids, and then the frantic mum dashing in to grab them and haul them out? The best part was when his toddler daughter burst in with a totally jaunty, funny strut with chicken-dance arm movements. She had a sense of utter confidence and a force field of perceived safety in her dad's presence. That poor, frantic mum felt terrible about the kids getting away from her, but what an accolade to parenting her daughter's confident attitude showed. If only everyone had that top-of-the-world feeling, and we could keep it all our lives. I might just start entering all rooms doing the chicken-armed toddler strut.

dealing with toddler shyness

Being shy, or 'slow to warm up' is a recognised, common personality trait. Some people are introverts, some extroverts. Some people seem like one but are actually more comfortable being the other. Most people are a mixture depending on the company and how familiar the situation.

After all, adults don't walk into a party and bellow 'Hello, everyone! I'm ME and WHO ARE YOU?' – not unless there has been BEER INVOLVEMENT. Toddlers often bond with their attentive family, friends and carers but warm to others slowly. This is wise and safe behaviour, and not to be criticised as being 'too shy'.

If your child can manage it, try to make the bottom-line requirement of a greeting 'hello' and 'goodbye'. Or, if that's beyond them, say: 'When you're ready, please say hello.' It's okay for them to cling to you, or hold your leg.

No adult or other child should be allowed to kiss, cuddle, pick up or touch a child who is reluctant. This is a very bad message to send to a child – that somebody else has the right to touch them when they don't feel comfortable. You may have to be firm with relatives hugging away willy-nilly. 'Savannah will kiss or hug you later, if she wants to. Until then, please give her some space.'

'Grigor, do you want to give Uncle Sven a hug?' If not, do not force them. Let them warm up to it themselves, if at all.

You don't have to identify or label your kid as 'shy'. 'She's a bit shy' usually sounds apologetic, as if all kids should throw themselves at strangers or people they haven't seen for a while. Help your kid learn to trust their instincts. Don't let people talk about shyness as if it's cute or an act, or not allowed ('Don't be shy' or 'How adorable, you're so cute when you're shy'). Negative reactions to a kid's shyness can push them further into social anxiety, and make them confused and feel they have to pretend.

'let girls be girls & boys be boys'

Kids should be free of the gender hang-ups of adults. If a girl is leading the game, she's not 'bossy' – she's the leader. If she's cross about something, she's allowed to be cross, and needs to learn how to handle it. A boy should feel comfortable to ask for a flower to be his facepaint design, or to be 'shy', or cry, or talk about his feelings. All kids are entitled to swagger, and fear, and to be boisterous, and to be praised for compassion, and imagination. Watch out for other people trying to stifle this, too. 'It's a bit sad that Grandpa thinks boys don't play with dolls, isn't it. I wonder where he got that wrong idea?' Let kids be themselves.

more info on being a boy or a girl

www.somekidsbooks.com
The fun picture books *Some Girls* and *Some Boys*, both by Nelly Thomas and illustrated by Sarah Dunk, are for any kid and show that we're all individuals – some girls like climbing trees or have short hair, some like toy trucks and some like pink stuff. Ditto for boys.

transcendsupport.com.au
Most kids who enjoy stuff that's 'non-traditional' don't reject their assumed gender, but some do – and need support and reassurance to be themselves. Resources are available for parents whose kids do consistently express thoughts and behaviours over a long time that show a strong need to identify with another gender. Transcend was set up by mums as a hub for information and support.

how to talk about grown-up things with toddlers

Grown-up concepts are things that need to be explained to little kids in language they understand, at a level of detail they can cope with. Usually it's best to give a simple answer to the questions they come up with rather than present encyclopedic lectures on subjects such as sex, death, fear, nudity, drug addiction, and why some female news-readers are required to look like Barbie dolls with shooty-up eyebrows.

Explaining body parts & functions

Sometimes we forget kids don't know what's happening to them. Unless they're really sick and uninterested, they could be reassured to know that vomiting means their body is trying to get rid of some food that had germs in it, or that the body is still waiting for the medicine to make their tummy better so it can do the right thing with food again; that they feel hot and bothered because their body is trying to burn up the germs; that they have a nasty rash but the ointment is going to go to work and start rubbing it out; or that having lots of naps is helping the body to fight the germs inside and make them strong again.

Kids should be given names for things that will help them communicate with others. Words such as 'poo' and 'wee' are pretty universal, 'tinkle' is less so, and 'shooting a rabbit' – as a phrase meaning to fart, as one kindergarten called it – is just plain nutty. Common terms for genitals are 'penis', 'willy', 'doodle', 'vagina', 'vulva', 'front botty', 'back botty', 'bottom' and 'private parts'. Basically, you need words that your family understands, but that will also make sense to a doctor.

Explaining serious family situations

Children sometimes have to deal with their parents' separation, divorce, addiction, or mental or physical illness, their own serious illness, and other difficult stuff. The most important ideas to convey are that the problem is not the child's fault; that some problems, such as psychological ones, can improve if tackled by parents and professionals together; and that the child is not alone – help is available and other kids go through these times too.

Enjoying being in the nuddy

Children under 5 don't associate themselves or others being in the nude with sex unless somebody makes that connection for them. You can tell preschoolers that some people don't like others being naked because they think it's rude, but that it's okay at home. (Do be prepared for the consequences of young children not knowing what's rude: when I was aged 4 I told the fruit-shop man conspiratorially, 'My mummy has a beard on her bottom.')

When your child wants privacy in the toilet or doesn't want to undress in front of others, respect this but be matter-of-fact about nudity and don't make them feel ashamed of their body.

Explaining masturbation

Some little kids, especially ones recently freed from nappies, might suddenly realise that various bits of their body feel very good when they rub them. Some boys will occasionally have a stiffening of the penis. The less fuss made, the better. Masturbating children can be told that because the activity involves their private parts, it's a private activity they can do in their room. Any more elaborate 'inappropriate' behaviour is almost certainly the result of the child having seen something, or been shown something by another kid, and it's best to take a low-key approach to finding out the cause.

Explaining gay

Most toddlers are perfectly fine with the idea that Uncle Todd has a girlfriend but Uncle Steve has a husband. Nobody has to talk about sex in this context to little kids. If they have any questions, answer them as they arise. If they hear negative comments from other or older kids, you can gently explain: 'There's nothing wrong with people loving each other.' As with all such talk, tell your child: 'Some people say mean things, but it doesn't mean they're right. Saying that isn't right, and we don't say things like that in this family.'

Explaining the news

Toddlers should not watch the news, or any violent or disturbing material, anywhere, including in waiting rooms. Kids cannot process the idea of constant bad news day after day. They can't understand where or why it is happening. If you do not need to have rolling coverage of disasters or news stories on a screen, don't. Much better to check alerts on your phone or watch the news when kids are napping or asleep. It's our job to shield them as much as possible. Sometimes kids do see something scary about a natural disaster, or they see a bad-news story, or somebody will tell them about it. Always be led by the kid. Ask what they think has happened, and respond gently.

One important idea to get across is: what you saw, or what was scary, has already happened, and it's over now. People came to help, and they cuddled the people in trouble. You can say: 'It's okay to be upset when bad things happen. I'm upset too. But it is not happening here, to us, now.' Encourage the habit that your kid comes to you with their worries – never say 'Don't worry about that' or suggest the worry is wrong or silly. Explain why they are safe, or will be safe. 'Why?' can be answered honestly, and age-appropriately: 'We don't know, but the police are going to find out.'

Explaining where babies come from

The arrival of a new baby sometimes prompts the question. A small child of, say, 2½ might be satisfied with 'Mummy and Daddy made you' or 'You grew in Mummy's tummy', and go off happily without any more questions for months or even years. But when the harder questions come, answer each question with an age-appropriate answer rather than explaining the whole palaver all at once. My mother showed me a diagram of fallopian tubes when I was 2, and frankly it was totes TMI.

Explaining death

Kids at different ages and stages see death differently. They often need to talk it through and ask the same questions over and over as they try to work it out in their heads. As with sex, keep pace with their questions and give them answers about what they're interested in, rather than piling onto them everything you can think of.

The permanency of death is probably the hardest concept for children to grasp, but there are many related questions – 'Did the baby die because I sometimes wanted them to go away?', 'Where is Granny now?', 'Will I die too?', 'When will you die, Daddy?' – that can be discussed when the child feels ready to raise them in an environment that encourages talk, questions and remembering somebody who is no longer alive. Children will gradually develop their own theories and accept things in their own way, but it's very important for them to feel they can talk about death at any time. Books read together can help to prompt questions or answer them as they are raised by the child.

In a grieving household, allow for kids being fully aware of a sad atmosphere if not the reasons for grief: allow them to cling, or to have 'time out' with other relatives or trusted friends who can have them in another room or take them to the park. It is normal and good for kids to have periods of play and happiness or be distracted, even if they are sad.

more info on kids' books about birth & death

Mummy Laid an Egg!
by Babette Cole (Random House, UK)
The older siblings explain to a shy mum and dad where babies really come from. One to bring out when your child eventually expresses interest in the nitty-gritty of how babies are made.

Badger's Parting Gifts
by Susan Varley (Collins, UK)
Old Badger's time to die has come, but everyone remembers something Badger gave them, taught them or showed them.

more info on talking about grown-up things

raisingchildren.net.au
On the home page of this reliable federal government–backed site, choose 'toddlers'
or 'preschoolers', then 'Connecting & communicating' for specific suggestions about,
say, anger, death and sex, and good hints on how to listen.

healthychildren.org
On the American Academy of Pediatrics site, search 'talking to children'. There are
fact sheets on how to talk about disasters, death, drugs and alcohol. Or search 'talking
to children about racial bias'.

betterhealth.vic.gov.au
Search 'trauma and children' on this website to find a wealth of resources about
children of different ages. Useful for families who need help with bereavement,
and with recovery from natural disasters or other events.

24

TODDLER BEHAVIOUR

Parents say 'no' and the baby understands. But usually about the same age as they start to walk, a toddler starts trying to control their world. They don't like this 'no' business. Teaching 'good behaviour' to toddlers combines many difficult elements: being cranky, reacting in the moment, feeling out of control, and ill-advised urges to have a tantrum. And that's just the parents.

what is discipline?

When people talk about discipline they often think it just means punishment. The point of discipline is not to punish a child, but to teach them to behave with kindness and consideration, and to understand the rules. 'Discipline' sounds a little bit like what English politicians get up to in expensive London dungeons with bored ladies called Mistress Nannypants.

Try to think of yourself as a coach, not a punisher. It's impossible for a child to have the mental capacity to put themselves in *your* shoes. But you can try to imagine you're a child attempting to work out the right way to behave – or what you can get away with. It's your kid's job to test the boundaries so they know where they are, and your job to keep the boundaries clear. Set reasonable rules early on – these can start when your child is 1 or 2 and build through their preschool years.

Here are some approaches you might find helpful.

⭐ Think of your child as your ally or apprentice, not the enemy.

⭐ Show your child the right way to behave.

⭐ Help your child learn when a behaviour is wrong, and why.

⭐ Recognise that your child may not understand or care why they're supposed to behave in a certain way. Explain when you can, but 'That's the rule' is a shorthand response. Toddlers are learning to be logical, but they're not there yet.

⭐ Give your child choices of things that don't matter. 'Apple or pear?', but not 'Sit still or hit your sister'.

⭐ Establish a small core of simple ground rules that are consistently observed, such as bedtime is 7 o'clock, no hitting, and you don't get what you ask for if you use a whingey voice – so the child isn't overwhelmed by trying to remember 56 rules.

⭐ Be clear that the aim is for your child to understand what are the right things to do, not to humiliate them or make them feel inadequate or guilty when they do something wrong.

'We have two rules for our 19-month-old son. Don't touch the power points and don't touch the bin.'
EMMA

Boundaries for kids: some ideas

* We must be kind and gentle with people and animals.
* Kids must be in bed at bedtime (with perhaps half an hour to read or play in bed).
* We don't scream or squeal loudly in this house.
* We use our words to fix a problem, not hitting or pushing.
* If we do the wrong thing or make a mistake, or yell, we say sorry afterwards.
* Parents are the bosses, but they let you choose some things.
* Everyone has to say please and thank you.
* We don't throw balls in the house.
* We don't throw our food.
* We have to try a new food, but if we don't like it we don't have to eat it.
* When we get a drink or a piece of fruit, we ask if anyone else would like some.
* Kids aren't allowed on the road without holding an adult's hand.
* Allowances will be made for a kid who is tired or otherwise having a hard time.
* There will be some time in the day for a kid who needs it to run and shout outside.
* We say hello and goodbye to people when we meet or they visit.

BLAST FROM THE PAST

'Never tell a child but once to do a thing; once is enough if it understands you. Then let it understand that disobedience is sure to be followed by punishment. Never allow it (a child) to ask "why".'
– Truly terrible advice from the *Northern Territory Times and Gazette*, 1915

'If I read another piece of parenting advice telling me to consider the child's feelings first when they are hitting me in the face, I will scream. Sometimes it's "NO!" first, then sort out the why later.' LAUREL

Boundaries for parents: some ideas

* Parents should speak to children with respect.
* Parents have decided never to hit. It is not an option.
* Parents need to say please and thank you, too.
* Parents will be consistent with rules and consequences.
* Parents will help children be likeable humans by teaching them manners and making sure they use them.
* If parents do the wrong thing or make a mistake, they say sorry.
* Parents will apologise if they have a tantrum or are rude.

* Parents are allowed to go into their room for quiet time.
* Parents must arrange time away or to be on their own to balance all the time they spend with kids.
* Parents will try not to throw their food.
* Allowances will be made for a parent who is tired or otherwise having a hard time.

'What works for one child will not necessarily work for another. Consistency, fairness, continuity and perseverance. My son is no angel and even angels wear you down in the end . . . Treat them how you would expect to be treated yourself. Don't back down. Once you've made a decision stick to it or they've got you sussed.' KIRSTIN

why is the kid 'behaving badly'?

It's always useful to know. Reasons can include:

⭐ They're starting to get sick.

⭐ They're tired. Maybe a nap or quiet time will help.

⭐ They're hungry. Produce a healthy snack (voila!).

⭐ They're confused. Give short, clear explanations or instructions.

⭐ The kid is having a non-specific bad mood.

⭐ They're bored with or understimulated by the general company or routine.

⭐ They're testing the boundaries. Be consistent with the rules and the consequences of breaking them.

⭐ Past annoying behaviour has been rewarded. A child who shouts 'DOOR!!!!' and has it opened for them has worked out the magic formula. It's better if they learn the magic word is 'please'.

⭐ They want everything to go their way. Acknowledge this and say you wish everyone could do whatever they wanted, but it doesn't always work like that. Don't be sucked into endless explanations of why not!

⭐ Their usual routine has been disrupted. Try to do something that gets you both back into at least one of your routines or a comfort zone.

⭐ There is an underlying problem. A trauma, a problem causing stress in the home or a worry (possibly even an overheard one), a developmental delay or hidden hearing problem, or a pain could be causing your child to change their behaviour. Deal with the family stress, getting professional help if needed: start with your family doctor.

⭐ Things escalate too quickly. The kid seems to go off like a rocket. Have you been accidentally setting an example?

⭐ The kid is desperate for attention. Even negative attention will show that you're interested in them. Give attention when they're not behaving badly.

> 'While the reasoning part of their brain, the cortex, is still being wired in, you have to be their cortex.'   HENNY

'There's nothing worse than arguing with a 2-year-old when you're 30.'   HELEN

Living in an unsafe situation

You will know already that toddlers watch adults and copy what they do. But the dangers of toddlers copying ugly or threatening behaviours in the home isn't the only risk. An aggressive or uncertain 'walking on eggshells' environment is fully felt by any small child. They are not 'too young to understand'. Even if they don't remember specific incidents later in life, their brain will be changed by their environment as babies and children. 'Significant adversity' – such as poverty and aggression or fear – means a very high risk of developmental delays in children, and can be measured as early as a few months old.

If you are living in a situation that is not safe, emotionally or physically, please reach out for help. Even if you feel you are not ready for drastic action, you can start to plan and hope, so you can remove yourself and your child from danger.

tantrums

Tantrums, or hissy fits, can start before 2 and last well past 3 years old. They are mainly a toddler's reaction to not getting their own way, and part of their development. Having a tantrum is an immature reaction to a problem, and many adults haven't yet grown out of such behaviour. Always make a kid safe by clearing the area around them, ensuring they can't hurt themselves or anyone else, and hug them if they'll accept it.

Tantrums start off as the best way a kid knows to express anger or frustration or tiredness: you need to help them learn other means. Here are some ways to do that.

⭐ Tantrums should be ignored whenever possible.

⭐ A tantrum chucker who gets what they want learns that tantrums work.

⭐ Reward the non-tantrum chucker and good behaviour.

⭐ Try to avoid tantrum 'recipes': tired kid, bright supermarket with lots of temptations, having to get in the car and be somewhere *immediately*, a toddler not being given any choices at all . . .

⭐ Try one of these: walk away (if at home); count to ten; do a meditation exercise; sing your favourite song to yourself, even if it's got a funny phrase in it such as 'Climb Every Mountain'; pop into the backyard for a moment. Use the 'time out' technique coming up.

⭐ After a tantrum, the kid could be in need of a cuddle because they've freaked themselves out.

⭐ Don't meet a tantrum with your own tantrum.

Tantrum solidarity

If you see a kid throwing a tantrum in a public place and their parent ignoring them, ignore them too and smile in a conspiratorial way with the parent before you move off without comment, unless it's 'Hang in there'. Don't judge or assume they need to 'discipline' their kid. Their child may have autism, or be drastically overtired because of a family crisis.

Responding to a meltdown

A lot of parents try to reason with kids when they're in full fall-about. This won't work, as the kid is concentrating all its energy on the flailing or yelling or crying. And you can't really reason with a person who is crying because their feet aren't hooves, or because they want to eat a banana without peeling it, or, well, just because. The first priority is to make everyone safe, before any talking.

So put your berserker-toddler in a contained safe place, and don't let them hurt another person or anybody else's things. They must not be allowed to hit siblings or parents or carers, no matter their level of frustration. It is not enough to say 'stop' or to say later 'That hurt your brother' or 'That made Mummy very upset'. You must stop it happening. You can ask other kids 'Can you just stay over there on the couch for a minute until Jaxon is feeling more calm?' See Chapter 23, Toddler Emotions, for how to help kids learn to identify, name and deal with emotions.

You can let a kid who's in emotional distress know you understand: 'You're having a hard time feeling so angry, I can see.' If a very upset child will allow being held, you can say: 'I can see how upset you are and I'm going to hold you for a moment.' If the tantrum is about wanting something not allowed, don't give in and allow it, as this teaches your child that tantrums work. Sometimes you just have to keep saying no and wait it out, wishing you were elsewhere, alone, and wearing a medal for patience.

'I do as he demands.'
GREER

whingeing

Not really naughtiness or defiance, whingeing or 'whining' is a hardwired tactic used by a lot of kids to get their way. If they learn that eighteen repeat whinges usually gets them what they want, then they learn to do it eighteen times the next time. Some parents do anything to give the kid what they want because the whingeing tone is more irritating than being locked in a giant jam jar with a flock of mosquitoes.

The consensus on this one is that you should ignore whingeing tones and explain that you will respond to a question asked in a 'nice voice' or a 'normal voice'. This way a whingeing tone is never rewarded and doesn't become the lever of choice. (Same thing goes for tantrums.) You'll have to follow up by really listening when they don't use a whingeing tone – that's the bargain. Kids may have to also be told that 'pleeeeeeeeaaaase' does not work, and that asking 67 times won't either. You must stick to this or you will be doomed to Endless Whingeing Hell. Distraction is often the answer to whingeing, so think about learning to tap dance.

I will tell you of the triumphant moment at my place when a pre-schooler visitor whinged to try to get a biscuit, and my kid said, 'Oh, that doesn't work here.' And the other kid said, 'Oh, okay,' and they both went off to play. I shall never forget it. I had my low moments as a mum but that one was an absolute classic. And it only took a few years. (A ha aha ha.)

general rudeness

Toddlers who make demands that would be rude coming from an adult need to modify their behaviour. Dictatorial demands are funny on one level, but it's your job to nip them in the bud. Help your toddler to be a more personable, um, person. 'Stop talking now' and 'Get me a drink' are not acceptable comments in polite society (sadly). Replying 'I am going to finish what I am saying' will do. And don't get the drink until you're asked nicely with a 'please'.

Extra-challenging kid behaviours

Sometimes a kid gets into the habit of epic tantrums or meltdowns or sulks, or inability to discuss the situation, or they find it difficult to sit still or follow instructions, or they develop obsessive behaviour such as headbanging, biting or headbutting. Get your kid-friendly doctor to check for any developmental or other problems that you might need a hand with (a kid with blocked ears can't hear instructions). Search 'biting' (etc.) on **raisingchildren.net.au** for extra info.

feeling out of control

If you feel you're not in control of your anger or reactions to your kid's behaviour, go see your child & family health nurse or family doctor: they have seen and talked this through with thousands of parents in your situation. You might need to take on a couple of new strategies, or get some more help or sleep so you're not so stressed, or there might be a simple physical reason your child is crying that can be fixed. Anything from check-ups to sleep-school training to counselling can be helpful for setting you right.

more info if you feel out of control

See 'Counselling and referral help for parents' in Chapter 2, Your Help Team.

Lifeline: 13 11 14
(general emergency 24-hour helpline)

Lifeline New Zealand: 0800 543 354
(general emergency 24-hour helpline)

BLAST FROM THE PAST
'Repeated yielding by parents often makes a tyrant out of the child ... and this disposition becomes a part of his personality. Many of these children grow up to be bullies or daydreamers and reach maturity as misfits.'
– Scary *Daily Mercury*, Queensland, 1949

strategies for 'fixing' behaviour

It's not just crying babies who can make parents feel rage. Toddlers and preschoolers can be maddeningly rude, shouty or difficult. Teaching kids how to behave requires patience, kindness and consistency. And sometimes those virtues are in short supply (I myself had a tantrum only this morning) – which is why the following will help.

- ★ Have a consistent approach to bad behaviour. (One parent should not be the lone 'disciplinarian' if there are two parents involved.)
- ★ Get as much help from outside as you can. Have a consistent, agreed-on set of rules that all parents and carers (including grandparents) know and follow.
- ★ If you find your anger and resentment rising, give *yourself* time out. Put the kids in front of something age-appropriate on the TV, go to another room and lie there, scream into a pillow, do relaxation techniques, read a chapter of a book – anything to get your frustration level down and reduce your fly-off-the-handleability. (It is so a word, shoosh.)
- ★ Imagine your kid was your best friend and was behaving the same way: your first reaction would not be to shout or say something rude.
- ★ Imagine you're in public, or actually go somewhere public to react.
- ★ Take every opportunity to rest and enjoy your own pursuits – a happier person is usually a kinder, more patient person.

> 'Between her and the dog I say "no" a lot: so my daughter knows not to dig up the garden and the dog knows not to throw food.'
> NICKY

Being on the same page about discipline

It's much harder to always be calm and consistent if you're a sole or single parent and don't have help in dealing with toddler behaviour, if your partner wants to hit a child and you don't (or vice versa), or if you've got yourself into a rut where you keep 'disciplining' but the kid's behaviour isn't changing. Perhaps you can do with some more support and babysitting help to let you have a break, and parent counselling to work out a united front with the kid; or you need to start afresh with some new rules and methods you can be consistent with.

Not smacking

Not hitting a child is a fundamental break we can make from the past. It isn't about fashion – it's about progress and finding new ways. Kids used to bounce around in a car without seatbelts a generation ago and most of them survived; it doesn't mean kids without seatbelts is a good idea. I know people say 'I got hit as a kid and I'm fine' – in fact, I heard a homeless drunk man say exactly that in the local playground once. Anyone who has hit their children can learn new ways of dealing with their anger.

Arguments against hitting include:

⭐ it doesn't alter many kids' behaviour – instead it teaches them that if someone is bigger or stronger or believes they are right, hitting is okay

⭐ it often results in them hitting other children, siblings and animals when frustrated

⭐ it punishes rather than teaches

⭐ it makes kids wary of their own actions and words in case they're wrong or frowned upon and will result in physical pain

⭐ it can escalate to worse abuse

⭐ it might have long-term effects because children are vulnerable to being emotionally and physically damaged.

An impulse to hit is something we have all felt. But it can be resisted, especially if you have a rule against it for yourself, and have some alternatives to try (see the Not Smacking section, coming up).

One sad comment to me from a mum was 'I hit him up to twelve times a day and it doesn't make any difference.' Another wrote 'Sometimes you feel like you're smacking them all day but they will eventually learn.' If it isn't working, you need to try something else. This section is for any parent who needs help with discipline that isn't working or who wants to find alternatives to smacking.

So many of the people who did hit – most often a slap on the hand or a swat to the bottom – told me they didn't like smacking but they still did it. I hope the ideas in this chapter will help them give it up.

'I use boring, long-winded lectures.' PAMELA

Disciplining someone else's child

⭐ You can't hit someone else's child.

⭐ You shouldn't yell at someone else's child (unless it's a shocked warning of sudden danger).

⭐ You can say to a child 'The rule in our house is [*whatever the rule is*] so when you're in our house or out with us, you need to follow that rule.' Toddlers should be able to follow simple house rules such as no hitting, no mean comments, and saying please and thank you.

⭐ It's okay not to ask a child back or not to let your child play at a house that has no rules and that you think could make for a dangerous or icky situation.

Ways to praise kids

Behaviour specialists agree that praising the good stuff is the most important way to change kids' behaviour.

⭐ 'I really like this painting. Tell me about it. Why did you make this bit red?'

⭐ 'You kept trying, even when it got harder and harder! That was so great.'

⭐ 'You are getting better at swimming, I can tell.'

⭐ 'It doesn't matter if you're the fastest.'

⭐ 'What a mighty effort!'

⭐ 'Thank you for spending that time making this. Aunty Maeve will love it.'

⭐ 'I really appreciate your help making the lunch. Thank you.'

⭐ It's important to be kind, and what you said to Tahlia just then was very kind. When Dad/Nanna/teddy hears about this, they will be proud of you.'

⭐ 'I love it when you do that.'

⭐ 'You are so good at that.'

⭐ 'You have lovely manners.'

⭐ 'What a great kid you are.'

⭐ 'I really like doing this with you.'

⭐ 'What a splendid job.'

⭐ High five!

> 'I always praise when they're good.'
> DEBBY

Body language – encouraging nods and smiles, eye contact, thumbs up, applause, handshakes – or stickers on a chart or on the hand can be good non-verbal things to add to what you've said.

~~~~~~ **more info** on bad-mood changers ~~~~~~

Wanda-Linda Goes Berserk
by Kaz Cooke (Penguin)
My picture book about having a tantrum and calming down afterwards, starring Glenda the hairy-nosed wombat.

Separating the behaviour from the kid

Although they might 'work' to stop a child's behaviour, or satisfy a parent's belief, some discipline approaches can do psychological harm.

⭐ It's very important not to crush the spirit of a child by making them feel they are a bad or terribly disappointing person. Humiliation can lead to real depression and sadness in a child. Make sure you get across that it's the behaviour you want changed, not the person. It's better to say 'My feelings were hurt when you said that. Let's think of a nicer thing you could say' than 'Get out of my sight. I can't look at you.'

⭐ Coldness or indifference in a parent is a much harsher punishment to a child than an adult might realise. An icy stare or similar cold-shoulder treatment can create inner panic and fear and an unspoken, desolate sadness because they feel that they are not loved.

⭐ Saying 'You're very, very bad' can make a child feel crushed and can have lasting effects on their self-esteem and confidence. Use something like 'Let's try that again in a different way'. If you separate being disappointed in them as a person from being disappointed in their behaviour, they know that changing the behaviour is a plus. But if you say you're disappointed in them as a person, all they can do is feel inadequate.

⭐ Shutting yourself in the loo or locking the kid outside the house can create a sense of panic in a child, especially if they have a temperament that makes this punishment very frightening.

A real 'sorry'

Everyone in the family should be able to say a sincere 'sorry' and have it accepted – but not if it's a stalling tactic before they do the same thing again, or a spat-out or shouted 'SORRY!' in very unsorry tones. Parents as well as kids should be able to be genuinely sorry and say so. This helps kids to understand the concept of pain to others, and hurt feelings, and gives them one way of helping make the situation better. If apologies are just as sincerely accepted, this should cut down on grudges, sulking, seething and revenge strikes.

'Appeal to their sympathies . . . once out at the shops I grabbed them and dashed for the public toilets. I was about to have an accident and they had to be quick! They forgot all about what they were making a fuss about because they had to save Mum from eternal public embarrassment!' INGRID

'Removal of the object they are fighting over is always useful.' KAREN

Possible bad-mood changers

These ideas have been suggested by parents – they're worth a try for a kid who's woken up on the wrong side of the bed (or cot):

* a bath
* safe water play
* prepare a snack together
* a drink of water – a dehydrated child is a tired child
* a favourite TV show (if they're older than 2) or book
* special toys put away for just this purpose
* have a cuddle and chat or quiet time
* promise a special made-up story at bedtime – and make sure you deliver
* go out and look for birds, butterflies, orange cars
* take them outside – even rugged up and waterproofed
* sing and dance together
* water the garden and pull out weeds
* allow them to rip something into pieces as a special treat (give them a newspaper or advertising guff from the letterbox) – older babies and young toddlers love this
* dress-ups
* go to see what's happening at the neighbours' or the shops
* bring out the playdough
* carry handbag-sized pencils, pads and other activities and games to head off trouble when you're out
* sing songs with actions they have to think about ('Incy-Wincy Spider', 'This Is the Way We Wash Our Hands')
* talk to a grandparent on the phone or video
* separate two kids if they are fighting and give them different activities for a while
* talk in funny voices and accents, make faces, walk like a pompous person – kids are fascinated by emotions and body language because they're trying to learn them
* 'hide' them and then 'find' them under the clean washing pile
* make a cubby with blankets and chairs
* swap roles – you be the kid and they the parent – and see what words they give you and how they behave as you
* make a puppet out of a toy by doing a voice for it, and have it chat away with your child – kids over 2½ will happily chat to a toy
* blow bubbles (for all ages).

the 'time out' technique

Different parenting advisers and parents have their own versions of time out, or quiet time. Parents who use time out differ about whether it's a circuit-breaker and cooling-off period or a punishment, but it's universally agreed by experts that it isn't meant to be used as a punishment. And time out needs to be balanced by praise for good behaviour, too. 'Time out' is really a technique for the over-threes, the age when they are developmentally ready.

manners

Some people don't bother teaching their children manners, but that's a short cut to having a child who is disliked. There's a difference between using the right words – please, thank you, thanks for having me, and hello – and common courtesy, which means learning to wait your turn to speak, not pushing people out of the way to get where you want to go, and consideration for others.

The pleases and thank-yous are pretty much a matter of automatic speech – children usually learn to say them before they really understand that they are forms of politeness. One parent's suggestion is that when you give small kids something like, say, a drink, hold on to it until they say thank you. And don't move a muscle until they say please.

The common, grating parental prompts include 'What's the magic word?', 'What do you say?' and 'I can't hear you'. (Swore I'd never say them. Said them all.) Praise the good manners when you get them.

People adore a child with good manners, and will give them lots of attention and unsolicited presents in shops and elsewhere just because they're so thrilled to meet one. A child will have an easier time of it if they learn that 'lovely manners' will get them further in life.

Kids learning to actually share is a different matter and needs to be reinforced with talk of people 'each having a turn': kids see that as fairer than the concept of 'sharing'. Talk to your child about who owns what so they understand that they don't own everything in the world. (You don't need a full-scale explanation of the global economy, just a notion of your blocks, Aunty Fatima's car, Caitlin's hairclips.) Help your child understand that their toys will always come back to them: after all, you wouldn't let just anyone walk off with your TV. If there are some very special toys they don't want to share, agree to put them out of bounds to guests and hide them away during visits.

BLAST FROM THE PAST

'A great deal of the bad manners of children is due to their mothers . . .
the people who spoil them the most are the servants.'
– *The Domestic Blunders of Women*, by 'A Mere Man', UK, 1899. So helpful.

General manners

General manners include:

⭐ saying please and thank you
⭐ saying hello when introduced to someone or seeing an acquaintance, and goodbye when leaving them (shy kids shouldn't be forced to do anything else in the way of conversation)
⭐ being kind and courteous to people and animals
⭐ not teasing
⭐ good sporting behaviour
⭐ no screaming, especially in public places (that shrieky squeal of excitement can be misinterpreted by strangers as distress, and is anyway very annoying and disruptive for others)
⭐ table manners, as they get older.

more info on dealing with toddler behaviour

raisingchildren.net.au
Choose 'toddlers' or 'preschoolers', then 'Behaviour' for hints.

How to Talk so Kids Will Listen & Listen so Kids Will Talk
by Adele Faber and Elaine Mazlish (Simon & Schuster, USA)
What every frazzled parent needs: good scripts for dealing with difficult situations, including tantrums. Some parents swear by the audio version for the car, and I am tickled by the idea of listening to it while the kids are in the back.

TripleP-parenting.net.au
The Positive Parenting Program (Triple P) website is a long-term success: an evidence-based parenting course developed by the Behavioural Family Intervention program at the University of Queensland, led by Dr Matthew Sanders, professor of clinical psychology. Learn online or go to your nearest classes. Dr Sanders' book, *Every Parent: A Positive Approach to Children's Behaviour* (Penguin, Australia), has practical ideas and clever, non-stressful, age-appropriate ways of dealing with kids. Covers whingeing, tantrums, being a bad sport, refusing to go to bed and food fussiness.

Raising Your Spirited Child
by Mary Sheedy Kurcinka (book and audiobook; HarperCollins)
A perennial favourite by a US parenting teacher that explains common reasons for behavioural problems and defiance, and offers practical advice on general changes to routines, sleep behaviours and other specific incidents.

How Kind!
by Mary Murphy (Candlewick Press, USA)
A picture book: all the barnyard animals do each other favours.

'If any of my boys threw a tantrum, it was often when we were in a shop and they wanted something and I said no. My advice is to walk away and pretend they aren't yours.'   DALE

25

TODDLER DEVELOPMENT

Toddlers do more than toddle. They climb,
fall, roll, burrow, mimic, squeeze, wedge, laugh,
rage, cuddle, and try to flee the general area.
Here's what to expect from your toddler – their abilities,
skills and achievements. And what to do if those skills
seem to be late in arriving, or come and go.

is your toddler amazing?

Yes, your child is amazing and also quite possibly a genius. In the sense that all kids are geniuses. Geni-eye. But don't tell anyone or even imply your child is a genius – especially not your child. Your child is allowed to be special. But your child is also allowed to be, well, not that great at some things, or not as advanced as some of their little mates. Achievements come at different times for babies and toddlers. Do all 36-year-olds have the same level of social skills and physical dexterity at jumping and umbrella twirling? Nope. And neither will toddlers.

Your job is to encourage your kid to enjoy things, explore things, and practise things in the guise of having fun and playing around. If you always say 'great job' they're going to give up trying to impress you, and get a big shock when they realise they are not brilliant at everything, not the centre of the universe and not quite as good at some stuff as other kids and quite furious and in denial (cue tantrum).

Your kid does something odd – I know because all kids do. They have a quirk, or a strange obsession or passion, or they're really good at something. Or really having trouble with something else. That's because they're normal, and they're weird. We're all a mixture of both. And remember, it's the weirdos who grow up to be amazing creative grown-ups. 'Weird' is not an insult. It just shows a lack of imagination in the person who thinks it's an insult.

outside advice

People you can ask about development include your child & family health nurse, your child-friendly family doctor, and if your kid is in childcare, the workers there. Professionals who spend lots of time with lots of different kids can be good independent observers and a source of useful info, because they see most kids of all ages come along in their own time.

Please remember the developmental milestones on the following lists are just a guide. Your toddler's personality could mean an earlier or later interest in books, or climbing, for example. But there are some missed milestones that mean getting a check-up is a good idea.

when to see a doctor about development

Throughout the lists below of expected development at various ages, you'll see the phrase 'See a doctor if'. It's not cause for alarm, it's just a good idea.

So, it's a good idea to go to the GP if your toddler has developed some social, speech or physical skills but then seems to lose them or 'go backwards'. Likewise, if your kid does seem to be developing at the accepted pace but tends to have massive emotional meltdowns when things don't go right for them. Also get along for a chat if your toddler doesn't react to big noises or sudden sights, if your toddler seems super sensitive to noise and always wants to get away from interacting with kids and adults, doesn't like eye contact, or has big differences in strength on different sides of their body.

It's always worth raising a worry: it will either result in calming reassurance, or you can find out what you need to do to get a hand with any problems or delays. Early intervention and loving help are the best way to handle it.

And please do have a doctor take a look at your toddler if somebody else suggests it might be a good idea. You might be upset at the suggestion that your toddler isn't 'normal', or is 'behind' in some way. But there is no insult or shame in a kid being slower at some things and better at others, or in a child having a quirky personality or interests. Most parents have had the thought, 'Maybe my kid has a problem, but I hope they don't' mixed with 'What if they do and it's my fault?', and 'Why doesn't everyone else mind their own business' mixed with 'I want to reach out to somebody about this'.

If you're not happy with a doctor's response, find another doctor, and another. You are the expert on your own kid and you always will be. Find somebody you can trust who can help you and your kid, or reassure you. If you're satisfied with the all-clear from a doctor, you can tell any busybodies: 'Yep, there's no problem, the doctor says. Are those new shoes?'

If you are referred for extra help in any area, or even start exploring a diagnosis of a developmental delay in one or more areas, it's normal to feel worry, shock, denial and/or anger. Some problems are little and temporary, others might need ongoing management and adjusting to.

'We had a session with a physio when my son hadn't started crawling. It was reassuring and helpful - and with her tips, he was crawling a week later!' KATHERINE

comforting thoughts

If you are referred for extra help in any area, or even start exploring a diagnosis of a developmental delay in one or more areas, it's normal to feel worry, shock, denial and/or anger. Some problems are little and temporary, others might need ongoing management and adjusting to. Here's some useful stuff to remember:

⭐ All kids have 'special needs' of some sort to a greater or lesser degree.

⭐ You will always be the expert on your kid.

⭐ There are lovely things about your kid.

⭐ It can take time to adjust to some unwelcome and difficult news.

⭐ There is help available that can help you overcome or manage your kid's needs and help you all enjoy life more.

⭐ 'Autism' seems to be the scariest 'label' and is a word often used by people who don't know what it means. Being 'on the spectrum' is not the same as having autism, and there is a huge range of different kinds of behaviours and abilities that can be wrongly labelled.

⭐ Not knowing is always worse. Sometimes a 'label' or at least a description of individual personality traits means you can start making positive changes for the better.

⭐ You will not be in this alone. There are experts to help you.

You don't have to tell anybody, or use the label or name a condition. You choose who to share information with. It's often good to have a private talk with childcare workers, or a carer or friends who look after your kid. Again, no need to use labels if you don't want to. Especially if they are irrelevant to the matter at hand. 'She really loves routine, so please stick to it as much as you can or there could be a meltdown' or 'Please don't correct Arthur's lisp – he will probably grow out of it, and our speech therapist says people drawing attention to it won't help.'

For more see Chapter 35, Special Needs.

> 'Nothing was wrong, she's just determined to do things on her own and that's how we have to parent her.' BREE

Toddler eyes

Many people believe looking at screens too much damages kids' eyesight. The truth is, the problem is caused by a related issue: not playing outside enough. Kid eyesight isn't fully matured until they're about 8 years old, and being outside is an essential part of that development.

Not spending enough time outdoors can cause kids to develop eye problems including myopia (also called near-sightedness), which means things in the distance look blurry. Myopia also increases the risk of sight damage later in life. There are two main reasons for myopia: genes and spending too much time indoors. The number of kids needing glasses and other treatment to correct their vision is rising rapidly worldwide because kids are spending less time outside.

Eye specialists agree that all children should play outside for about ten hours a week, to protect the development of their vision and eyes. Even an hour a day will have some protective effect. Older children who spend more than two hours a day on screens have a much higher incidence of myopia.

Sometimes letting kids play outside makes things difficult because it requires more supervision, especially if you don't have a fenced yard – but it's important. Encourage a childcare centre and, later, school to have regular, shaded outdoor play. Playing outside with simple toys or nature boosts kids' immune system and confidence, and helps kids learn spatial judgement, ball skills and other useful developmental tools. See 'Sun care' in Chapter 33, Health, for how to protect kids.

Have your kid's eyes tested at an ophthalmologist (eye surgeon and specialist) or optometrist (health professional often attached to glasses-frame shops). Check first, but this should be covered by Medicare.

wheeeeeee!

toddler physical activity

Official guidelines by experts say that for full development, toddlers need to be active for 'at least three hours a day' – not in a row, but altogether, added up. Toddlers do not need to do any organised running races or gym-style exercise folderol. 'Activity' means hurtling around in a playground, dancing, jumping, skipping and balancing.

This age is a good time to add some other things, like swapping smaller, lighter balls with soccer-ball-sized balls for a bit of kicking, then throwing, handling and, eventually (all stand) catching. Kids will self-regulate their intensity, having a rest or a scheduled sleep and then going again later. Exercise and activity can be full-on, or gentle and slow.

Some communities have organised toddler activities, maybe even with 'gym' in the title, but the key is to make sure they're run by somebody who understands toddler development and provides fun, relevant, achievable games that involve movement for littlies and adapt to age and ability levels. Swimming lessons or pool play with an adult can also be good. (See Chapter 32, Safety & Injuries, for more on pool rules; and swimming lessons.)

Some people worry that we 'wrap kids in cottonwool' and that they are missing out on fun activities with any risk, because we fear injury. Toddlers can still explore the world relatively safely, with your help. Later, when they've done plenty of romping and supervised climbing and running, and developed ball skills, they can gradually expand their boundaries.

~~~~~~ more info on toddler physical activity ~~~~~

health.gov.au
Search on the Australian Health Department site for 'physical activity recommendations for children' to find a brochure. Scroll down for 'tips and ideas children 0-5'.

How much screen time is okay for toddlers?

We are raising the first generations to know about smartphones and personal tablets from birth – babies know very early that there's a little magic device that can take and show photos, play music, record their voice, tell mum what to do, captivate dad.

Scrolling and checking social media and news feeds are addictive behaviours that affect brain chemicals. A toddler loves to have an effect on the world – to make something else appear by swiping, for example, is a thrill, especially when the app or game is designed to keep babies and toddlers interested, and quiet while you drive home or do a chore or have a minute's peace. The phone or tablet is a portal to books, cartoons, songs, contact with relatives . . . There's no in-built 'that's enough' instinct. It doesn't turn itself off (as long as it's charged) and the material on it – at least in terms of one person's ability to find and watch or consume or play it – is limitless.

Recommended screen times below cover the daily combined use of all screens: live or streamed TV, movies, hand-held games, apps, and any use of computers, tablets and phones. All screen time is not equal: child development experts all furiously agree that quality beats worrying about quantity. In other words an hour of good-quality TV for a preschooler is infinitely better than a half-hour of a violent game. Family or friends screening a movie or TV show should always choose one rated G for the youngest person who is there – not be guided by the oldest or most persuasive kid in the room.

Some apps and games are useless in terms of learning or development, or even psychologically harmful – there are apps for little girls to pretend they're getting cosmetic surgery. Electronic games that have positive role models for both girls and boys, and promote thinking or might encourage a 'real world' adaption, but these are aimed at older kids and are not for babies or toddlers.

Screen time before the age of 2 is associated with a very much higher risk of a delay in speech development and less ability in reading. It is also believed to affect learning and development of communication, attention abilities, and social skills later on. Many children are already starting kindergarten with below-average physical, communication and speech skills because much of their interaction is them being silent, using screens.

Unsupervised device use and social media are unsuitable and bad for toddlers.

Recommended daily maximum screen times

Under 18 months old: no screen time.

⭐ 18 months to 2 years: occasional 'together-use' – with an adult – watching a TV show or using an app.

⭐ 2 to 5 years: one hour maximum 'together-use' – with an adult.

⭐ Older than 6 years: Parents should set family-rule limits. Experts generally say kids should have a maximum daily use of 2 hours and, where possible, days without screen use.

⭐ No screens 2 hours before bedtime, as their light messes with the brain's understanding of night and day. (For more on this see Chapter 20, Toddler Sleep.)

Ask other parents and kids, and consult media sites, to 'curate' – carefully edit and choose – what your kid does see online. Make sure your kids understand the real world, with all its bumps and bruises and moments of boredom that spark creativity and problem solving.

〰〰〰〰 **more info** on screen time for toddlers 〰〰〰〰

healthychildren.org
The American Academy of Pediatrics site recommends screen-time maximums, and has a screen-time calculator and a guide on how to make a plan so everyone knows the recommendations and rules. On the home page search 'family media plan'.

commonsensemedia.org
An American website that recommends good games, apps and websites for kids, mainly older than toddler age.

Parents' screen time

Parents should be aware that when they choose to look at screens while their toddler is close by, the child gets a message. 'That thing is far more interesting than me right now' is not a good message for very young children.

'Teach them what an "inside voice" is for when they need to stop shouting embarrassing stuff in public.'
SANJANA

'There's no point trying to make a toddler do something they don't want to, tbh. Will get you nowhere.'
BEK

talking with a toddler

Talk to your child and give them space to talk back.

Explain what you're going to do and why, before you do it. Kids pick up an incredible amount just by listening and repeating. Their brains are making millions of connections, including the right uses and placement of words. This applies to all ages.

Don't 'correct' a misuse of a word, but instead use it correctly yourself in a reply. 'I putted my hat.' 'Yes, you put on your hat: that was a good idea!' instead of 'Don't say "putted": that's wrong.' If your kid isn't talking much, try not to anticipate their needs too efficiently, so that they are encouraged to ask for what they're after, instead of pointing. Or offer them a choice, in words, and wait for the response, in words.

Use simple terms to explain things, but now and then add some words that will help them build a bigger vocabulary – kids of this age can understand all sorts of words as long as they hear them in context, and it will stop you going mad from using only 'cat sat on mat'–type vocabulary.

See Chapter 23, Toddler Emotions, and Chapter 24, Toddler Behaviour, for more on talking with toddlers.

'Choose your battles wisely.'
KELLIE

'Acknowledge kids' big feelings without "fixing" them. "It's really hard to leave the park, isn't it? It's so fun here and it's frustrating that we have to do shopping for dinner instead of playing for longer. We could say 'bye, bye' to the fun park?". Get on the same side of a problem.'
SUNSHINE

toddler development milestones

These milestone times are averages, and they will vary between toddlers depending on how much practice they get and what they're interested in, and because they're individual.

1 year to 18 months old

Physical development

Your toddler aged 1 to 1½:

- ⭐ can see things further away and try to get them
- ⭐ is shuffling, crawling, bum-dragging, or staggering along holding on to furniture like a little drunkard, just walking or walking alone, perhaps moving with a tentative, stiff-legged totter, with feet wide apart for extra balance
- ⭐ may be climbing onto ladders, chairs, boxes, tables, uncles
- ⭐ can let go of something with controlled movement
- ⭐ starts to stack things inside or on top of each other
- ⭐ uses a spoon more deftly
- ⭐ is learning to get simple clothes off and to help get them on
- ⭐ starts to drink from a cup, or a bottle without a teat.

Emotional & mental development

Your toddler aged 1 to 1½:

- ⭐ is bonded to one or two consistent carers at home
- ⭐ may develop separation anxiety when they start walking or improve rapidly at walking – this can happen with other new developments too
- ⭐ is developing their memory
- ⭐ may remember how to do a task or action they saw up to four months ago
- ⭐ often says 'NO!'
- ⭐ is showing great interest in books
- ⭐ is starting to ask or look for things that are not in sight
- ⭐ is affectionate with familiar pals, but can be wary of new folk
- ⭐ gets excited about something they can anticipate, such as a present
- ⭐ if frustrated might hit, kick, scratch, claw or bite to show their frustration.

Communication development

Your toddler aged 1 to 1½ probably:

⭐ begins talking, has a vocabulary of a few words and may put two
   or more words together. Girls often progress more quickly than boys

⭐ will start to pick up more words every day, somewhere around
   18 months old

⭐ understands more when listening to a conversation, even if they
   don't have the skills to join in yet.

Between 1 & 1½ years old, what can you do to help development?

Pull-along or push-along toys are good fun. Encourage outdoor play with balls and sand, and supervised water play, climbing, swings and slides: it helps them to develop physical skills and to exercise – and tires 'em out so they have a good sleep. All play involving objects with wheels, such as prams and ride-on toys, or with water needs constant vigilance. Even 'doing the dishes' in the sink is water play (always supervise the play, and make sure water is drained away).

Let toddlers 'help' you with chores: give them a feather duster, a sponge for rudimentary wiping work, a wooden spoon and bowl for stirring something safe while you're cooking. And they'll enjoy picking things out of the clothes basket to be hung up by you.

Teach your toddler to put their head back for washing off shampoo. Toddlers usually hate water on their face and eyes, which may be a survival instinct.

As the kid gets more mobile and can reach to tabletop level and climb up bookcases or chests of drawers, do another safety check of the house and places you regularly visit (see Chapter 32, Safety & Injuries).

Read your child simple stories and together look at picture books with images they can point to and name, or flaps they can lift.

Play different kinds of music. Sing and dance together. Make up songs with familiar names and words in them.

See your doctor if your 1-year-old isn't having a go at babbled phrases and doesn't seem to understand any familiar words, or doesn't show interest in a new face, or can't roll a ball or play peekaboo; or if between the ages of 1 year and 18 months, can't stand up by themselves, or get around with one crawly method or another.

See your doctor if your 18-month-old toddler can't stand and walk on their own without holding on to something, or can't stack blocks on top of each other or try a scribble with a crayon after being shown how, or if they show no difference in affection or interest between a stranger and a familiar family person, or they're never keen on interacting with others, or if they have no clear words they use, or they can't understand short requests, or if they're not pointing at things or presenting things for your inspection.

18 months to 2 years old

Physical development

Your toddler aged 1½ to 2:

★ is getting better at that stiff-legged walking style, and maybe going faster

★ runs straight-legged

★ can see things in the distance

★ understands the purpose of things – a bowl is stirred, a page is turned, a shoe goes on a foot

★ can throw a ball, but catching is still hard

★ climbs stairs and other things – and can go down (usually on their bottom, if they get practice on stairs in their home)

★ is still testing a few things in their mouth

★ can take off their hat and other clothes, but putting them on is harder.

Toddler feet & shoes

When a baby is first learning to walk, and practising their exciting new skill, they need to do it with bare feet. This helps them 'feel' the ground, develop balance and train their brain to receive messages. Lots of kids first walk in cute ways: flat-footed, and perhaps 'pigeon-toed' with toes pointing inwards, or with outward toes, or on 'tippy-toes'. If they're still doing that after the age of 3, see your GP or a podiatrist (university-qualified foot specialist). If your child isn't walking before age 2, also see your doctor.

Delay shoes till at least two months after they first walk, and keep feet bare whenever possible. (Obviously shoes are necessary when there's sharp ground or an urban injury is a possibility.) Shoes should be professionally fitted if you can (at a shoe shop) so your kid's feet can be measured. It's totally normal to have one foot slightly bigger than the other.

Shoe soles should be flexible (not flat and hard). Sadly this means more expense for an item your little tacker will fast grow out of. Better to have one or two pairs of better-quality shoes than a basket full of crappy plastic ones. Shoes should already feel comfy in the shop.

'One friend still likes to remind me how I made my children get back down and crawl, after they went from rolling to walking without doing the steps in between. I still stand by it! They had fun because I bought a tunnel and cut shapes in cardboard boxes. So much educational research to say that crawling is important!' SAMANTHA

'At one she was not only walking, climbing, a climber who saw everything as a challenge to be conquered. It seemed like she was never really a baby, but a tiny person with a mission.' ROSE

Emotional & mental development

Your toddler aged 1½ to 2:

- ⭐ has clear feelings of wanting to do things by themselves
- ⭐ as well as recognising themselves in the mirror, experiments with moving their head and making faces. Kids often try out emotions in the form of face-making
- ⭐ is terribly, terribly BUSY
- ⭐ can amuse themselves for short periods at the same activity
- ⭐ will try to help with housework chores
- ⭐ is affectionate
- ⭐ is quick to feel frustration and possibly has tantrums
- ⭐ should understand simple directions and what's required for regular events but can't be relied on to remember instructions
- ⭐ may remember or describe more dreams, and may have nightmares
- ⭐ may develop fear of things such as dogs, people in animal suits, water, heights, or anything else that it makes sense to be scared of, as a survival tactic
- ⭐ shows sympathy for other children who are distressed
- ⭐ wants to explore and touch everything
- ⭐ can't anticipate consequences but can learn from very specific events (the last time I touched that oven thing it hurt so I'm not going to touch it again)
- ⭐ can express jealousy and selfishness
- ⭐ is a peekaboo demon.

Communication development

Your toddler aged 1½ to 2:

- ⭐ is developing more words and language skills, such as using very simple sentences, as well as full-on 'nonsense' chat. Most amusing.
- ⭐ is copying sounds, actions and reactions from adults
- ⭐ is learning lots of names for things
- ⭐ learns bits of songs
- ⭐ will tell you or show you if something is in the 'wrong' place
- ⭐ will show how they are feeling and respond to the obvious feelings of others
- ⭐ likes a five-minute warning before a new activity ('Very soon we'll need to put the blocks away and go to the shop', 'Let's put on our shoes because we're about to go down to the park to find some good sticks').

Between 1½ & 2 years old, what can you do to help development?

Play chasey with your toddler. Kick a ball together. Play throwing and catching games, with the emphasis on them throwing and you catching. Toddlers find it easier to catch something that's not hard and unyielding, and not too small (tennis ball) or too heavy (basketball). Try light, smaller-sized beach balls, not too tightly blown up, and, even better, adult-palm-sized beanbags.

Beg, borrow or buy a ride-on 'bike' without pedals for them to zoom around on, or a wee scooter.

You can start to teach washing and drying their hands; stringing large beads; the idea of sorting colours and shapes; identifying everyone, including themselves, in family photos; playing in sand; stopping at the kerb and other road safety actions; playing in safe water in the bath or outside; songs; and matching words to situations and feelings.

Help your toddler learn to dance on their own feet, although you may need to hold hands. Develop some favourite songs and playlists. Make music together with saucepans and rattly things.

Read to them, look at picture books together and encourage independent looking at books. Make up and tell stories: toddlers often love to contribute, frequently trying to exactly copy your stories but eventually coming up with independent details.

As with a younger toddler, use lots of different words when you speak to your child; don't 'dumb it down'. A child of 2 can understand what 'awesome', 'fragile' and 'shemozzle' mean, and using lots of words gives them a wider range of reactions and explanations. They also have fun saying them. You have to converse with kids for them to understand the language: you can't just sit them in front of a screen. They need to ask questions and use words in different contexts to see which ones fit.

Try not to say 'no' all the time; instead try out some variations and distractions. 'Hey, why don't we do a jigsaw puzzle instead!' 'You know what, if you hold your cup with two hands instead of one you don't spill the drink inside.' 'Well, it's not an ice-cream day, but you can choose whether you want strawberry yoghurt or a banana milkshake!'

'Sometimes, toddlers just need to do things in their own time.'
TILLY

See your doctor if your 2-year-old can't walk on their own, or go up and down stairs while holding a hand or onto the wall; or they don't try to feed themselves with a spoon, or help to dress themselves; and if they always use toys to bang together, throw or drop, rather than using them in conventional ways (cuddling dolly, vrooming a car) or in more imaginative ways ('teddy is going to the shop'). Also see your doctor if they don't seem to be learning new words and putting a couple of them together ('go up' or 'meow cat'), or if they have meltdown tantrums when you can't understand what they're trying to say.

2 to 3 years old

Physical development

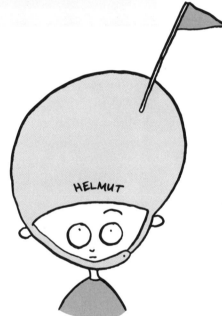

Your toddler aged 2 to 3:
- ⭐ can jump up and down when asked
- ⭐ can stand on one leg
- ⭐ runs around confidently
- ⭐ may be showing signs of right- or left-handedness
- ⭐ can get the lid off some things and open some doors
- ⭐ is starting to get good control of a pencil or crayon and makes marks on paper
- ⭐ can pick up and put down small things and turn pages
- ⭐ can build a tall tower from several blocks
- ⭐ can feed themselves and use toddler cutlery – comes with practice
- ⭐ goes *down* stairs by putting two feet on each stair before the next one, but goes *up* one foot per stair (and needs to use the stair rail or the wall for support)
- ⭐ has a more adult sense of taste, and a reflex against bitter tastes
- ⭐ can learn to ride a trike with pedals
- ⭐ may become very aware of nappies and want their dirty ones changed, but may not yet be ready for toilet training (for more see Chapter 22, Toilet Training).

Emotional & mental development

Your toddler aged 2 to 3:

★ has a more developed sense of who 'I' and 'me' is

★ understands more conversation and simple concepts and feelings – 'I'm cold', 'over there', 'falling down'

★ understands more than they can show – they're learning emotions and social skills

★ may not recognise a different skin colour, but may be curious if they hear others refer to it

★ can understand simple explanations

★ is working out how to get their way (including tantrums if they work)

★ remembers rhymes and information they enjoy

★ understands more concepts – boats go on the water, birds fly

★ likes to help and enjoys routine things

★ wants to be more independent and to get their own way

★ imitates sounds, actions and reactions, with some personal variations.

Communication development

Your toddler aged 2 to 3:

★ understands more words from listening to conversations

★ can repeat words several times, or stutters as part of learning (most stuttering usually stops within a year or so)

★ wants to participate in conversations, singalongs and group activities

★ asks questions about the right words and actions to use

★ chats away, building daily on their vocabulary if given the opportunity

★ tries more complex sentences, such as 'Please go down there'.

Between 2 and 3 years old, what can you do to help development?

Obviously there's a big gap between 2 and 3 years old: don't see these suggestions as stuff your kid must be able to do by the stated age, but as something they're already doing by that age – or will pick up in the next six months to a year.

⭐ Stick close to them, although this is never foolproof, because they want to investigate things all the time. (What's behind here? What happens if I throw this down the loo? What will this feel like squeezed between my hands?)

⭐ By the age of 3 your child might find a trike with pedals fun, or prefer a scooter. And you can help them practise their 'ball skills' – have fun with balls.

⭐ When reading together, ask your kid to point out and explain things in familiar books, or to guess what's happening in new ones.

⭐ If your child – and you – aren't getting at least some fresh air and exercise every day, think about how to change this so they're not at risk of becoming bored, or falling behind in developmental or eyesight skills.

⭐ Give them more music, more art, more nature rambles, more water play, more books, more jokes. Enjoy and share the small things in life that are fun for you to rediscover and all new for your kid: animal-shaped clouds, a big red truck, the way a wombat moves.

⭐ A kid this age might enjoy one quarter of a grown-up sports event such as footy, but rarely the whole afternoon: try to see things from their point of view. Time is much slower for little people.

⭐ Rotate batches of toys so your kid sees them with new eyes.

⭐ Give them crayons that have intense colours – better to buy one good set with strong colours, or oil pastels, and look after them a little more carefully, than to have ones with pale, wimpy colours. Talk about the colours.

⭐ Understand that kids this age prefer to play next to each other rather than with each other: one with a truck, one with a spade, for example. Sharing toys can be a challenging concept.

⭐ Make screen use occasional, not a daily activity. Kids need to interact with others to learn the listening and verbal skills essential for the first year of school.

⭐ Organise playtimes with other kids by using childcare or swapsie arrangements with other parents – your child develops social skills and you get some time to yourself here and there.

⭐ Check out council, local and state library and community websites and noticeboards, and social media groups and alerts, for kid-friendly parks, playgrounds, events, free book-readings, festivals, crafts and special celebrations.

⭐ Everything you do and say will be repeated or acted out, so if you blow up every time something goes wrong you're teaching tantrums, and if you punch the wall whenever you're angry they will too. See Chapter 23, Toddler Emotions, and Chapter 24, Toddler Behaviour, for advice and 'scripts'.

See your doctor if your 3-year-old doesn't try to do things for themselves such as dressing and eating, or seems to have difficulties with tasks that use smaller objects (like threading plastic beads), or can't walk up and down stairs on their own without support, or can't run or jump. Also see the doctor if they're not interested in playing with other kids, or in 'pretending' games. Or if they don't recognise feelings such as anger or sadness in others, or are not able to name their own feelings, or if their speech is difficult for their family and close friends to understand, or they're not putting a few words together into an almost-sentence. Also see your doctor if your 3-year-old is happily doing wee in a potty or loo but still does poo in their nappy, or if they don't mind loud noises at home but cover their ears with unfamiliar people or in places like shopping centres, or plays with other kids at home but won't at childcare or kinder. Being referred to a specialist by your doctor doesn't mean there's anything scary – it's just what specialists are for, so you get the best advice, help and/or reassurance.

'Observation: toddler's fave form of protest is the sit-in. Or the lie-down dead weight style action.' EMMA

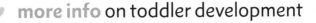
more info on toddler development

healthdirect.gov.au
This health hub administered by the federal government gathers many reliable links on various subjects. On the home page choose 'Health topics A–Z', then 'Babies and Toddlers' on the drop-down menu, then choose from food, exercise, health checks and more.

BLAST FROM THE PAST

'Prince Edward of Kent's daily routine . . . the toddler Prince and his baby sister Princess Alexandra spend most of their time at their parents' lovely Buckinghamshire home, and on sunny days they play in the garden from early morning to late afternoon. He has a sleep directly after lunch – in the garden if it is fine.'

– *The Australian Women's Weekly*, 1937

26 TODDLER toys & games

The list that follows of fun toys and games
for 1- to 3-year-olds was compiled from
suggestions by parents and doctors.

As in Chapter 17, Baby Toys & Games,
these have a bias towards cheap fun.

toys for toddlers

★ cars, trucks, trains ★ large click-together blocks ★ a plastic picnic set ★ baby dolls and a baby doll's stroller ★ plastic tools and a construction hat for girls *and* boys ★ books ★ large potato stamps and paint for printing ★ safe musical instruments, if you can stand it ★ stickers ★ any dress-up clothes ★ a box of bandaids, which can get emptied and filled, emptied and filled, over and over ★ coloured wooden blocks ★ adult shoes to stomp about in ★ a tricycle or scooter ★ a tea-party set ★ a set of plastic cups of different sizes, and a plastic bucket or two, to take to the beach ★ a wipe-clean magnetic drawing slate ★ kid-sized kitchen utensils to pretend to cook with ★ biscuit cutters, rolling pin and playdough (if using homemade, add food colouring and see 'Play dough' coming up for a note on safety) ★ a small train set ★ ladybird beetles in various incarnations ★ plastic frogs ★ plastic bangles or rings to stack and roll ★ wooden or plastic farmyard animals ★ balls ★ audio books or music ★ a bubble-blowing set (but an adult needs to work with the child on this one) ★ toddler jigsaw puzzles with big pieces ★ a toy phone ★ coloured chalk for drawing on the footpath ★ old purses and handbags with funny things in them, or pretend money or an EFTPOS card (what have we come to), for shopping games ★ a spinning top ★ 'letters' and a posting box to put things into (a shoebox, or an old tissue box with the plastic flaps removed)

Button battery warning

Button batteries in toys and other items, when swallowed, can cause permanent disability and even the death of babies and toddlers. See the 'Button batteries' box in Chapter 32, Safety & Injuries, for more on this and other good things to know to avoid injuries.

BLAST FROM THE PAST

'There are no toys at Montessori playgroup. I give them a bowl full of nuts and the children have to put the big nuts in one container and the little ones in another.' – Kindergarten teacher, *The Times*, Victor Harbor, Queensland, 1991

Toddler activities & games

★ draw and paint using non-toxic, washable poster paints
★ **pretend to be dinosaurs** ★ playing pretend to
fix things ★ play pretend games, such as daddy mouse and baby
mouse ★ read a book from the library about stars and the moon
then go out and look at them ★ 'do the housework' – toddlers are the
perfect height for dusting skirting boards and low bookshelves (hide precious
knick-knackery) ★ play dentist or doctor check-ups – white shirts are good coats,
and many cheap shops have plastic doctor toys such as stethoscopes (but many
of these have choking hazards, so buyer beware) ★ paste using bits of fabric,
paper, pictures torn from magazines, cut-up streamers, and make a scrapbook
together ★ look at and talk about alphabet and number posters ★ have a puppet
show with bought puppets, your child's stuffed toys, or sock puppets with button
eyes that you've made ★ **cook a cake or muffins** and clean up the mess
together ★ sing songs together ★ make a tent or cubby with boxes, cushions and
blankets ★ cook bread and have a nap while it rises ★ draw roads on a large
piece of cardboard (or a flattened cardboard box) and get your kid to place cars
and street signs, and shops and houses of blocks, around the roads ★ blend fruit
with yoghurt to put in moulds, then in the freezer for popsicle-style treats. ★ keep
cardboard boxes and give your kid the lot, plus sticky tape, coloured paper and
paints, to construct whatever they want to ★ **make up a story** that goes
around: you say a bit, they add to it, and so it goes on ★ read books ★ make
pictures, letters or postcards to send to friends and relatives, and end with a trip to
the postbox or by sending an email ★ bring out the dress-up box and have everyone
in the family join in ★ dress up in someone else's old gear – perhaps Nanna's, or
Dad's shoes. ★ put on some music and dance ★ **play musical statues**
when the music snaps off everyone has to freeze ★ subscribe to a geographic
photography magazine or get a set from the op shop or grandparents – find
pictures of animals, cut them out and paste them on cardboard to
make a 'zoo' or a wildlife park ★ do scientific 'speriments' with
bottles and containers of coloured water with bits of leaves ★

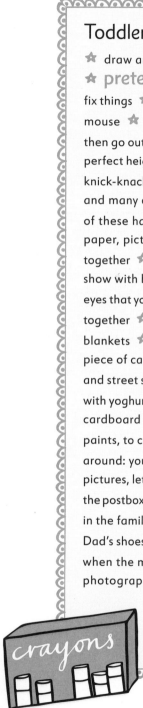

✱ invite a friend over to play ✱ Stand the kid into a cardboard box with their legs out the open bottom of the box and let them pretend they're a car ✱ collect all the old Christmas and birthday cards and let the child cut and paste them ✱ go to the library, ask what's good for toddlers ✱ sort the washing into piles and fold it ✱ play dominoes or cards (surprisingly good fun even if the rules aren't yet grasped – invent or go with the flow) ✱ make your own wrapping paper and cards for birthdays that are coming up ✱ dance party! The more fun you can make it, the better – roll up a rug, choose a music playlist, and add mood lighting if possible ✱ do some face painting (you'll need the special paints in advance) ✱ have a video conference with a grandparent or friend ✱ use an umbrella and gumboots under the shower ✱ play hopscotch ✱ make yourselves morning or afternoon tea and have a grown-up pretend chat ('How are you?' 'How's work?' 'What's been happening?') ✱ go through recipe books together with bookmarks or tags and mark things that look like they'd be fun to make or eat ✱ blow up a balloon and play volleyball or soccer or footy ✱ set up a hospital – use dolls and teddies as patients and tear up old sheets for bandages ✱ supply a bucket of pegs and dry clothes to peg to a clothes horse ✱ make the room really dark and play with a torch and create shadow pictures on the wall ✱ make sandwiches and cut them into shapes with biscuit cutters ✱ use playdough or real dough for cutting out shapes with biscuit cutters (see 'Playdough' coming up for a note on safety) ✱ make pasta shapes or spaghetti, put in a little oil to help separate them, and let kids 'play with their food' – squishing stuff helps them learn what their hands are 'telling' them (same with sand or playdough) ✱ go puddle stamping or make mud pies or collect neighbourhood leaves ✱ play at recognising colours – find all the red things in the kitchen, or all the blue blocks, or point at things and clothes while you're out and say the colours, then start asking what colour things are ✱ Toddlers love the idea of pretending to have a tea party or picnic – they can draw the food and you can cut it out and put on paper plates.

Playdough

Homemade playdough recipes usually have a large amount of salt in them. A high concentration of salt can damage a child's internal organs. Kids, especially babies and toddlers, should be supervised so they don't eat homemade playdough (they'll probably hate the taste anyway). The commercial stuff should be a reputable brand: it shouldn't contain salt.

Outside activities

Many 'inside activities' can be simply moved outside onto a ground-floor verandah or into the garden, or to a local park:

⭐ Collect examples of fallen leaves, blossoms, twigs and other interesting things.

⭐ Identify things you can see in the distance and in the sky.

⭐ Drive or catch public transport to a park, river or beach, and explore. Go armed with supplies, a good weather forecast, sensible shoes and hats.

⭐ Short trips more often will make for less 'hitting the wall' than rarer, longer trips.

> **BLAST FROM THE PAST**
> 'All toddlers . . . find a cart to pull along, and load with luggage, soul satisfying at some time, and sand and water are acknowledged necessities for happy development and growth.'
> – *Coolgardie Miner*, Western Australia, 1936

BLASTS FROM THE PAST

'Horses Tails: From the nursery window . . . you must all watch carefully, and when you see a horse in the distance, guess the colour of its tail! As the horse gets nearer and nearer, the excitement becomes intense . . . Roadside Whist: On a walk, points are awarded for seeing a man carrying a parcel, a man carrying a baby, a tinker, a child with a hoop, a chimney sweep [and many more].'
– E.M. Baker (editor), *Indoor Games for Children and Young People*, 1912.
Other suggested games include 'playing shop', follow the leader,
'British prisoners' and quoting hymns.

MATCH THE KID WITH THE PARENT!
draw a line to match them up

A. SHOCKING OLD CYNIC

1 CRUISY BABY

B. CALM, SKINNY POET

2 ALERT, SPORTY GIRL

C. EXCITABLE BANK CLERK

3 ECCENTRIC, CHUBBY CAR-OBSESSED TODDLER

THAT'S RIGHT! IT COULD BE ANY OF THEM!

PART 3

everything else

YOU NEED TO KNOW

PARENTING STYLES

Some people have a philosophy for their parenting. It might be 'I'll do what my mum did', or 'I'd never do what my mum did'. You might be a 'helicopter' or a 'greenie' or 'slightly terrifying'. You might follow a book, or a website, or muddle through without a set of ready-made values and guidelines. You might be like a magpie and take bits and pieces that take your fancy wherever you find them.

choosing a parenting style

Some of the 'philosophies' listed in this grab bag of approaches are just general ideas that you bring with you to parenting ('Rules are important') ('I hate rules'). Others are educational philosophies with their own handbooks and organisational network.

You'll already have some sort of a philosophy based on your own experiences and expectations, even if you don't have a name for it. It's good to be flexible enough to question why you're doing things, whether they work and what might work better. There's no shame in saying, 'Jeez, I never expected to be up against this problem. I think I need a new solution.' That's parenting.

No parenting theory is right for everyone. That's about the most scientific it gets, I reckon. You might find a method works well for your first child but just makes the second child look at you as if you've got to be *kidding*.

If a guru or theory isn't working for you, don't blame yourself or your kid. Try another approach. See Chapter 24, Toddler Behaviour, for other ideas and hints.

A family of families

Families come in many formats – sole and single parents, extended families, lots of siblings, no siblings, two dads, two mums, three dogs, grandparent and kid – and with many different philosophies, including strict, free-range and dog-worshipping. All sorts of families can raise perfectly delightful and rascally kids.

'I'm a divorced special needs parent: the best advice I got was my 70-year-old mum saying "Do what's right for you and everyone else can just go fuck themselves".' INSTALADY

'Being a young mum doesn't make you a dumb mum. It's okay to ignore "helpful" advice! No, I won't be giving my baby brandy when she is teething, thank you very much!' ALLISON

Why you can't get judgey

You don't know why that kid is screaming in the queue for the check-outs. You don't know if the baby in the pram wearing a helmet has a protective parent or a congenital skull condition. You don't know anybody else's background, or financial situation, or emotional state of mind, or whether they are subject to abuse behind closed doors. You don't think babies should wear navy? You think that woman over there should be breast-feeding her baby? Did you know she's undergoing radiation treatment, so she can't? I'll tell you what gives me the irrits. Too-cool-for-school parents who refuse to play their kids kid-music because they'd rather listen to their own dirge-like hipster music. And my heart sinks when I see a little kid drinking Coke out of a bottle because I know they'll probably have toothaches and pain later. But I'll tell you what else I know – until anyone asks my opinion, it's none of my beeswax. I don't know what led them to that decision, and I have no jurisdiction.

How to respond to unwanted advice

Here's some useful phrases:
- ⭐ 'Is that right?' (Then ignore it.)
- ⭐ 'I'll take that on board. If you want any extra information, I'll let you know.'
- ⭐ 'We're following our own doctor's advice.'
- ⭐ 'Thanks, but we'll be okay.'
- ⭐ 'I'm so glad that worked for you. This is working for us.'
- ⭐ 'I'm experimenting. This is my guinea-pig child.'
- ⭐ 'Thanks – if I need some more advice I'll definitely ask.'

Parents on social media

Conventional rules of social media say:
- ⭐ Check your privacy and other settings. Even with copyright 'protection', once something is on social media, you have effectively lost control of its further use. You might want to restrict access to family photos and news to a small group of family and friends.
- ⭐ Social media is forever – even if you delete a photo or a post it will still exist somewhere.
- ⭐ You should never post pictures of other people's children, or tag them, without asking permission.

- ✪ You should never announce anybody else's news about other parents or families without permission, including but not restricted to their pregnancies, illnesses, kids' achievements, divorces, hangovers, holiday plans, milestones, etc.
- ✪ 'Mummy', 'daddy' and 'grandparent' bloggers should know that one day the children will use newer, more powerful social media to post whatever they like about their parents and grandparents and their embarrassing moments.
- ✪ Until the teenage years, kids shouldn't use any social media, or have control over their app-buying or emails.

attachment parenting

This philosophy is based on parental closeness with the baby and child – its basics include breastfeeding, sleeping with your baby, and carrying them in a sling most of the time. (See Chapter 8, Baby Sleep, for safe sleeping advice and the risk factors that make co-sleeping inadvisable.) Having one consistent carer rather than several is emphasised; in almost all examples given it seems to be the mum who is supposed to do most of the attaching. Parents are encouraged to respond immediately to their child's wants. Attachment-parenting advocates do not believe in leaving a baby or a child to cry, even for very short times.

At its best it's a warm and loving approach. At its most useless it turns parenting into a world where the baby runs everyone else ragged, an overtired baby is picked up instead of being helped to a desperately needed sleep, the kid turns into a smug dictator, and any problem with the child is blamed on the mother for not being attached enough.

more info on attachment parenting

pinkymckay.com
Australian parenting expert Pinky McKay has a child-centred and relaxed approach.

attachmentparentingaustralia.com
Support groups, links, resources and positive personal stories.

the 'raising happy children' approach

Seems obvious as a concept, doesn't it? It's not a cohesive philosophy with an organised group, but it's the priority of many parents, some of whom didn't have happy childhoods themselves and are seeking new ways of relating to their kids, with an eye to making them feel generally happy, safe, self-confident and resilient. The assumption is that good behaviour will follow.

my mum is a thespian

At its best the happy children approach is a great thing to aim for and will minimise stress. At its worst it could mean children grow up without knowledge of the real world and are shocked and ill-prepared for institutions and people who aren't motivated by kindness and patience – in other words, much of the real world. It's also important that kids feel secure about being able to express their natural feelings, including anger and sadness. Several books have the phrase 'happy children' in their title.

~~~~~ more info on raising happy children ~~~~~

100 Ways to Happy Children: A Guide for Busy Parents
by Dr Timothy Sharp (Penguin, Australia)
A dad and psychologist uses research to recommend ways to make a happier family and help kids enjoy life, cope with disappointments and cooperate.

The Complete Secrets of Happy Children
by Steve Biddulph with Shaaron Biddulph (HarperCollins, Australia)
The Biddulphs' focus on 'soft love' (touch, praise) and 'firm love' (discipline through teaching and being involved).

parenting with routines & rules

This philosophy rests on getting babies and kids into strict routines that suit the adults as much as the kids. There's always a posse of child-rearin' rope-and-brand-'em types who ride the rodeo of parenting advice. These advisers are often nannies or child & family health nurses from the UK, or men from America, but not always. They favour rules and routines. Some parents consider them life-saving sheriffs, others want them shot on sight (okay, okay, enough with the metaphor).

triple P

Sometimes it's hard to just react in the moment. It can help if you have rules, have kindly but firm and consistent responses to infractions, and have scripts ready. Triple P (Positive Parenting Program) is a really great, kindly, practical parent-education program that has helped many Australian parents. It was developed by Professor Matthew Sanders and the Parenting and Family Support Centre in the Department of Psychology at the University of Queensland, and is based on international research into child development and parental roles. The program helps parents learn skills and strategies to deal with kids, and offers help with kids' behaviour as well as with particular issues. It can be used to help target specific behavioural problems or be used by professional agencies, and can help stop the abuse of kids. See Chapter 24, Toddler Behaviour, for more on this and other resources for consistent parenting.

more info on Triple P

TripleP-parenting.net.au
Every Parent: A Positive Approach to Children's Behaviour
by Matthew Sanders (Penguin, Australia)
The official website and book of the Positive Parenting Program.

'I'm the expert on my kids.'   WENDY

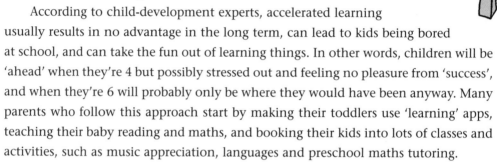

maximising potential, accelerated learning or 'hothousing'

Many parents like to maximise their child's development by doing specific things to stimulate and encourage their child. Accelerated learning is the movement by parents to give their child an advantage by having them learn or accomplish things before most kids their age do.

According to child-development experts, accelerated learning usually results in no advantage in the long term, can lead to kids being bored at school, and can take the fun out of learning things. In other words, children will be 'ahead' when they're 4 but possibly stressed out and feeling no pleasure from 'success', and when they're 6 will probably only be where they would have been anyway. Many parents who follow this approach start by making their toddlers use 'learning' apps, teaching their baby reading and maths, and booking their kids into lots of classes and activities, such as music appreciation, languages and preschool maths tutoring.

Unfortunately many of the parents who believe in this way of teaching children are persuaded that their kids need special advantages. Research shows that children learn all the time, in great leaps and bounds, just from doing things that are fun, including chatting, playing outside, pottering and making a cake. The upside of the accelerated learning approach is that knowing what development stage your child is at can help you introduce new games and fun activities. The downside is that everyone feels under pressure, and expectations of a genius child are almost always met with disappointment. There's a reason they call that 'overachieving'.

~~~~~ **more info** on maximising potential ~~~~~

aaegt.net.au
Choose 'Useful links' then 'Kids' for an approved list of fun puzzles, games and online sites useful for all kids. The Australian Association for the Education of the Gifted and Talented also has advocacy advice for parents of kids with advanced learning capabilities.

'helicopter' parenting

This is the rather scornful name given by others to parents who always seem to 'hover' (like a 'copter) over their children: parents who accompany their child around a children's party, play every game with them and supervise every activity. Helicopter parents say they're 'involved'; others say they're stifling. I do wonder why some people think 'helicopter' parents are worth more disapproval than 'neglectful' parents, but that's Judgeyland for you. (Okay, we all live in Judgeyland. I just try to look like a tourist.)

Upside: parent is engaged and involved. Possible downsides: kids never learn to amuse themselves and feel under constant scrutiny.

relaxed parenting

This approach isn't strictly defined, but it scorns the reliance on a guidebook to look after kids: parents should stop worrying so much about whether they're doing the right thing and whether their child is in danger; parents need to learn to trust their own judgement; and parents need to back off from pressuring their kids with lots of expectations, classes and planned activities.

The upside of relaxed parenting is that the parents are calm, and so maybe the kids are too. Downsides include the sinking sense of recognition that being too 'relaxed' can mean neglectful or uncaring. 'No rules' can produce a child who feels adrift, without guidance or boundaries or a feeling of being cherished. Because the rest of the world has rules and conventions, a kid who is a stranger to them all can end up being seen as disruptive, rude and self-centred.

~~~~ **more info** on being a more relaxed parent ~~~~

All Joy and No Fun: The Paradox of Modern Parenthood
by Jennifer Senior (Hachette, Australia)
A smart book about expectations and how to get more fun out of parenting.
Easy to read, with real-world examples.

'If Mum's happy, then everyone's happy, that's my motto.' NICOLE

raising girls & boys differently

Some parenting philosophies emphasise the differences in development between boys and girls, encouraging parents to treat boys and girls differently. You should never lose sight of the fact, though, that each child is an individual, and their individual character, and lovely quirks, and personal interests, will always be far more important than their gender.

the green, natural or new-age approach

Generally, any or all of these things will be embraced: breastfeeding, reusable nappies, recycling, organic food, herbal remedies, no rules for behaviour. And these things rejected: disposable accoutrements and plastic containers and toys, chemicals of any description, consumerism, 1950s-style repressive discipline, the bouffant hairdo.

At its most useful this approach offers the central idea of treading lightly on the earth, which we can all benefit from and aspire to. At its least useful it involves turning away from the real world to isolationist activities, groups and websites and creating an echo chamber, just like some strict religions.

Beware of 'natural' parenting sites or resources that point to anti-immunisation groups. See Chapter 34, Immunisation, about how these groups have become increasingly extremist and dangerous, posting lies and abuse. Also see Chapter 33, Health, for how natural therapists can work with your doctor, who needs to be the primary health adviser for your family, and why homeopathy never works.

'If everyone, including the adults, has a clean bum and a full tum at the end of the day, you are winning. Anything else you get done is a bonus.'   CATH, a midwife

keeping up with parenting issues

You can bookmark parenting websites and forums for browsing in those rare moments of freedom, if you're not out dancing on a table.

~~~~~~~~ **more info** on keeping up with ~~~~~~~~
parenting issues

nytimes.com /topic/subject/parenting
New York Times writers and readers blog and share news stories and feelings.

A Step Up for Step Families
by Marcia Watts (Independent Ink, Australia)
A thoughtful guidebook on the practical and emotional issues of a blended family, by a mum and step-mum who's also a relationships counsellor. At **stepfamilies.com.au**.

Don't lose you

Sure, some things change forever when you become a parent. Priorities. And for some people, what makes them cry. You might never want to watch the news or a violent movie again. Or you might want to take up roller-wrestling, to get you out of the house Thursday nights. Whatever you do as a parent, don't forget to take time to be you. Look at stuff you're interested in online that isn't baby or kid related. Borrow a book *you* want to read when you take junior to storytime at the local library. Tell your friends with no kids you still want to be asked out to things and for them to keep asking even when you can't go, or to come over with takeaway occasionally. Keep studying, or drawing, or gardening: do your thing when you can. A happier parent is a better parent, and an engaged parent is the best kind of role model.

tap tap *tap tap*

28 DADS

Being a dad is marvellous – and boring and complicated and hard and hilarious and exhausting, and makes you proud and furious and bewildered and tired and more full of love than you thought possible.

This whole book is for dads as well as mums and other parents – but here's the men-only section. Much of it, but not all of it, is about dads with lady-partners. But gay or straight: welcome, mate.

good on you, dad

For caring enough to read this, for choosing to be a better dad than some fathers in previous generations, for wanting to work out how to do it even if you haven't had a good dad role model in your own life, for being a real partner in this parenting biz – thanks. Really.

new dads & sex

Many blokes are astonished to find out how much parenthood gets in the way of a sex life. Here are some reasons your partner could be uninterested in sex.

⭐ Her body has not been truly her 'own' for a long time. Especially if she's breastfeeding, she may feel 'everyone wants a piece' of her.

⭐ He's tired all the time.

⭐ Her libido (sex drive) isn't what it used to be because of hormone changes.

⭐ She doesn't want to get pregnant again.

⭐ She feels unattractive because of weight gain or loss, bosom changes or stretch marks.

What you can do

⭐ Keep talking about it.

⭐ Make her *feel* attractive as well as telling her. (Show it by your actions.)

⭐ Get help with housework.

⭐ Wear three condoms at once or do something else sensible about contraception – then everyone can relax.

⭐ Be patient.

⭐ Ask her what she wants.

As the stupid shampoo ad says, 'It won't happen overnight, but it will happen.' See 'Having sex again' in Chapter 3, Look After Yourself. You might also like to read 'Your post-baby body' in that chapter to help understand any new worries about body image.

> 'We need to know not only that women can do what men can do, but also that men can do what women can do.' GLORIA STEINEM

being a real partner to a new mum

One minute there's a floaty pregnant woman demanding that the baby come out, and the next minute she's an exhausted wreck saying she can't cope, her bosoms don't work, she'll never be able to be a good mother, boo and boo-hoo. Not much to be done, chaps, except pitch in and be true to the word 'partner', emotionally and around the house. It can be tricky, especially in the early days with all the raging hormones and exhaustion and bosoms akimbo-but-off-limits.

Then you go back to work, or she does, and someone will have a crying baby thrust at them every night after her long, hard day and the other one will wonder how come they got signed up as Cinderella in a cyclone.

This is your chance to be a real hero. Listen, sympathise, don't try to solve everything immediately, do everything you can to reassure your partner that she'll work out the breastfeeding or it doesn't matter if she has to bottle-feed, and talk about being in it together and riding it through. This would be a good time to dip into any spare money for a weekly cleaner, even for just the first eight weeks, or to get your relatives and friends to bring food, fold washing and make themselves useful.

Women and men at home can feel trapped in a new role they can't get out of – 'housewife', 'milking machine' or 'walking zombie'. Without making it a competition, sympathise and say you have mixed feelings about the responsibility of keeping the money coming in (or vice versa – whatever your individual situation is). If it seems like she's very anxious or has gone 'blank' or is artificially alert, or you're the one with those feelings, talk about it. Talk to your doctor. This is incredibly common, and very treatable.

Many dads love to have their kids for hours on end – they hang out for the prospect. And many understand that parenthood is a joint venture. Having a supportive partner in these early days can make all the difference for women at home, between having the mild blues and thinking they're going mad. Partners, especially those who are at home full time, can do with regular nights, mornings or afternoons off at the weekend.

'It can be very overwhelming for dads too. We kept in close touch with family and friends, and the local mother-and-child health nurse for reassurance that we were doing the right thing. Sharing the home duties helps too.'   SCOTT

There's no reason why men can't become as competent as women at being a parent, if you don't count the bosoms business. Mums don't have a monopoly on baby knowledge. If you feel 'frozen out' or elbowed aside when you're trying to learn and bond with your baby, speak up, and talk about it.

things dads need to know

You probably have just as many parenting instincts as your partner. You'll be learning new things all the time for the next few years. Talking honestly with other parents will show you that feeling scared or inadequate is not unique or strange.

The more you do things, the better you'll be at them. This includes nappy changing, bathing, getting clothes on and off a wriggler, and talking to your baby.

Anticipation is needed – try to think ahead about things that might happen and how to deal with them. A lot of mums say dads need to be better prepared. Don't wait until you're out of baby formula to buy the next lot, for example. Have baby painkiller in the cupboard. Get the kid a coat and hat before the first really cold days of winter. If you go to the supermarket for milk, get bananas and toilet paper too.

Stuff doesn't just 'happen'. It often happens because your partner has made it happen. Women can often do six things at a time while planning another four in their head. Men often think and do only one thing at a time. Either develop the so-called womanly ability, start working off lists, or explain that you'll get the six things done even if it takes a bit longer. Think about what wouldn't be done if your partner suddenly wasn't there. Many dads wouldn't know how to make an appointment at their kid's hairdresser, find somewhere to take them for swimming lessons, tell a doctor their kid's habits and routine, or organise a birthday party, complete with invitations. But there are a lot more dads now who do know how to do this stuff, and actually do it. Hooray.

> 'My number one piece of advice for a new mother would be to ask the midwife in hospital to help your husband give the baby its first bath. After that, never suggest in any way that you are more competent or better in any way at caring for the baby. If he is parenting from day one he will get good at it, and it's very sweet to see a daddy confidently nursing a little bub!' JUNINE

Sometimes it drives women crazy when their partner asks them what to buy at the supermarket every time, or how to wash something. Sometimes we have to be reminded that you men want to do it right, that you don't want us to be mad at you for doing it wrong. But don't fall into the trap of being 'one of the kids' who always needs to be told what to do.

If you want to know more about how to do the housework properly or how to decipher those strange cleaning symbols on clothes labels, you know what a search engine is.

Count yourself in, dad

Most importantly you need to bond with your baby too, and this can take a while. The best way is to get to know your baby by spending time together, changing nappies, having quiet chats (you can say anything to a baby – they just like to hear you and see your face, and love it when you sing, even if you're terrible at it).

Don't let your partner, family members, in-laws, friends or people in the street make you feel bad that you're learning how to look after a baby. If you do the wrong thing, that's just a step towards doing it the right way – or your way, which doesn't have to be how everyone else does it, as long as it's safe.

Looking after babies is too important and difficult and rewarding to be left to only one gender. It's all hands on deck.

'The reality is he's out of the house for 10 to 12 hours a day. Five days a week. He would dearly love to spend more time with our son, but by the time he gets home the baby's often asleep. Also I'm more than happy to do most of the housework as I'm the one at home. Before we had a baby we had a cleaner, so neither of us had to come home from work and clean the house, but we can't afford that luxury now. No matter what your views are on sexual politics, equality, etc., it's pretty hard not to start living a 1950s lifestyle if the parent at home is the woman and the "working" parent is the bloke. And our son and I agree: he's a top dad!'   KATE

the parenting partnership

Parents should talk about whether they see their roles as 'the same and supporting each other' or 'different but supporting each other'. It's not a good dynamic when one parent is the 'expert' and the other parent abdicates all responsibility for knowledge and understanding. Very often the 'mum always knows best' thing comes from generations of social conditioning and reflected the only control women had. If your partner thinks you're incompetent, ask them to teach you.

Talking about it will help.

⭐ A man might need to acknowledge that his wage is not 'his' money alone, and he won't be 'babysitting' his own kids or 'helping' with housework: he's an equal co-partner in parenting.

⭐ A woman might have to admit it doesn't matter if the dad dresses the baby in an unmatching outfit, and that it's scary to suddenly lose all the authority and skills and experience of a job, and be thrown into something that's so unpredictable and unfamiliar.

⭐ Both parents need to spend lots of time with babies and toddlers, so they can develop 'instincts' about when things are wrong, as well as the fun times.

dads & housework

If you're a stay-at-home dad for the day, week or year, you have to do housework as well as look after the kid(s). You are a dad, not just a Big Toy. (A lot of the time you will get to be a big toy.) In this arena I think you need to do the housework properly, even the bits you don't 'see': think 'dirty' – the loo needs to be done at least weekly, even if the state of it hasn't yet alarmed visitors.

A list of weekly or daily tasks can help, if you're a list man. Talk about who will do what, and to what standard. When kids are little-little, 'tidy' is probably asking too much, but 'not disgusting' is achievable, especially if the bins go out on time.

> 'I pay someone to come on Sunday mornings and hubby and I go out for brunch (think of the cost as "marriage insurance"). We tried going out to dinner but were falling asleep at the table by 9 p.m.' KASIA

～～～ more info for dads ～～～

Parent helplines and services that have info for dads as well as mums are listed in Chapter 2, Your Help Team.

websites for dads

raisingchildren.net.au
Click on 'grown-ups' on the home page, then choose 'Fathers' on the drop-down menu for lots of helpful fact sheets and videos. Under 'Early days', click on '10 tips for new dads', or just click on any subject you want to know more about. This is the best general parenting site; it is funded by the federal government and has trusted medical and other info.

thefatheringproject.org
A non-profit site to support and cheer on dads, with lots of practical ideas, and links to support. Affiliated with the University of Western Australia.

fatherhood.com.au
The Fatherhood Project is a non-profit, independent Australian organisation that promotes family togetherness. The website has lots of hints.

🥝 fatherandchild.org.nz
The Father & Child Trust charity has info and suggested resources for all sorts of dads, solo, teen, at-home, working, and new.

dad.info
England's premier dad site provides a good hub, some funny articles and helpful practical info.

mrdad.com
US author Armin Brott has many columns and books about all kinds of fatherhood. The website has links to his *Positive Parenting* podcasts.

🥝 How to Dad
In the tradition of amiable deadpan Kiwis, Jordan Watson went viral with his 'How to hold a baby' video. Use your search engine to find his stuff.

～～～

~~~~~~ more info on picture books ~~~~~~
about dads

thekidsbookshop.com.au
Use the drop-down theme menu at this online shop to find books about 'dads' or with a
daddish flavour for babies and toddlers. There are some grandpa ones, too.

What Dads Can't Do
by Douglas Wood (Simon & Schuster, USA)
A gorgeous story about companionship between a small crocodiley creature and a dad
crocodiley creature. Dads and kids will get different frissons.

My Dad
by Anthony Browne (Corgi, UK)
An inventive writer and illustrator looks at all sorts of dads.

Mister Seahorse
by Eric Carle (Philomel Books, Australia)
Mrs Seahorse lays her eggs on Mr Seahorse – then he and other marine-based dads
look after the babies and kids. From Mr Carle of *Very Hungry Caterpillar* book fame.

BLAST FROM THE PAST

'There ought to be schools for fathers . . . many and many a mother is
discouraged, dissuaded or even prohibited from breastfeeding because
the father . . . fears she may lose her elegance of person if she nurses the baby.
No man can ever more truly call himself a gentleman than when in the home,
and for mother and baby he plays the part of a gentle man.'
– *The Express and Telegraph*, South Australia, 1922

the special uses of blokes

(Obviously the talents listed here aren't exclusively male, but this whole list generalises about things so shut up.)

- ★ Blokes can let mums know they're not in parenting alone, even if the adults don't live together.
- ★ Blokes can be secretly smug because a baby usually says 'Dadda' before 'Mumma'.
- ★ Blokes can be especially good at understanding the boisterousness of little boys.
- ★ Many blokes can perform the extremely useful task of getting their girls interested in ball skills and sport.
- ★ Blokes can share going-to-bed settling duties.
- ★ Blokes don't have to be the strong disciplinarians, just present a united front with their partner.
- ★ Blokes can show kids that they enjoy being with them, which builds their self-esteem.
- ★ Blokes can show boys it's okay to cry, dress up, and play with dolls and tea sets.
- ★ Blokes can show girls how to climb, kick a ball, and use tools.
- ★ Blokes can be affectionate and available to kids, which gives children a sense of safety and confidence.
- ★ A bloke who is careful and kind to his partner is showing his kids how to behave. Kids learn by example more than words.

dads & dangers

Don't lead, herd

Blokes can be great at encouraging kids to take little, safe 'risks'. Make sure you read Chapter 16, Baby Development, and Chapter 25, Toddler Development, so you know what to expect of your kids in terms of their thinking and sporting skills, and Chapter 32, Safety & Injuries, for common ways kids get hurt, such as driveway accidents. When crossing a road, hold a kid's hand all the way across. Kids need to hold hands across the road until they're much older. If you haven't got a hand on a kid, make sure your eyes are always on them. When you're walking or cycling, herd, don't lead – leading requires taking your eyes off 'em.

An infuriating checklist for men

* Bring in a vast wage.
* Work flexible, part-time hours.
* Be fabulously artistic and amusingly unpredictable but also totally reliable.
* Be competent at all kid stuff but never usurp or contradict mother superiority.
* Make partner feel attractive and sexy.
* Be endlessly supportive.
* Talk.
* Shut up.
* Talk again.
* No, not about that.
* Oh, for heaven's SAKE.

dads at the doctor

Doctors are used to seeing dads with a list from their partner of what to ask the doctor, and jotting notes of what the doctor says to tell their partners. Nothing wrong with that – but don't forget to watch how the doctor behaves with your kid, too. It's part of your job to find a kid-friendly doctor.

dads who need help

It's common for dads, like mums, to find themselves trying to deal with parenting or postnatal depression or anxiety, irritability, or a feeling of inability to cope. If your partner is anxious or depressed, or behaving in a way that concerns you, help and advice are available to you, too.

more info for dads who need help

howisdadgoing.org.au
1300 726 306
Support and advice dads' site from Perinatal Anxiety & Depression Australia, a non-profit group. ('Perinatal' just means 'before or after the birth'.)

Mensline
1300 78 99 78 (24-hour)
mensline.org.au
Counselling and referral help with relationships, kids, separation, stress, work, whatever you need.

stay-at-home dads

Sadly, SAHD (sad!) is the acronym for a Stay-At-Home Dad, so I think we all should avoid that like a full nappy on the train. Being a bloke at home with a baby or larger brood might mean that you are on deck at home one or two days a week, and working in the office the rest of the time, or that you are the full-time primary caregiver.

The reality is that it's less common to find a full-time stay-at-home dad who's at home indefinitely, or for a good while when the kids are little. More common are part-timers who share working days and juggle with their partner, and maybe other relatives or childcare arrangements.

BLAST FROM THE PAST

'Men who stay at home to raise young children should be entitled to up to a year off work, the South Australian Minister for Labour said yesterday. "In families where mum is earning more, it would make economic sense to have dad at home."'
– Bob Gregory, quoted in *The Canberra Times*, 1990

your role as dad

Establishing your authority as a confident parent can be tricky. Many full-time carer dads (and other dads) receive annoying advice, scrutiny or criticism. Or bizarre over-the-top praise for doing what women do without comment.

You may not want to origami the baby singlets in the way your mother-in-law suggests. You may want to roll them into tight balls and volley them into the top drawer from the far side of the room while you pretend to be in the Olympic folding team. If you're happy with your own routine or methods, a good response to

'Ten years I have been a stay-at-home dad. My life has changed forever. I've lost a lot of money and a bunch of workmates, but the relationship gains with my children and my partner are immense. Would I do it all again? You betcha!'   DAVID

unsolicited advice is 'Thanks for that' or 'I'll take that on board'. Then ignore it. If necessary, say 'We're pretty happy – this way is working for us.' 'Us' is good. It's like the royal 'we'. It suggests solidarity.

Unless safety or health is involved (for example, no, you can't throw a baby into the air madly – it can detach a retina), you can dress a toddler in unmatching stripes and florals and use a tea cosy for a hat without fear of medical emergency. Nobody hands an apprentice pilot Flight 94 to New York and says 'Have a crack at flying that, mate'. Parenting means learning on the job, but go easy on yourself for not being perfect straight away – or ever. 'Perfect' parents are not only fictitious but a fictitious pain in the fictitious arse.

'We find out what women have known for decades. You can't truly be a star at work if you're truly serious about being there for your kids as often as they need you. There will always be some hot shot who's willing to give up more to get where you could go if not for what you need to do at home.' JONATHAN KRONSTADT, stay-at-home dad and author

I'm going to miss you darling!

PAY PACKET

29

PAID WORK & CHILDCARE

Some parents give up work outside the home, others work part time or full time. Some parents share both roles. And everyone's busier than ants at a picnic.

who works where, when?

At some time in their life, most mothers mix part-time, casual or full-time work and being at home with their children. Men, too, either share that mix or restructure their work to be more flexible if they can. There's also lots of parents sharing custody, and many sole parents (most of whom are women). This chapter isn't a blueprint for restructuring your life – it just presents options and ideas on making decisions.

The 'which parent stays home when?' conversation

⭐ Are you both offensively wealthy and never have to work at all, ever?

⭐ Who's on contract? Who has a permanent, well-paid position with great benefits? Who earns more? Who wants to stay home more?

⭐ Can you do a year off work, or would it make more sense to sort of job-share, with one partner working at home three days a week?

⭐ Whose workplace is the more flexible and family-friendly?

⭐ Which workplace offers better prospects for the future?

⭐ Who needs to keep up the superannuation payments?

⭐ Who needs to 'keep their hand in', keep their name in the industry?

⭐ Which parent will inevitably take some sort of hit to their career because they're a parent? (Hint: the answer should be 'both'.)

⭐ Who wants to try some part-time study mixed with part-time childcare while the other one gets paid?

⭐ Have you had a go at it and decided that it's the best thing you've ever done and, what's more, you're good at it? Or have you given it a red-hot go and decided you can do it three days a week max without going shrieky-crazy?

⭐ What cleaning, cooking and shopping requirements will be filled by which partner? Staying at home isn't all fun and games: some of it is drudgery as well. All the drudgery shouldn't be left to whoever's unpaid, regardless of gender.

> 'When they had children, my friend's husband said she would have to do all the housework because she was at home, or if she got a job, the cleaner's fee or childcare had to come out of her wage. She was shocked: they hadn't discussed it and were on totally different pages. The marriage didn't last.' SHAUNA

The impossible dream

No, you cannot work from home and look after kids full time. No, no, no. Seriously. Not. You can work from home if you have childcare options, and somebody to help or get paid for doing the housework . . . but a toddler on the keyboard is a mental health and safety issue, and a serious productivity hazard.

You can juggle kids and work, but you can't do both at exactly the same time, especially before the kids are old enough to know when to stop weeing on clients.

staying home

As well as dealing with all the brand-newness of being a parent, you might be coming to terms with another huge transition: the change from paid work 'out there' to home work that's unpaid and undervalued.

Unfortunately many parents (and non-parents) have a failure of imagination about what it's like for somebody doing it differently, and make 'judgements' based on their own experience and choices, or even on prejudice. This is especially potent for mothers because it feeds old-fashioned notions of what a 'good' or 'bad' mother is. Mothers who work outside their home might have more independence, a better superannuation account, more money, different clothes, *and* extra guilt and stress and exhaustion.

Mothers who stay 'at home' might have more time to stay in their pyjamas, less stress (or more), more isolation, fewer options, less money, less power in a relationship – or more. People at home might love it, or resent it; people at work might be relieved, or feel cheated of time with their baby. Some aspects of being at home with kids are mind-numbing – and so are some aspects of paid work. Some women go part time, some find a job that allows school pick-up, others try to continue their career or find new work that can be done at home.

For many people, the cost of childcare is so high that the advantages of returning to work are not immediate financial ones: it's more to do with keeping their name known or a position in the hierarchy, and maintaining skills, and superannuation. For others, paid work is a financial necessity.

Stay-at-home dads

See 'Stay-at-home dads' in Chapter 28, Dads.

Housewife is a dirty word

I don't know anyone who wants to be called a 'housewife'. You might like to call yourself:

- ⭐ a homemaker
- ⭐ a stay-at-home mum/dad
- ⭐ a home executive
- ⭐ the chief executive officer of your house
- ⭐ a full-time mother/father/parent
- ⭐ a part-time nanny, driver, cleaner, teacher, medical triage officer, retail consultant, stylist, home decorator, chef, events coordinator, project manager, company director, entertainment facilitator, arbitration expert, and so on
- ⭐ the boss
- ⭐ Countess.

juggling paid work & unpaid work

Most parents are involved in part-time or full-time paid work, especially as their kids grow older. Well, unless they simply swan about their hobby trout farm or something. Many parents choose to work from home if they can.

If you work for a business, find out what policies your employer has on flexible and family-friendly work practices and hours. Ask your union about entitlements in this area. Your local employment office will have information and training opportunities for people wanting to re-enter the workforce after kids arrive. Be careful of 'work from home' ads – many of them are scams.

The world of constant juggling and adjustment, of feeling guilty about home and guilty about work, is familiar to lots of us. Only you can judge whether you've bitten off more than you can chew, or whether spitting some out will make you feel better. Or if some element of mad scramble will be normal from now on.

more info on juggling paid work & unpaid work

fairwork.gov.au
On the home page of this government site, click on 'Employee entitlements' then 'Flexibility in the workplace'. Or under the 'Find help for' box on the home page, click on 'Parents & families'.

business.gov.au
This Australian government site has hints and practical info on businesses in general, and you can also search 'home based businesses'.

australianunions.org.au
Many mums, especially, return to casual or part-time work, and some are exploited. This union site details your rights. Click on 'Help At Work'.

The Wife Drought
by Annabel Crabb (Random House, Australia)
Journalist Annabel Crabb provokes a conversation about work-life balance and task divisions between men and women.

scamwatch.gov.au
On the home page of this Australian Competition and Consumer Commission (ACCC) website, pick 'Types of scams' then 'Jobs & employment' to see a list of warning signs and known job scams. (No real job will come from getting an unsolicited email.)

employment.govt.nz
Infoline: 0800 800 863
On the home page of this government website, click on 'Leave and holidays' and then 'Parental leave' on the drop-down menu to find info for publicly and privately employed and self-employed people.

workingforfamilies.govt.nz
Infoline: 0800 774 004
Find out about financial support entitlements, and assistance for childcare or housing.

childcare

This person is a childcare worker. She has a more important job than the CEO of a big bank and is paid eleventy million dollars less. If only we could afford to pay her a squillion dollars with performance bonuses and share packages out the wazoo. If only it was easy to decide how much childcare you're going to need, or not need, in advance and where to find it. Here's some info to help you work it out.

How much care do you need?

Only you can decide how many days of childcare, if any, are okay for your kid and how much you can afford. Only you can decide whether being with your child 24 hours a day, seven days a week, is good for you or them – or is going to turn you into a shrieky-mad harpy. Only you can decide whether your child needs or wants to be with other kids their age. Only you can decide whether particular grandparents are energetic, willing and capable enough to provide a stimulating environment for a baby or toddler all day, or for several days in a row. Only you can decide who wants or needs to be at work, whether you can juggle part-time or full-time rosters, and all the rest of it.

BLAST FROM THE PAST

'The Collingwood creche was "a rather shabby looking place at the lower end of Gertrude St". It took the children of mothers who are usually the only worker in the family, aged from 7 weeks to 5 and 6. There is no government assistance. Parents must go out to work or starve ... The charge is fourpence for one child, sixpence for two, and ninepence for three.'
– *Fitzroy City Press*, 1890

Childcare waiting lists

The first thing to say about childcare is to get from your local council the details of centres within reach and put your baby's name on the waiting lists NOW, even if your baby is 6 weeks old and you don't expect to want part-time care until they're 2 years old. Waiting lists for childcare centres can be several years long. Put your child's name down at a couple of different ones and take a good look at them when you're ready. If you move to another area, the first thing you should do is put your child's name down in the new area. If their name comes up before you're ready, you can always defer your place.

In fact, anyone who ever has sex should probably call a childcare centre first, just in case.

So-called studies on childcare

Anyone with a like-minded opinion can cite a 'study' that says childcare will turn your child into either an aggressive, attention-seeking prima donna or an antisocial throwback. Others will back up their opposite view with 'statistics' that 'prove' childcare makes your child a more well-adjusted genius with advanced development skills and social sense.

You get to choose what's best for you. Maybe you have your child at home with you every day, or you work full time and have a nanny, or you use part-time creche or full-time childcare, or your parents look after the kid sometimes. It's important to realise that mothers can do no right, and everything about the idea of childcare or no childcare that can go wrong will be blamed on a mother, not a father, even if you have a husband with mutton-chop whiskers and a waistcoat who makes all the decisions.

Of all the studies conducted by people in various countries on different kinds of childcare, not one makes an assessment of what's best for an individual child, and in particular not one of them is about your child. You can't base a decision about your kid's welfare on a childcare study of 11.3 children in Helsinki conducted in 1982, even if it does make the news because the results are controversial.

Studies come out now and then saying 'Childcare is brilliant!', 'Grandparent care best', 'Grandparents not a good educational environment', 'Childcare is crap!' Ignore all that. Sit down and think and talk about what you'd like, and then see if you can make it happen. Stay flexible. The only way to work out what kind of childcare is good for your kid is to work it out according to their needs, the needs of your family and what's available, and by watching your child's progress and communicating honestly and openly with the carers you've checked out. If you have access to a childcare centre that is staffed by loving and cheerful, well-trained people, with a sensible ratio of staff to children, and your child is happy to go, and the activities are varied and age-appropriate and the other kids are mostly well adjusted and untroubled, you're already ahead of the game.

childcare options

Childcare definitions vary from state to state – in some places kindergarten means a preschool childcare centre for kids aged 3 to 5; in others it means an educational program in the year before school starts, or the first year of school. Costs will also vary: check with centres and government services about subsidies available to families whose combined household income is below a certain level. People in remote or rural areas will have fewer formal childcare options but probably lower fees than in the city.

informal family arrangements

Many people use informal or formal arrangements with grandparents, either to give themselves a break here and there or so they can go to work. This can be great, but only if you have the right kind of grandparents, and it isn't full-time.

You'll just need to feel your way in making a decision, but a good indicator is whether a grandparent regularly offers to help and actually turns up, and follows your requests. (I know one friend who found out her dad was giving her toddler a coffee every morning.) Another good indicator is a grandparent who seems stimulated by the encounters, and engages the kid rather than simply 'being there' and then feeling exhausted. Lots of people also have regular or irregular swapsies with siblings or friends to give themselves a break.

BLAST FROM THE PAST
'The Prime Minister Paul Keating and the Leader of the Opposition John Hewson are late converts to the child care issue. The catalyst for their conversion seems to be that a viable child-care policy will be crucial to who wins the March 13 election.' – *The Canberra Times*, 1993

formal home or family day care

Many local councils license people to look after kids in the carer's own home, from one morning a week to full-time, long-day care. Government subsidies should apply for fees at approved homes. Check if a home is accredited, and check with the relevant department and local council about whether it's regularly monitored by official inspectors, and if any complaints have been made. Make your own unscheduled 'inspections'. Check the ratio of kids to carer, and who else visits or lives there and has contact with the children. A family home will need more, not less, regulation and modification than a purpose-built centre with qualified workers.

more info on family day care

familydaycare.com.au
The Australian peak body for family day-care providers has a site that explains the concept, and can put you in contact with your nearest operator.

childcare centres

A formal day-care centre has professionally trained staff and must comply with a huge range of government regulations, from the kind of fencing and equipment needed, to staff ratios and what to do with the pooey nappies. The Australian Children's Education and Care Quality Authority assesses the quality of each site.

Visit all the centres in your area. One person's popular and groovy centre is another person's nightmare. Some childcare centres are community run, others are profitable companies. Most are purpose-built or in a modified building and have large rooms, an outdoor play area and lots of organised activities. Most also have a full- or part-time cook on site to provide meals. (Ask if the cook is considered part of the staff-to-child ratio: obviously it's better if they're not.)

Some childcare centres will take babies from 6 weeks old; others start at age 1 year. Some allow half-day attendance; most don't. Kids can be booked in from, say, 9 a.m. to 4 p.m., or longer or shorter hours, depending on the policy of the centre. They usually charge for a whole day even if you only want care from 10 a.m. to 4 p.m.

Childcare centre fees

Fees are sometimes calculated by the hour. Check with the centre whether you might be eligible for government help with them. (See also 'More info on finding childcare' coming up.)

Think carefully about the fees. They can't necessarily be seen as a direct trade-off against the mother's wage, or the father's, with a conclusion that one would be better off staying home full time. Mothers who stay home for a few years traditionally lose more superannuation benefits and seniority and experience. Many couples prefer to try to juggle some part-time work each, or make another arrangement that means child work and paid work are shared.

Possible childcare advantages

★ Staff are usually dedicated beyond the call of duty and certainly the pay packet.

★ Childcare helps parents have a more balanced life.

★ It can allow a parent to be a better parent because they have breaks.

★ It helps parents stay out of poverty as it allows them to take paid work.

★ It comes closer to the sharing kind of childcare in a tribal environment than does the isolation of one person at home with a child.

★ Toddlers and preschoolers tend to adore the child-centred routine.

★ Trained staff know lots of songs, games and tricks for the right age group, and tend to have the energy to make giraffes from egg cartons.

★ Some centres put on more staff than are required by regulations.

★ Staff can focus on the children as they don't have to perform other tasks during the day such as the washing and shopping.

★ Kids get the opportunity to socialise with other kids of various ages.

★ Some centres are community run and the profits are directed back into facilities for children.

★ Programs for optimum development have been prepared by professionals.

★ A structured, kindly social environment can help children overcome shyness, aggression and other social problems.

★ Day care is a much better environment for a child than a home where things are difficult.

★ Good childcare is good for kids.

Possible childcare disadvantages

⭐ Long hours in a childcare centre, such as 8 a.m. to 6 p.m. five days a week, are generally accepted to be not the best situation for a very small child.

⭐ Australian staff-to-children ratios could be better, and they should be standardised nationally.

⭐ Many good childcare workers leave because the pay is so outrageously crappy.

⭐ It's a high-pressure job and some workers are better at it than others.

⭐ Many centres are run for profit and governments don't put enough money into childcare.

⭐ A parent can come to rely on childcare and get locked into a work schedule, and then it's harder for them to adjust when their child needs a break or fewer hours, or is sick.

⭐ Childcare centres can have small outdoor areas. A child at the same centre for years, or doing very long hours, can be understimulated by the never-changing environment.

⭐ Not enough men want to be childcare workers.

⭐ The childcare available to you may not match the personality and needs of your kid.

⭐ Bad childcare is bad for kids.

Questions to ask before choosing a childcare centre

⭐ Is the centre affiliated with a religious group or based on a particular philosophy?

⭐ Is there lots of space inside and outside?

⭐ Are the carers covered in cuddly kids or does the place seem a bit stand-offish?

⭐ Do the staff speak respectfully to the children?

⭐ Do the children look interested and happy?

⭐ Do the staff seem to get on well together?

⭐ Who works or lives on site? Can I meet them all?

⭐ Is it always like this? (Allow for reality – imagine if someone came to your place at a bad scheduled time.)

⭐ What sort of meals do they serve?

⭐ What activities and programs are available, and how do they encourage creativity, fun and development?

⭐ What is the staff-to-child ratio?

⭐ What discipline measures are used?

Questions to ask when your child has been at a childcare centre for a while

⭐ Is my child adjusting?

⭐ What does my child like doing?

⭐ Who are their special friends?

⭐ Is there a day, morning or afternoon when the mix of kids creates a nasty or difficult dynamic for my child?

settling into childcare

If possible, especially in the first days and weeks, spend as much time as you can helping your child to settle and bond with the carer or carers, or the nanny. It can be a delicate situation leaving a child you know will be happy two seconds after you leave, but meanwhile is weeping piteously and clinging to you for dear life. Some kids initially need to be 'eased into the day', yet will end up hardly giving you a backward glance as they race to an activity ready for them on the kid-sized tables at childcare or to hold Granny's hand and wave you off to work.

Let your child know you are going and what time you'll come back (even if they don't quite 'get' times). Check later with the centre or carer to make sure any tears on your departure cleared up after you left, and that your child isn't showing signs of continuing separation anxiety or sadness throughout the day. Feel free to check up on their progress during the day even if they weren't upset when you left: you can tell your kid you rang when they were happily playing in the sandpit and they'll feel secure and become aware of the bridge between home and the childcare centre, or between you at work and them at home.

Make sure the carer or carers know they can talk to you openly about your child's feelings, demeanour and development, because you won't get snippy.

guilt about childcare

The real key to dealing with guilt is to make sure your child is having a happy, stimulated, social childhood, whatever childcare options or combination you choose. To do that, you have to spend enough time with your child to know them very well.

The other way to minimise guilt is to try to look very dispassionately at your set-up and honestly assess whether your kid is happy and thriving after a few weeks of care. Don't make your decision based on other people's theories, what your mother thinks, that survey in Finland or the experiences of anyone else's children.

~~~~~ **more info** on finding childcare ~~~~~

startingblocks.gov.au
This Australian Children's Education and Care Quality Authority site will help you check the quality ratings and accreditation of childcare providers near you, and ask the right questions of centres.

humanservices.gov.au/individuals/families
Click on 'Child care' for government info on fees assistance.

Centrelink Family Assistance Office: 13 61 50
Yeah, good luck with getting through to that.

BLAST FROM THE PAST
'The Victorian Railways Nursery at Flinders St station took children from 2 weeks old, and supplied them with cots with rubber wheels, toys, and mini cars, scooters and trikes, and 2 playrooms (one outside). In December 1936 the crèche averaged 114 children a day and one day in the week before Christmas in 1936 it looked after 180 clients.'
– The Age, 1937

a nanny or au pair

This is probably the most expensive form of childcare because you're paying one person's wage, without any subsidies, and you need to organise tax and superannuation. Nannies tend to live offsite and should be paid proper wages and benefits where appropriate.

An au pair (it's a French expression) is a live-in childminder and home helper, often a foreign worker or student who accepts lower than usual nanny rates because they get their meals and a room to live in for free. Most au pairs are in Australia on a working holiday visa.

Hiring a nanny or au pair through an agency means it's easier to pay their wage, and their superannuation (if they work enough hours to qualify); know their training and work history, and be assured they've had a 'working with children' check; agree on a job description; and get emergency replacements when necessary.

You should have a job interview personally and ask lots of questions, and person-ally check all references and qualifications. When you interview, make sure your baby or child is with you. Watch how the nanny interacts with them.

You need to sort out upfront, before the nanny or au pair starts, what housework or cooking aside from kid food is included in their responsibilities. You should also make your expectations clear: for example, friends of the au pair can visit, but no taking the baby to the pub for a shandy.

Waiting lists for kinder & preschool

It can come as an enormous shock to parents who discover that their kid is not automatically given a place at a local kindergarten, or even an enrolment in the nearest government primary school. This can be an informal and unofficial lottery involving 'first in, best dressed' and subject to what's available in your area. Get onto waiting lists as soon as you can, although this will not guarantee your child a place.

clean
hands

30

family food

You might be an expert whizzer in the kitchen already,
able to conjure up a family supper from some stale cumin,
a choko and half a packet of freeze-dried mackerel.
Or you might be serving a toddler truffle-oil bavarois
of nutkin fern imported directly from a family-run
vineyard in Sardinia. On the other hand you might be
shocked – *shocked* – to find that coffee is not a food group.

cooking for babies & toddlers

Most people start off having to learn everything about feeding babies and toddlers and so they begin with lots of books, worry about it all the time, compare notes with other parents, freeze little ice cubes of colour-coordinated pureed things, and then a few months later find the kid is eating whatever the grown-up department is having that night and the books are propping up the wobbly end of the kitchen table.

It's smart to introduce a wide range of food to your baby and toddler from the get-go, but there's never any guarantee this will result in a child who will eat everything. Lots of babies love everything they're given and then gradually get sterner about the whole caper when they become toddlers (see Chapter 14, First Food, for info on babies and eating).

What is guaranteed is that once most people have children money is tighter, and 'eating in' becomes the norm. If you weren't previously into cooking, it's a good time to start.

Beware of child-centred cookbooks imported from overseas that are full of elaborate recipes and theme food served as pictures on the plate. One book suggests you construct a Merry Meatball Pony and Liver Log Cabin. This way lies MADNESS, I tell you. US and UK books are always full of recipes for things such as cod and cilantro (it's coriander) and never have any tropical fruit – it's just the wrong hemisphere.

Honey

It is very rare, but honey can introduce botulism bacteria to babies and can contribute to kids being 'hooked' on sweet-tasting things for comfort. Experts agree: don't give honey to a baby under 1 year old.

'My kid loves the idea of "eating the rainbow" every day with different colours of fruit and vegies to get all the right vitamins and stuff – some days we have to go out and get another colour.'   DAVE

'I told my 3-year-old daughter that peeled broad beans were called bean lollies. She loved them.'   AHEM, ANONYMOUS AUTHOR

〰〰〰〰 more info on food safety for 〰〰〰〰
babies & kids

See the list of food choking hazards in Chapter 14, First Food, and Chapter 19, Toddler Food. (Non-food choking hazards are in Chapter 32, Safety & Injuries.)

foodsafety.asn.au
For info on preparing, carrying around and serving food to tots while avoiding food poisoning, go to the Australian government–funded Food Safety Information Council's site.

〰〰〰〰〰〰〰〰〰〰〰〰〰〰〰〰〰

cooking with kids

A lot of recipe writers don't seem to understand that cooking *for* kids and cooking *with* kids are entirely different kettles of mashed fish. Most cookbooks supposedly teaching kids to cook are exclusively devoted to totally crap, sugary things. Sometimes cooking something savoury is an extremely useful way to amuse the tinies *and* get some dinner at the end. The world has enough toffee apples – in fact one is too many. (To make your kitchen safer for babies and kids see Chapter 32, Safety & Injuries.)

Good things to cook with kids

You might like to try making:
- ⭐ biscuits, savoury slices and gingerbread folk – kids can cut the shapes with biscuit cutters or a blunt baby knife
- ⭐ veggie muffins – measure, sift, pour, stir, spoon
- ⭐ sandwiches – butter, fill and squash down
- ⭐ pancakes – you fry and they sprinkle on savoury bits or fruit, then roll or fold
- ⭐ smoothies – kids can cut up soft fruit with a blunt knife and chuck the chunks into the blender, pour in the milk and a dollop of yoghurt (no raw eggs allowed for babies and toddlers because of salmonella risk)
- ⭐ pizza – the kids add the decoration to a cooked, cooled pizza base or a ready-made one
- ⭐ mashed, squished and extremely distressed potatoes.

How kids can help

You could let toddlers:

- ⭐ 'help' plant and pick things in the garden, or 'help' choose things at the market or shop
- ⭐ 'help' work out shopping lists and look for items in the supermarket
- ⭐ 'help' with meal preparation: smash fruit, sift flour, mix batter, tear lettuce into bits and so on.

BLAST FROM THE PAST

'Half cover a cauliflower with boiling water and cook for 30 to 45 minutes.'
— *The Radiation Cookery Book*, 34th edition, 1948

---

more info on family cooking

Kids' books about eating, and cooking-with-kids and family food cookbooks, can be sourced at **kidsbookshop.com.au**, publishers' websites, online bookstores and your local chain or independent bookshop.

marketfresh.com.au
Fresh fruit and veggie info, including a chart to identify unfamiliar fruit and veg, when what's in season and what you can do with it, family recipes, kids' food and school-lunch ideas, from the Melbourne Market. Click on Resources, or Healthy Eating Recipes.

The Cook's Companion
by Stephanie Alexander (Penguin, Australia)
Giant book on everything you need to know about kitchen equipment and techniques, what to look for when buying, how to store foods, and which foods go well with other foods, as well as recipes.

healthy food & drink choices

Breakfast

By far the best breakfast for a kid is one that doesn't come in a packet covered in brightly coloured pictures and marketed as 'children's breakfast cereal'. Much better: an unprocessed breakfast cereal like rolled oats, shredded wheat, wheat bricks or muesli with no dried fruit or whole nuts. If you put in some milk and real fruit, which contains natural sugars, your child will get used to the taste without added sugar. This will also give your child a more sustained energy boost than the oversweet, 'non-nutritious' packaged breakfast cereals.

Most commercial children's breakfast cereal is made of grains that have been so overprocessed there's no nutrition left in them. Then vitamins are added – sort of like sprinkling in a crushed vitamin tablet. Preservatives and flavouring and a frightening amount of sugar are then added. Beware of the claims that all these pre-packaged things have 'essential vitamins and minerals' and other goodies. Your child is better off getting those nutrients from real, fresh food.

'Energy' foods

Kids don't need to eat sugar in foods, or 'energy' foods (usually code for 'sugar-and-salt-packed'), to have energy. They get energy from normal foods in their diet, including protein and carbohydrates. Give kids real fruit instead, and avoid commercial dried fruits, fruit 'bars', strips and 'roll-ups'.

Drinks

You'll save money and your kid will be healthier if you get your little one 'hooked' on water as the only regular drink offered. Milk as well as water can be offered through the day. Give your kids full-fat (not 'light' or low-fat) milk before the age of 2 unless your doctor recommends otherwise. Full-fat milk has the extra nutrients and food energy that little ones need. Avoid drinks of milk before meals as they 'fill up' a little tummy without the extra nutrients and fibre provided by food.

Most bought drinks for kids have from one or two up to an astonishing eight teaspoons' worth of sugar in a serving. It's believed one fizzy drink a day can add as much as six unwanted kilos to an adult in one year. They're not good for babies and toddlers. Pieces of fruit give a child fibre and experience in chewing. Kids don't need fruit juice and it can damage their teeth. Avoid giving drinks of milk in bed in a bottle, as the slow swishing about and residue in the mouth can cause extra tooth decay (see also Chapter 36, Teeth).

If a toddler has constant access to water during each meal, and in, say, a safe sippy cup that can be taken on travels and left on the table or the floor during play-times, or from a filter system or a cold tap, they should be getting enough fluids on a self-serve basis. If a toddler is constipated, drinking more water can help.

What NOT to give your baby or toddler:

- ★ commercial fizzy drinks, colas, lemonades
- ★ shop-bought fruit juices in bottles or little boxes
- ★ slices of citrus fruit to suck on
- ★ home-juiced drinks
- ★ juice-bar-mixed juices in large containers with straws
- ★ powdered stuff added to milk
- ★ flavoured milks, flavoured mineral waters, cordials
- ★ energy drinks and any drink with caffeine, including cola, tea and coffee, and many herbal teas
- ★ bought bottled water instead of tap water (tap water has fluoride in it to help keep their teeth healthy).

Fancy drinks for special occasions, like parties, can be the non-sugar versions of cordials or fizzy drinks, or water with a drop of food colouring.

BLAST FROM THE PAST

Menu for Mansion House children's ball given by London's Lady Mayoress: 'Boar's head, soles *en mayonnaise*, lobster salads, lamb cutlets *à la* Victoria, larks *à la* Ripon, turkeys, sauce *béchamel*, game pies, galantine of chicken, roast chickens, ham, tongue, creams, orange jellies, clear jellies, meringues, *éclairs*, petit gateaux, trifles, maids of honour.'
– *The Mercury*, Hobart, 1910

more info on healthy food & drink choices

Anyone can call themselves a 'nutritionist'. Most celebrity and food folk on social media do not have the right qualifications or experience to advise on what kids should eat or drink. Many are paid or given free stuff to recommend products:

daa.asn.au
The Dietitians Association of Australia website has a ton of fact sheets. Choose 'Smart Eating for a Healthier You', or search 'children'.

choice.com.au/babies-and-kids
For lots of reports and info sheets on healthy products and dodgy ones for kids, scroll down to 'Feeding your baby' and 'Feeding children' on this independent site.

raisingchildren.net.au
On this Australian government–backed site, choose the age group of your kid(s) then 'Nutrition' or 'Nutrition & fitness' for lots of good info.

cyh.com
On this South Australian government health site, choose 'Parenting and Child Health' then 'Nutrition' for heaps on healthy foods, how to read food labels, cooking, good breakfasts and more.

childrensfoodeducation.org.au
Website of a charity that promotes an understanding of health, nutrition and healthy food choices for kids.

'Low-fat foods'

It can be very confusing, but low-fat foods are usually very high in sugar, most of which the body converts into fat. Best to avoid them for tinies. Low-fat foods are not suitable for babies and toddlers unless you're individually advised by a doctor or a dietitian.

dietitian or nutritionist?

Anyone can call themselves a nutritionist. A dietitian is a professional who has the qualification 'Accredited Practising Dietitian' (APD). APD means they've successfully undertaken tertiary study approved by the Dietitians Association of Australia and are recognised by Medicare (which may fund some visits) and private health funds. For more info visit the Dietitians Association of Australia website (daa.asn.au).

vegetarian & vegan parents

Because humans have evolved to need meat, any radical change from this needs careful thought when small kids are involved. Many vegetarian parents allow their young children to eat meat, and many vegan parents give their kids meat, dairy products and eggs because they see it as the best way for their kids to grow and develop in the early years. Many will seek out organic meats, free-range eggs and other products that are aligned to their philosophy. Many parents are content to allow their kids to make up their own mind later about whether or when to become a vegetarian or a vegan, which is most likely to happen in the teenage years.

Any form of vegetarian or vegan diet you are on during pregnancy and breast-feeding, or that you are giving your baby or children, needs to be okayed by an independent dietitian who knows your individual needs. A paediatric dietitian at your nearest children's hospital or community health centre, or at a private clinic, will help you make sure you're meeting the special needs of babies and kids.

Vegetarian and vegan diets for kids

Medical experts and child development specialists say that babies and toddlers should not be on strict vegetarian or vegan diets. Most vegetarian and vegan parents choose to give their kids some non-plant-based protein.

'Planting a few simple vegies and watching them grow with your littlies, then harvesting, cooking and eating them together is a really lovely activity to do together. Kids learn where food comes from, and the fun in cooking and gardening.' ANNA

Like all kids, older vegetarian children need lots of healthy food and not to just fill up on high-fibre food with low nutrients. They'll need a wide range of protein foods, dairy products, fruit (including avocado), chopped nuts (nut pastes until they're 1 year old), seeds, protein such as eggs, and soy products. They will also need special care to get iron, calcium, iodine, fat, and nutrients such as B12 and zinc.

organic food

Organically produced foods make for fewer damaging chemicals in the environment, and foodie folk swear it tastes better. After very large studies and analyses of all available data, scientists believe that there's no proof of increased nutritional benefit.

Organic vegies and fruit should be washed thoroughly to rid them of bacteria as well as 'spray' residue. For local organic matters, such as suppliers, click on 'Resources' on the home page of the Organic Federation of Australia website (ofa.org.au).

restricted diets for kids

Any program for weight gain or loss in kids needs to be a response to a medical diagnosis and must be discussed with and supervised by your family doctor, perhaps in consultation with a specialist dietitian. Kids should not be put on 'diets' or have any food group or common food excluded, including wheat and dairy, unless it is on medical advice. Medical advice doesn't include the suggestions of friends or family, a suspicion of an allergy or intolerance, or the advice of a natural therapist, chiropractor or other non-medical adviser. Some babies and children have become sick, died or almost died because their parents put them on extreme diets, including raw food, non-dairy formulas, and other regimes. Fad diets such as 'paleo' can also cause kids to miss out on important nutrients. Eczema and asthma are not cured by changed eating habits.

food allergies & intolerances

Many children have allergies or intolerances to various foods, which can include milk, wheat, nuts, shellfish, strawberries, kiwifruit and oranges. An allergy is a reaction by the immune system against something, such as a food, that most people don't have a problem with. You'll probably start with suspicions and instincts, or the food allergy will suddenly become obvious because of a serious or visible reaction such as mouth itchiness or a rash. Any violent reaction to a food or drink that involves breathing difficulties means you need to call an ambulance straight away, as this can be anaphylactic shock which needs emergency treatment.

Food intolerances happen when the body is unable to process a certain kind of food because of, say, enzymes not working properly to break down the sugar in milk (lactose). This intolerance is often avoided by giving kids soy milk, some yoghurt and other lactose-free stuff. Using soy milk and goat's milk doesn't prevent allergies.

Your doctor will help you isolate an allergy or intolerance. It's very important to have your suspicions professionally confirmed.

Australia is at the forefront of allergy research. The Murdoch Children's Research Institute says useful preventative strategies can include breastfeeding in the first 6 months if you can, starting solids from around 6 months, letting kids play in the dirt and not using antibacterial sprays in the home, and getting enough vitamin D (see 'Vitamin D' in Chapter 33, Health.)

Some reputable studies have found that there is a smaller incidence of some food allergies in babies who live in rural areas, with a dog, or with older siblings under the age of 6. The theory is that they may be 'protected' by contact with more germs that encourage a robust immune-system response. Some researchers are convinced there is also a genetic element.

A little bit can do you good

In the past, parents were told not to give babies certain foods in case they became allergic, but we now know that this exclusion advice may worsen or even create some allergies, and that it certainly doesn't prevent them. Now, experts say they've learnt from research that the immune system may be 'trained' by trying lots of different foods early to avoid potential allergies.

Doctors now say babies need to try a wide range of foods from 4 to 6 months onwards, to get them used to it. Trying little bits of new foods also helps babies and toddlers accept new tastes. Foods to introduce early and keep offering in the first year include dairy products, fish, wheat, egg and nuts. Don't give whole nuts, which can cause choking: try ground ones or nut pastes such as peanut butter. (See Chapter 14, First Food.)

Allergy recovery

Research continues into the 'causes' of and protective effects against allergies. A treatment for peanut allergy, which affects about three in every 100 babies, has been devised as part of a small study at the Murdoch Children's Research Institute in Melbourne. It's based on specific probiotics given with specific amounts of peanut flour, and has 'cured' many children, changing their lives. The signs are hopeful that in time we'll know more about allergies, and even be able to cure some.

Many children 'grow out of' allergic reactions if they keep having some of the food in small amounts, but this requires specialist medical advice. It's too dangerous to guess how much and when. Your family doctor can refer you to a specialist, who can give you a program to follow.

BLAST FROM THE PAST
Recipe for saveloy sandwich: 'Saveloys. Butter. Bread. Tomato Sauce.'
(You can guess the rest.)
– Laraine Leyland, *Food for the Road* cookbook, 2002

∼∼∼∼∼ more info on food allergies ∼∼∼∼∼ & intolerances

allergy.org.au
The latest advice on feeding babies new foods, and avoiding or managing allergies, from the leading Australian and NZ specialists (Australasian Society of Clinical Immunology and Allergy). On the home page choose 'Patients & Consumers' to get info on finding a specialist, anaphylaxis, food allergies and other issues. Click on 'Schools & Childcare' for info on carers and supervision, and anaphylaxis training.

raisingchildren.net.au
Search 'food allergies' and 'food intolerances' for fact sheets.

mcriallergypal.com.au
The Murdoch Children's Research Institute has created a free app to help manage a kid's allergy and share info with carers.

allergyfacts.org.au
An Australian charity set up to help families with children who are at risk of severe allergic reactions caused by foods such as nuts, seafood and eggs, or by contact with latex, bee stings or other triggers. Sells cookbooks.

31

KiD
eQUiPMeNT

You're going to need some stuff. A bed, a car seat,
a pram. And 987 other things that all fit into a
'baby bag', or the tray of a twin-cab ute.

choosing your kid equipment

It's usually best to shop at a section of a department store or a store that sells different brands of baby gear so that you can compare prices and know that most things will be covered by the required safety standard. Each item should have a tag showing a current, certified Australia and New Zealand safety standard (AS/NZS) label: often a tick in Australia and a logo in NZ.

Do your homework, especially if you plan to buy second-hand stuff – it could be unsafe, illegal or superseded. And if you're acquiring something second-hand, get hold of and scrupulously follow the manufacturer's directions about construction and use. If there's no paperwork, check whether the gear conforms to the current safety standard and check out the instructions – often they're online. Remember, standards can be updated. It might have been up to standard in 1997, but is not now.

For some bizarre reason not all the safety standards are enforced by law (although those for cots and car seats are, for example) and some equipment is not yet covered by a standard, including baby slings. And I'm always horrified to see that years-old copies of my books for parents are sold on second-hand sites, with outdated medical and safety info (I update the books every year). And parent forums that have 'life hacks' can be terrifying.

dangerous toys & equipment

A flood of cheap imports that are not checked and do not conform to safety standards, a huge increase in the number of shops that stock this kind of stuff (think '$3 shops'), hand-me-downs and a thriving second-hand market online mean many parents unwittingly buy unsafe, outdated, damaged products for their kids. Just because you can buy it does not mean it's fit for purpose, or even legal, or safe.

Unsafe things sold for babies

These are downright dangerous or potentially dangerous.

★ Bumpers: these soft, padded sidey-bits that tie onto cots stop the free flow of fresh air, and babies can get their heads wedged underneath and suffocate. Yes, they're in all the fashionable shops and ad pictures. They shouldn't be.

⭐ Baby walkers: they're still sold because they can be convenient for parents, and babies enjoy them. But every safety mob between here and Neptune says they don't help kids learn to walk properly and cause a lot of accidents.

⭐ Bouncy things: many safety experts say these are dodgy for babies and too much of a risk. A bouncinette should always be used with a restraint. It should be placed on a safe surface where it can't travel over the edge of the stairs or table or kitchen counter, and never near a heater or a fire. It should be abandoned as soon as the baby can roll. Babies love to be reminded of womb-like feelings so they enjoy baby bouncers or bouncing swings, and hammocks of any description, but all these products are notorious in hospital emergency departments. They're legal, but not advisable.

See Chapter 32, Safety & Injuries, for more on how to make your home safer and deal with accidents.

more info on dangerous toys & equipment

www.productsafety.gov.au
An Australian Competition and Consumer Commission site with safety alerts and product recalls on baby gear. Choose 'Products' then 'Babies and Kids'. Or 'Recalls' then 'Browse all recalls' then 'Babies and kids'. Search 'mandatory standards' to see which products have to conform by law.

choice.com.au
The independent Choice (aka the Australasian Consumers' Association) often finds safety hazards when testing kids' equipment. Members have access to all reports and reviews, or you can pay a very small fee to open a specific report. Some info is free.

consumer.org.nz
New Zealand's consumer organisation: members get free advice from independent user and test reports and an advice line.

cots & beds

Most people skip the bassinet stage and go straight to a cot. This is one of the most important items to check all the safety features on. Rustic, vintage or otherwise non-safety-standard cots can be deadly. Also see 'Making a safe sleeping place' in Chapter 8, Baby Sleep. Three quarters of portable cots and a third of fixed cots sold from 2011–2018 were found to be dangerous, according to *Choice*.

prams

Some prams convert to a stroller. Think about the weather, year-round, where you live. You'll need a wet-weather cover and a sunshade or an umbrella. All new prams and strollers should have swively wheels for easy manoeuvring. If you walk to the shops a lot, get a sturdy pram with a large metal shopping basket underneath. If you live in an upstairs, walk-up flat, you'll need something that folds into a light, convenient package that can be hauled upstairs. Do you need to get the pram into and out of a car or bus? (Don't take the manufacturer's or sales assistant's word for it – fold it up and down yourself a few times in the shop, and try lifting it.) Make sure the pram is comfortable for both you and your partner to push – some have adjustable handle heights. A pram should have a safety standard label.

Pram & stroller safety

All prams are more dangerous if the person wheeling them is on a phone. Mobile phones distract parents from their baby's safety.

Don't push a pram or stroller out in front of you onto the road first when crossing. It's amazing how many people will stand between two parked cars with their pram or stroller actually on the road in front of them. You feel safe because you're further away from the traffic, but your child could be in danger.

Two thirds of strollers sold from 2011–2018 had serious failures, according to *Choice*.

PRAM

shopping

The earth is not flat – all wheels will roll

No piece of ground is exactly flat. Every constructed piece of ground is deliberately engineered *not* to be flat, and this includes footpaths, traffic islands, river or lake paths, bike or running paths, paved walkways and lookouts, street footpaths, and train or tram platforms. They are *all* designed for water drainage in the rain to have a very gradual and invisible slope towards the tracks or the river or the street.

Any pram or stroller left without a brake on will automatically, silently, slowly or quickly roll towards the edge and topple over. The rule is: if your hand is off the pram, the brake has to be on. Always park a pram at right angles to an edge, but keep the brake on because there could be an angle that way as well. It's not safe to leave a baby sleeping in a pram, or a toddler sleeping in a stroller, unsupervised.

strollers

Babies can't go in strollers until they have good sitty-up control, usually at about 6 months. More expensive strollers are usually more comfortable for long walks or shopping. Strollers need to have a five-point safety harness so a toddler doesn't make a bold bid for freedom when you least expect it. A stroller also needs good brakes and a shelf or basket underneath that is large enough to hold your baby bag or shopping. Bags hanging from stroller handles destabilise the whole shebang. Jogging strollers can be harder to get in and out of a car, and may not fit easily or at all on public transport: Choice has rated some brands unsafe, but a good jogging stroller can be great for long walks or different terrain.

more info on prams & strollers

choice.com.au
Search 'prams and strollers' on the home page of this independent consumer website for reviews and a buying guide.

productsafety.gov.au
On the home page of the Australian Competition and Consumer Commission's site, search 'prams and strollers' for buying info, fact sheets and recall news.

highchairs

You'll need a highchair with wide-apart, stable legs; a lockable tray so the bub can't whack it up and down on their fingers; and a harness that goes around the waist and then over the shoulders, with a strap between the legs that goes up to the waist strap. If you consistently strap your baby in, as you do in the car or stroller, they'll assume that's the go and not fuss (fingers crossed).

Always put the kid in the highchair yourself: don't let them climb in themselves. Don't leave the room when your baby is in the highchair. Kids are known to do sudden acrobatics you never thought possible, without a safety net. And they can push against a table or another chair with their feet, which can tip their highchair over – usually backwards. A good highchair's label will show it complies with the safety standard.

more info on highchairs

Search 'high chairs' (two words) on **choice.com.au** and **productsafety.gov.au** for the usual info.

baby carriers & slings

Many mums and dads find having the baby strapped to their front leaves their hands free and lets the bub stay nicely swaddled and soothed by a heartbeat. Buy a sling or carrier with proper safety instructions, and follow them. Some babies have been suffocated in, or injured falling from, slings.

Babies in a sling must:

⭐ constantly have their mouth and nose exposed to open air

⭐ be firmly wrapped to you, and more vertical than horizontal

⭐ be showing their whole face when they are in the sling

⭐ be positioned with their chin up, not sunk onto their chest, and not be curled around like they were in the womb

⭐ have their back and neck supported by the material of the carrier

⭐ not be near a hot drink.

Who can use a sling?

Ask your family doctor whether it's safe for your baby to be in a sling: most safety instructions say babies under 4 months, especially premmie ones, shouldn't be carried in slings. A structured sling can make any baby's hip problems worse, as can some positions in a sling. So far there are no official Australia/NZ safety standard requirements for baby slings. Any sling should come with formal safety and usage recommendations. See 'More info on baby carriers & slings' coming up.

Structured baby carriers

These are the front ones with padding and straps, or the backpack-style ones for older babies, and they often have metal frames.

Make sure you get one from a reputable baby shop, and try it on in the shop with your baby in it. Make sure your baby can't slip out. A waist belt for the carrier provides essential stability and transfers some weight to your hips as the baby gets heavier. Any baby carrier for older bubs should have good back support for you, and back and neck support for bub. If you're paying heaps, what are you getting for your money?

⭐ Check the weight suitability. Is your baby ready, or about to 'grow out' of it?

⭐ Check the washing instructions to see if they're practical. Dry-clean? A ha aha haaaaa.

★ Padded shoulder straps and no-rub metal frame edges are important. Check they are strong enough. Many baby carriers have no metal parts.

★ Check online instructions to make sure a second-hand carrier has all its bits and they're in good order.

more info on baby carriers & slings

rednose.com.au
On this important baby safety website, search 'baby sling' for a safety video and more.

productsafety.gov.au
On the Australian Competition and Consumer Commission's product safety site search 'baby sling safety' for a fact sheet, or 'baby slings and carriers'. Also check whether any carriers have been recalled.

choice.com.au
Search 'carriers and slings' on this independent consumer website for a guide.

consumer.org.nz
The consumer organisation of NZ has a guide to buying and using baby carriers.

On your bike

Having a baby on a bike in a safety standard approved seat, even with the regulation helmet on as well, is not necessarily safe. A small person on a bike in an accident, even with a helmet on, is likely to suffer much more serious injuries than an adult. The combination of speed + metal objects that weigh tons + a baby = nothing good.

Extra safety concerns also exist for bikes towing a baby carriage: even if the trailer has a flag on a flexible stick, it's much lower than anything drivers expect to see associated with a bike.

Child bicycle seats are covered by a legal standard. All people on or being towed or pushed by a bike must also be wearing legal standard helmets. Many parks and trails have safer bike paths for tootling along with a baby or toddler.

family cars

If you're buying a new family car, check recommendations and the publicly available safety results. You'll need a car that has or can have an anchor point installed for baby and child restraints – a car with no back seats won't do. A car with back doors will make your life 100 times easier when getting kids in and out.

Proximity alarms, lenses and video-checking systems are not a guarantee of safety and can promote false confidence, according to car accident authorities. Blind spots occur in all vehicles, especially low to the ground. Large four-wheel drive cars are over-represented in accidents where children are hit in their own driveways – and a child hit by a four-wheel drive is statistically very much more likely to die than if hit by a regular car. (For the same reason, have any bull bar removed from the front.) Station wagons can be fitted with a cargo barrier so dogs and other heavy stuff don't fly forward in an accident.

~~~~~~ **more info** on family cars ~~~~~~

ancap.com.au
The Australasian New Car Assessment Program grades cars on their crash and other safety test results.

baby & toddler car seats

You'll need a new baby restraint or toddler car seat that's certified to the current safety standard. A registered fitter can help to install it correctly. Second-hand car restraints must be less than ten years old and have no Velcro. They must not have been in an accident or have been bought overseas. If you don't know the answers to these questions because yours is second-hand, get another seat.

⭐ Babies up to 6 months old must go in a baby capsule fitted to the back seat, facing the back of the car.

⭐ After 6 months old (with good head control), babies should stay facing backwards if they still fit in their restraint with a built-in six-point harness – some restraints are designed to last till your 'baby' is up to 2 or 3 years old. Some restraints will 'convert' to face frontwards for later so you won't have to buy a new one.

★ Kids aged 4 to 7 must be in a front-facing child seat with an in-built harness, or in an approved booster seat with a lap-sash seatbelt fastened in an approved, adjusted way.

★ All kids under 7 must be in the back seat of a car in approved restraints.

★ Kids who are in the smaller range for their age may have to wait a little longer to 'graduate' to the next seat option.

Info on which child restraints to use is based on individual height and body control. Newer restraints have shoulder markings that indicate when a kid is ready to graduate to another restraint.

~~~~ more info on baby & toddler car seats ~~~~

Most child car seats are fitted wrongly by their owners. Many car insurance companies have 'fitting stations' to install or show you how to do it correctly.

childcarseats.com.au
All the info on which car seat or booster you need for which kid. Check the latest Child Restraint Evaluation Program (CREP) results for car seats. Find a fitting station near you in NSW, Victoria or WA.

kidsafe.com.au
Kidsafe is independent and non-profit, and is full bottle on safety requirements. Click on your area on the map of Australia, then find 'child restraints' on your state's website.

road safety authorities
Ask for registered restraint fitters near you.
ACT: 13 22 81
NSW: 13 22 13
NT: 1800 720 144
QLD: 13 23 80
SA: 13 10 84
TAS: 1300 135 513
VIC: 1300 360 745
WA: 1300 780 713

🥝 **safekids.org.nz**
Non-profit mob with fact sheets on car restraints.

Trampolines & bouncy castles dangers

It's sad news for jolly jumpers but according to medical experts, children under about 7 should never go on a trampoline. It's because of the injury rate the experts see from all trampolines, even ones with net sides or in a supervised play centre.

Injuries can happen from landing anywhere on the mat of the trampoline, on the springs, on the frame, on the ground, from headbutts, from landing on any body part and from collisions. Trampolines cause more injuries in the US than any other play equipment or sport except skiing, including 'monkey bars', slides, bikes, skateboards and tree-climbing. That's because of the velocity that kids can get up to, the 'bad' ways they can land, and the unusually serious bone breaks that occur.

Likewise, toddlers shouldn't go on bouncy castles, 'moon bounce' houses and cubbies, or other home and party inflatable novelty constructions and activities. The rise of home-use inflatables has caused an exponential rise in injuries. Even a child alone on a bouncy castle is at risk of injury, but being on it with other children is a huge risk for broken bones, bruises and other injuries from awkward landings, 'ejections' (being pushed or falling off), falls and collisions with other kids, especially heads and limbs, and especially bigger kids connecting with smaller ones.

Bouncy castles have also blown away with a child on them, or deflated, covering children unseen in the middle of layers of heavy plastic. Inflatable bouncy houses with safety sides and a few mesh 'windows' can be much hotter than the air outside.

Doctors say no kid under 6 should be on bouncy stuff. Always an adult watching. One kid on at a time. No kids of mismatched sizes and weights at the same time. No flips, tumbling, wrestling, hitting, eating, sleeping . . . oh, you get the picture. And get all kids off it, quick, if it starts to lose air pressure.

ye olde bouncy castle

equipment beyond the basics

You might want one of these.

⭐ A portable or folding cot for guests or travelling: for babies to be as safe away as they are at home, these need to be absolutely bang-up to the latest safety standard, and the instructions must be strictly followed for their special assembly and use.

⭐ Stair guards and door 'gates': you can get expandable or swinging hinged safety standard barriers from baby shops.

The baby bag

You don't have to have a wildly flash, celebrity-endorsed designer bag. You need one that stuff can't fall out of – so it needs to zip up. Consider a backpack or courier-style cross-body bag with a long strap, so your hands are free. Say goodbye to the teensy clutch purse or the lone wallet for several years, unless you're happy to gaffer tape them to your head.

What to put in the baby or toddler bag

⭐ nappies
⭐ bottles
⭐ wet wipes
⭐ spare baby clothes
⭐ plastic bags
⭐ sunscreen and hats
⭐ antiseptic no-rinse handwash
⭐ bandaids
⭐ the kitchen sink
⭐ a wad of cash
⭐ a bar of chocolate
⭐ a small inflatable craft of some description
⭐ a spare pantsuit made from caravan upholstery
⭐ a spare teddy

32

safety
& INJURIES

As I said in *Up the Duff*, my book on pregnancy,
the only way to childproof a house is to never
let a kid into it. But you can make it much safer.
And you can avoid lots of common dangers if
you know about them. Here's the lowdown.

When to call an ambulance with an injury

Call an ambulance on 000 (or 111 in New Zealand) if your child has:

* been unconscious or is unconscious
* a convulsion (a fit)
* stopped breathing and needed or needs resuscitation
* a suspected injured neck or back (don't move the patient)
* a suspected broken bone – support it with your arm and hand or a pillow and keep the kid still until the ambulance arrives
* a serious head injury
* had an electric shock
* a burn bigger than the palm size of the baby or toddler, or one that's on the face, inside the throat, or on the hand or genitals
* anaphylactic allergic shock – a rapidly spreading red rash and swelling that affects breathing; this is very rare and usually triggered by an insect sting, a drug or a food
* gone blue around the lips (it means they're deprived of oxygen) – the 'blueness' can be less obvious in a kid who has dark skin, but look for a difference in their gums, and around the lips, eyes and fingernails
* been sleepier than normal afterwards
* difficulty breathing after an injury, fall or knock.

When to go to the doctor with an injury

See a doctor straight away if your child has:

* concussion – signs and symptoms following a knock or injury include vomiting, confusion or memory loss, headaches, floppiness, tiredness and difficulty concentrating
* a severe cut or a deep wound
* something inserted into an eye, ear, nose or other body opening
* a burn (any burn on a baby, or any burn larger than a pea on a toddler or preschooler) – burns can take a few days to fully develop, so it's always worthwhile having them checked.

first aid

You should take a first-aid course so you know how to:

* ⭐ perform CPR (cardiopulmonary resuscitation)
* ⭐ treat a broken bone until you get to a doctor or the ambulance comes
* ⭐ get a child away from an electrical charge without being injured or knocked out yourself
* ⭐ help a person on fire to stop, drop and roll
* ⭐ recognise when you can move an injured child and when you shouldn't
* ⭐ stop bleeding by applying pressure until help arrives.

～～～～～～ more info on first aid ～～～～～

redcross.org.au/first-aid
stjohn.org.au/first-aid-training
Doctors say parents should do a first-aid course and/or a paediatric first-aid course.

kidshealth.schn.health.nsw.gov.au
Click on 'Child health and safety', then choose 'CPR' on the drop-down menu for an online course on this Children's Hospital at Westmead Kids Health site.

raisingchildren.net.au
For info and fact sheets, on the home page search 'CPR' and 'first aid'.

first-aid kit

Keep a first-aid kit anywhere the child often goes – home, car, grandparents' house – and always out of their reach. Safety experts say you should store your home first-aid kit 1.5 metres off the ground in a locked cupboard, but I don't know anyone who has such a thing. Just be as safe as you can – perhaps a plastic toolbox on top of a high cupboard with a child lock on it (child locks are available at hardware and baby shops).

The best remedies for minor accidents are antiseptic cream and perhaps an adhesive strip (for small cuts and very small burns), icepacks (for small bumps and bruises), sympathy and kissing it better.

A home first-aid kit should include the following items.

⭐ Painkiller: baby and kid versions of paracetamol and ibuprofen can be taken at different ages – check with your doctor about which to get, and see 'Painkillers for babies & kids' in Chapter 33, Health.

⭐ A tiny cup, dropper and/or no-needle syringe with measurements, for giving medicine.

⭐ Cottonwool balls or the less wispy gauze squares – good for cleaning cuts or infected skin.

⭐ Antiseptic cream or liquid – lightly apply it to a cleaned cut or sore.

⭐ Sticking plasters for minor cuts and sores. (I can't say B*nd%#d because it's a brand name, but if you know anybody who says 'sticking plasters' you are in the Royal Family.)

⭐ Sterile gauze dressings – these are useful for larger cuts and sore areas.

⭐ Bandages.

⭐ Waterproof tape, to keep on bandages or eye patches.

⭐ Thermometer (optional) – ask your pharmacist or doctor which sort to get for a baby or toddler.

⭐ Little squeezy pouches of saline solution – these are useful for washing eyes or getting something out of an eye.

⭐ A 'drawing' ointment for coaxing out splinters or glass – ask your pharmacist.

Fundraising organisations that sell first-aid kits include the Red Cross (**redcross.org.au**), St John Ambulance (**stjohn.org.au**) and the Royal Life Saving Society (**royallifesaving.com.au**).

First-aid kit surprise

A good thing to have in your first-aid kit is something to distract kids. We used lollipops (I think one was in there for three years). Otherwise, stickers you can put on their skin or some other safe novelty distraction can be excellent when you're doing something with antiseptic that makes a kid want to yell the house down.

'kidproofing' your house

Most safety stuff is available at the hardware or baby-gear shop. You'll need:

- ⭐ A tested, working smoke alarm in all bedrooms, all living rooms and the kitchen. If yours aren't electric, change the batteries once a year. Some do this every summer daylight-saving switch; others put a calendar reminder in for every 1 April.
- ⭐ A fuse box fitted with a safety switch that turns off the power if someone is getting an electric shock.
- ⭐ Power-point covers so a baby can't stick a fork in one.
- ⭐ A fire extinguisher and a fire blanket in the kitchen (say the firies).
- ⭐ A poisons/medication cabinet or first-aid kit that can be locked or placed up high, inaccessible to a climbing toddler.

Common dangers for kids

Injury is the biggest cause of death in kids now that we've got a good immunisation program and much better medical management of illness and conditions. Because of safety regulations and awareness, the rate of injuries is less than in the past, too.

The more mobile a baby gets, the more dangerous the house becomes. So while your baby stays put when you wrap them up like a parcel, it's a good time to make the house safer. Babies and toddlers reach development 'milestones' at different times: yours could be an early 'roller' or 'climber'. Or a great 'escaper'. These days, common dangers to kids include poisonings, car and pedestrian accidents, drowning, choking, suffocation, burns and electrical accidents.

Also check out Chapter 31, Kid Equipment, on what to buy that's safe, and 'More info on first aid' earlier in this chapter.

Kidproofing checklist

Tour your own house with new, paranoid-parent eyes. Are there drycleaning bags hanging over clothes? Stairs with no risers, or nothing to stop a baby hurtling through the bannisters? A dodgy fireguard that could be squeezed around? A hair dryer near a sink filled with water? Ceremonial sword? Rocket launcher? A maniac in the woodshed?

This checklist is essential for your house, and also useful for places that your kid might visit as a baby or toddler, such as relatives' and friends' houses.

⭐ Reorganise cupboards so that the following are on higher ground, safely out of reach or in a cupboard with a child lock: poisons; cleaning products, including dishwasher powder or tablets; washing-machine powder or pouches; vitamins (can be toxic to children); alcohol; cigarettes; matches and lighters; prescription medications; illegal drugs; all batteries; pesticides; plastic bags; mothballs and camphor; soaps and shampoos; cosmetics; essential oils; and sharp things such as needles and scissors.

⭐ Put safety locks on all drawers and cupboards that kids can reach.

⭐ Set your hot-water thermostat at 50 degrees Celsius or lower, to reduce the chance of a burn. All hot-water taps should be inaccessible to children.

⭐ Suffocation hazards: lose the habit of storing plastic bags in a kitchen cupboard or drawer: tie tight knots in all plastic bags and store them high up, if at all. Lock and/or get rid of old fridges, trunks and other suffocation hazards, especially in garages and sheds.

⭐ Remove any pull-cords on curtains or blinds and make inaccessible any string-like decorations such as bunting and Christmas lights.

⭐ Put guards or other barriers on beds, bunks, ladders, balconies, stairs and all upstairs windows (flyscreens are not strong enough to stop a kid falling out of a window). Kids under 2 are most at risk from head injuries.

⭐ Anchor TVs, chests of drawers and other furniture and fixtures to the wall.

⭐ Keep out of reach all charging stations and remote controls and other things with batteries (see 'Button batteries' coming up).

⭐ Banish fridge magnets, or use the large floppy kind without an inserted or detachable magnet (see 'Magnets' coming up).

⭐ Remove from upstairs balconies and verandahs any chairs, tables and other items that can be climbed on, and/or keep doors to upstairs outdoor areas locked, with the key kept somewhere inaccessible.

⭐ Remove heavy pot plants. Toddlers and preschoolers can topple them accidentally, or on purpose.

⭐ Get rid of rugs or install non-slip pads on the rugs' edges, and use rubber non-slip mats in the bath and next to the bath and shower.

⭐ Consider plastic 'covers' for coffee and other table corners.

⭐ Check that windows and doors are fitted with 'safety glass', which breaks into non-cutting pebbles, or are covered with an invisible film that holds shards. Most landlords are required to do this.

⭐ Put stickers at toddler height on windows and clear-glass doors so kids don't bump into them.

~~~~~~ **more info** on a home safety checklist ~~~~~~

kidsafe.com.au
Search 'safety list' on this non-profit site for its list of dangers.

safekids.org.nz
New Zealand's national child injury prevention service has fact sheets on everything from dog-bite prevention to sun-care advice.

Toys

Most toys sold here are labelled with an international safety standard (ISO) that our government accepts. But many toys slip through without being inspected for safety standard compliance (especially in 'cheap' import shops). Some toys safe for older kids are dangerous for smaller children. Check toys for loose or missing bits, and damage, every few weeks. See 'Dangerous toys & equipment' in Chapter 31, Kid Equipment, for more on recalls and safety standards.

Headphones

Personal devices can be great for older kids to listen to books or music, but anything with 'strings' – wires – is a strangling hazard for toddlers and babies, and accidental high volume can damage hearing. Babies and toddlers must not use headphones or earplugs. Some people take babies and toddlers wearing wireless special-purpose big industrial noise-protection earmuffs to concerts and car racetracks, but those aren't usually good environments for kids anyway.

Button batteries

All batteries are swallowing and choking hazards, but button batteries are a special, deadly danger. These small, coin-like lithium batteries contain electrical currents that burn body tissue. Their corrosion can cause catastrophic permanent injuries. It can be very hard for doctors to diagnose this (it can cause coughs, vomiting or no visible symptoms, and sometimes doesn't cause significant pain as the damage is being done).

Babies and kids have found batteries in toys; games; remote control devices (for the TV, automatic window blinds, air conditioner, car, roller door); hearing aids; kitchen and bathroom scales; kitchen timers; cameras; wireless lights, including torches; flameless candles; thermometers; calculators; watches; musical birthday cards (dispose of them immediately after opening them and listening together, and don't display them); and gift, novelty, party or promotional items that lightup. Also beware of open or accessible packets of spare batteries, new packets of batteries in shops and supermarkets, and 'old' batteries not disposed of.

Toys that conform to regulations should have batteries in a screw-down compartment – but not all toys conform. Safety experts suggest parents keep in mind that lithium batteries are as dangerous as guns and pools. If you know or suspect your child has swallowed a battery, don't try to make them vomit, and don't give them anything to eat or drink: take them to the emergency room, and tell the staff your suspicions. If possible, take the packet of batteries with you as the serial number on the packaging will help medical staff identify the battery.

~~~~~~ more info on button battery dangers ~~~~~

thebatterycontrolled.com.au
Safety site with info on how to store, use and dispose of batteries, supported by an alliance of battery manufacturers, Kidsafe and the Australian Competition and Consumer Commission.

batteryrecycling.org.au
Find out how you can safely dispose of batteries near you.

Magnets

Magnets can be dangerous for kids to swallow, especially if they swallow two, or if they swallow a magnet and a piece of metal, which can then trap pieces of the bowel between them, causing small rips. Kids can find magnets in fridge magnets; 'easy-closing' phone covers and cupboard doors; 'executive' toys; construction toys and home ornaments with high-powered magnetic silver balls and 'rare-earth' magnets; audio equipment; headphones; fishing reels; novelty lights; torches; toys; and electric-guitar pick-ups.

kids & cars

Kids as pedestrians

Based on accident records, road safety authorities say that kids up to the age of about 10 to 12 should be supervised when crossing roads. Until then they don't have the brain connections and memory development to follow road rules at all times. This is impractical for some kids who walk to school, so serious road safety drills are important. I once observed a school crossing without a guard for several days, to gather data to request one. There was lots of rule ignoring, and attention problems with some kids. Hold the hand of any kid under 7 to prevent unscheduled stops, wandering or dashes; holding the hand of older kids is okay, too.

Hold hands with or closely herd a kid across a road – never 'lead'. You can't see what a kid behind you is doing on a crossing. Sometimes they stop or wander off course. I've seen a small child sit down in front of a car at a crossing while their parent strode on, talking on the phone, and the light changed. The kid was too low for drivers to see but other pedestrians saved the day. The parent was still oblivious.

If your kid's on a bike or scooter, keep your hand on the helmet or handlebars all the way across so you know where they are.

Kids see marked 'crossings' and 'lights' as safe, and often don't check to see whether lights have changed, or if cars are slowing or have stopped.

The freezing game

You can teach a fun safety trick to your toddler as soon as they're old enough to 'stop' or 'freeze'. It's basically the same as the old party game called 'statues' where you freeze when the music stops. With the safety version you say 'FREEZE!' at unexpected moments (you can stop in a curious pose, too, as part of the fun), and then after a few moments release them with 'and, go again'.

Then, if your child is running or moving somewhere dangerous, such as into the path of a car, or going towards an unfamiliar, snarling dog, you can say 'FREEZE!' and they will automatically stop – perhaps just long enough for you to grab them out of the way. It's especially good when you can see a car reversing down a driveway towards the footpath – the driver can probably see you but not the shorter toddler.

Kids in hot cars

Don't leave a baby or a kid in the car. Ever. More than 5000 kids a year are rescued by cops or passers-by after being left in cars. Each year, children die because they got too hot in a car. Ambulance services are called to thousands more who have been left in cars, or locked themselves in the car with the keys. It doesn't matter if you are going to be quick, they're asleep, the air conditioning is on, or the keys are in the car. Cars have been stolen with babies and children in the back seat.

It can be 20 to 40 degrees hotter in a closed car than the temperature outside, which means on a typical summer day it could reach 50 degrees in your car in less than five minutes and 70 degrees within ten minutes. Three-quarters of the possible temperature rise happens within the first five minutes after the car door is closed. Having a light-coloured car doesn't make much difference. Cracking the window open does not drop the temperature enough. The smaller the baby, the quicker they become overheated and dehydrated.

If you see a child locked in a car, call 000. Follow the dispatcher's instructions. If they tell you to break a window, break one away from the child. This won't be easy. Modern car windows are resistant to rubber mallets and shoes. Look for a pointed object – the metal spikes on a car front-seat head rest, a screwdriver, a small metal hammer – and aim for a corner of a window: it's the weakest point. Avoid the centre of a window, the strongest bit.

Every year some kids die because they are left in a car all day by accident by a tired or distracted parent, who usually forgot that they didn't drop a kid at childcare. The toddler falls asleep, and the parent drives to work and parks somewhere that nobody notices there's a child in the back seat. This is especially a risk when the usual daily routine is broken. One suggestion to avoid this is to always put your wallet, handbag and home or work keys on the back seat, so you always have to look into the back seat before you leave the car.

kids in the kitchen

Once your wee cherub is toddling, and ready to 'help' you to cook and wash up, make some new rules for the kitchen: never let your kid play with something that could be dangerous at another time.

Teach kids from the earliest age that stovetops and oven fronts can be hot and microwaves can have hot things in them. Small children have seen you touch a cold oven door or clean the hotplates. They also probably won't make the connection that somebody else's stove or oven might be hot.

Some parents have a rule for kids: hands behind your back when looking at the hotplates or through the glass door of the oven, or when a cake mixer is going, for example. Balance the specific taboos with lots of things they *can* touch, pour, stir and measure. Don't deep-fry anything in hot oil until your youngest child is 32. Chips can be done in the oven on trays brushed with oil.

Also: no running in the kitchen! Keep urns, kettles and coffee machines well out of reach. And make sure there are no dangling electric cords. Most children's scalds are from hot liquids such as tea, instant noodles, soup, coffee and water, and are usually on the hands, or on the face and chest when they pull a mug, bowl or container down on themselves. Many microwaves have very tempting button-opening functions that toddlers would love to have a go at. Crawlers and toddlers are at special risk.

Ditch placemats, coasters and tablecloths, which are all easily slid by kids towards themselves, bringing something hot along. Grandparents tend to have a spectacular amount of tabletop folderol, so ask them nicely to pop it away during visits.

Sitting in a highchair is a good spot for an older baby or toddler who is 'helping' by mashing or cutting something up for you to put in the cooking. Or if your older kid is up to it they can stand on a solid chair to reach the bench.

Stovetop

If you only have one or two things on the stove, use just the rear burners. Always turn saucepan and frying-pan handles away from the front of the stove so they can't be grabbed or knocked. Check out safety guards for stovetops, which prevent toddlers from pulling things down on themselves.

If you're cooking on the stovetop and have to leave the kitchen, turn off the hot-plate. It's better to be delayed than on fire. (What a splendid motto.)

Ovens & microwaves

A microwave oven will heat random bits of the food to scalding temperature yet often leave the container cool to the touch, so anything cooked or warmed in a microwave must be thoroughly stirred, rested, cooled and tested before being given to children. Don't put glass bottles in a microwave: they can break. Some microwave ovens heat more strongly and more quickly than others, so be careful with unfamiliar ones.

If your ordinary oven is close to the ground and hot to the touch when it's on, try to rig up some sort of barrier, such as a bit of a playpen, so that the oven or whole kitchen is out of bounds.

With food cooked in either kind of oven, be careful when taking lids off as steam can burn severely.

~~~~~~ **more info** on home safety ~~~~~~

kidsafe.com.au
Kidsafe (the Child Accident Prevention Foundation of Australia) provides advice and fact sheets on how to minimise dangers. It runs seminars on home, pool and farm safety and has lists of home safety hints for babies under 1 and toddlers.

safekids.org.nz
The New Zealand national child safety program has fact sheets, checklists and guidelines.

burns & scalds

If your child is scalded (with steam or hot water) or otherwise burned, call an ambulance if the child is a baby, or if the burn is larger than the toddler's palm size (Australia 000, NZ 111).

Follow the instructions given to you over the phone while you wait for paramedics to arrive.

Otherwise, quickly and calmly:

1   If there's a scald, whip off any wet clothing on or near the burn (the liquid can continue to burn), unless the material is sticking to skin.

2   Do not use ice, iced water, butter, lotions or ointments, or a covering of any kind. Those things will make the burn worse. Use the nearest cold tap to keep running water going over the burn for at least twenty minutes or until the ambulance arrives. If you are on tank water or can't run the tap for this long and the burnis on the arm or leg, fill the bath or sink and immerse the burned area in the water. Replace the water if it heats up. This will help alleviate pain and stop the area burning deeper. It's important to keep the rest of the child warm. Give the child a painkiller.

3   You need to call an ambulance if:
   ★ the burn is on a baby
   ★ the burn area is bigger than the child's palm
   ★ a serious burn is on the face or head
   ★ the burn area is whitish and not hurting (signs of a deeper, damaging burn)
   ★ the child is very quiet despite a bad burn
   ★ the burn was caused over some time (for example, a hand on a heater wasn't taken away immediately).

   Most burns in kids need to be seen by your doctor the same day: tell the office staff when you ring why the appointment is urgent.

4   After twenty minutes of cooling the burn with water, if you have to transport the child, cover the area with a clean, wet cotton pillowcase or tea towel (no towelling fabric). You can also use cling wrap.

5   Take the child to hospital or your nearest doctor. You'll need medical advice for anything more than a very small scald. All burns to a baby must be seen by a doctor as soon as possible.

Going hot & cold

Neither hot nor cold packs are a good idea for bubs because babies can't tell you whether they're too hot or too cold, and any bump or bruise on a bub needs to be checked by a doctor straight away.

Icepacks from the freezer shouldn't be applied for longer than ten minutes to a toddler who's had a bump, and should always be well wrapped in a tea towel or other fabric before being applied.

A wheat bag or a 'hot' water bottle can be useful as a comfort, and to ease the pain in a tummy or a sore ear; it's more of a comforting prop than a remedy. To avoid burns, the bag or bottle must be heated only to slightly warm, never hot, whether you're using a microwaved wheat bag or hot water. All hot water bottles are subject to splits and leaks without warning. Wheat bags should be regularly inspected for holes; and to prevent grains from leaking out and being swallowed, they should be covered twice (that is, securely sewn into another cover made from sturdy fabric – a good job for a home-sewing fiend, I mean friend).

Some wheat bags have caught fire or caused burns. Don't buy a homemade wheat bag. Buy one with heating instructions from a proper shop, and follow the instructions. 'Hotspots' inside a heated bag can smoulder and burst into flame, especially if the bag is put under blankets or clothes. Allow two hours between each time you heat a wheat bag in a microwave. If the bag smells charred or burnt, let it cool completely on a bench, then throw it away.

wheat bag

CPR

CPR stands for cardio-pulmonary resuscitation – also known as 'mouth-to-mouth' or 'rescue breaths' and chest compressions.

choking

First aid for choking is difficult because it's so frightening for everyone, and because there are different recommendations depending on whether the obstruction is mild or severe, whether the kid is able to cough up the obstruction, and whether they are conscious or unconscious.

If the kid is unconscious, send for help and start CPR. Follow the instructions the ambulance service gives you over the phone until the paramedics arrive.

If the kid is conscious but unable to cough up the obstruction, put the kid over an adult's knee with their head lower than feet, and give five hefty whacks in the middle of the back between the shoulder blades. If that doesn't dislodge the object, alternate five back whacks with five pushes on the chest, a bit like CPR but very firm, and quicker.

Choking risks include things that are swallowed or inhaled – which can include almost anything (see 'Choking hazards' on the opposite page).

more info on how to do CPR

www.healthdirect.gov.au/how-to-perform-cpr
Different instructions for doing CPR on adults and children and on babies up to 1 year old.

raisingchildren.net.au
Search 'CPR' for instruction sheets on babies and children.

Choking hazards

Choking hazards can include beach shells, coins, sewing bits and bobs, button batteries (which can also cause death and injury in other ways: see 'Button batteries' earlier in this chapter), marbles and rocks used as decorative garden or pot-plant surfaces, earplugs, hairpins and hair decorations, jewellery, bread tag-ties, bits of balloon, small balls, buttons, little bits that come off toys or teddy bears, and lots of food.

See the various types of food choking hazards for babies and toddlers in Chapter 14, First Food, and Chapter 19, Toddler Food – they can be hard or soft lollies, raw apples, meat, nuts, bits of carrot, uncooked peas, uncut grapes, fruit pips and pits, hot dogs and sausage meat, strips of bacon, marshmallows and popcorn. (All of these things can also be pushed up a kid's nose or into an ear, while they're experimenting.)

more info on choking hazards

productsafety.gov.au
On the home page of this government site search 'choke check' to download a rectangle shape to print, cut out, roll and sticky-tape so you've made a cylinder. Anything that fits into the cylinder is a choking hazard (it's very roughly the width of a cylindrical nail-polish bottle and about as tall as your little finger).

raisingchildren.net.au
Search 'choking first aid' or 'how to stop choking' on this government-approved site for a downloadable fact sheet of illustrated choking first-aid instructions.

kids & water

Toddlers and older boys are statistically the most at risk of drowning in their own or a relative's pool – but it takes only seconds for any kid to drown, or to develop permanent brain damage from near-drowning. For every drowning there are lots of drowning 'injuries'. All it takes is a couple of minutes to lose consciousness, and the next stage is brain damage or death. For every drowning there are many more 'miraculous survivals' or 'successful CPR' that result in permanent brain damage or disability.

Drowning danger areas include home pools, the beach, public pools, baths, ponds, dams, spa baths, wading pools, pop-up pools, paddling pools, inflatable pools, clamshell sandpit shapes, buckets, tanks, water features, pump systems, toilets and recurrent puddles. Kids can drown in a couple of centimetres of water. More people drown at beaches, rivers and creeks than in swimming pools, but small kids are more likely to drown in home pools or a bath.

All swimming-pool fences in Australia must comply with an Australian safety standard that includes mandatory measurements and a required form of lock. A pool needs an approved fence, with a self-latching, self-locking gate – the same goes for anywhere else you visit with a pool or pond. Many people who think their pool fence meets the current standard are wrong. A local council will come for free to inspect a fence and gates and give an assessment.

Kids almost never cry out and often don't make a splash when they crawl, slide, climb or fall into water or they begin to drown at the beach or in a pool. They don't call for help. They usually sink out of sight. An adult should always be at arm's length from a toddler in the water with their eyes 'on' the child. One-on-one swim instructors aren't just being encouraging when they walk the length of the pool next to a kid with a kickboard: they're also ready to jump in.

I've seen a few incidents that could have resulted in drowning: in one, a kid sank from sight in a hotel pool while her babysitter chatted to another adult; in another a preschooler crawled into a backyard pool without a sound; and I was rescued as a small child from the deep end of a pool, where I was sitting on the bottom happily looking up. I was supposed to hold onto the edge but I forgot. I could swim. I just didn't.

It's important that kids learn to swim, but no child or adult is drown-proof, no matter their experience and capabilities.

All children in a pool or at the beach should be supervised individually with 'eyes on' by an adult, not an older sibling. The supervisor should be at arm's length or firmly holding, especially in waves at ocean beaches.

In a pool, keep kids under 5 no further than an arm's length away from you, and lock your eyes on kids under 12. Don't rely on lifesavers or pool attendants. They have to watch a lot of people in changing conditions: you have the responsibility for your kid. One of the medical consultants for this book told me that a paediatrician she knows religiously made his kids (even as teenagers) get out of the pool area if he had to leave to answer the phone or go to the front door.

Don't assume that other people have made an environment safe. Often there are no fences and gates around private ponds, dams, river bridges and paths. Keep hold of your kid's hand in places like this. Think about the set-up where your kid might visit or stay with relatives. Older children and adults can leave doors and gates open no matter how many times they're reminded.

If you have a children's party at your home with a pool, make access to the pool impossible, and station an adult who knows CPR to watch the pool at all times. If kids are in the pool as part of the party, you will need multiple supervisors at all times.

more info on water safety

royallifesaving.com.au
The Royal Life Saving Society does more than train beach and pool patrols. The website has fact sheets and info on swimming and resuscitation lessons, children's pool party rules, pool area safety checklists and more. Choose 'Families' to start.

homepoolsafety.com.au
Info on why you can't assume your pool fence and gate are safe, a safety checklist for inspecting pool areas, fact sheets on resuscitation and supervision, and safety pointers for dams, boats, rivers and public pools. Also info on swimming and lifeguard skills and lessons. Another Royal Life Saving Society site.

swimaustralia.org.au
A non-profit organisation of swimming coaches and teachers that accredits swimming teachers and schools nationwide. From the main page choose 'Development', then 'Parents'.

kids & poisons

Make sure any medication is kept up high or in childproof containers in your handbag. This goes for relatives' homes and places your kid regularly visits, too.

Other common poison risks for kids include essential oils; cleaning products; dishwashing and laundry detergent powder, pods and pellets; cosmetics including perfume and acetone; garden and garage chemicals; and poisonous flowers, berries, leaves or mushrooms.

An expert is on call 24 hours a day, every day of the year at the Poisons Information Centre (number below). Put the centre's number in your phone and on the wall or fridge with your other emergency numbers, and call immediately if you think your child has swallowed something poisonous. If your child has swallowed medicine, a chemical or something else packaged, have the packaging with you so that you can identify any details needed. Don't try to make your kid vomit unless advised by the Poisons Information Centre or an ambulance dispatcher.

~~~~~~~~~~~~~~ more info on poisons ~~~~~~~~~~~~~~

Australian Poisons Information Centre Emergency Hotline: 13 11 26 (24 hours)

0800 764 766 (0800 POISON)
poisons.co.nz
New Zealand National Poisons Centre.

rch.org.au
On the home page of the Royal Children's Hospital in Melbourne website, choose 'Children's Health Information', then 'Kids Health Info'. Choose 'P' from the A–Z list then 'Poisoning Prevention for Children'.

Slides

Don't go down playground slides with your baby or toddler on your lap.
Adult weight + kid on slide = most common case of toddler broken legs, and ankles.

farm & rural safety

I can't believe I need to say this, but no baby, toddler or other child should be allowed as a passenger on a quad bike or motorbike on a public road or any place anywhere ever, including a farm. Quad bikes are the leading cause of injury and death of kids on farms despite it being illegal for a kid under 16 to be on one, even as a passenger. Farms also have extra dangers, including heavy equipment, pesticides, animals, electric and barbed wire fences, and dams. It's better to corral the kids in a playpen or fenced garden area with shade than to take on the impossible task of fencing off everything else.

more info on farm safety

farmsafe.org.au
Choose 'Children on farms' on the not-for-profit Farmsafe Australia site.

Shoosh about the placebo effect

A friend used to tell her sick or slightly injured child she needed a 'placebo'. This totally backfired when some idiot busybody told the child the truth: a placebo meant it didn't work. So don't actually say 'placebo', but remember all the non-medical tools for your first-aid kit: 'kissing it better'; a strategic Bandaid for show; a sticker reward for being brave; a similar treatment on a teddy; a distracting new book or an old favourite; a special song or chant you do after a bump or bruise ('Bruise, bruise go away, don't come back another day'); the special dressing gown and slippers on – whatever it takes to convey sympathy and useful ritual. This is basically what homeopathy is – but cheaper.

animals & kid safety

The list of unsuitable pets for health, safety or conservation reasons is quite long and includes poisonous or venomous creatures; anything with large jaws and a genetic history of instability, guarding or attacking (that is, many breeds of dog); native or other usually wild animals; and fragile or prey animals that are easily harmed or frightened. Also elephants. And Crazy Ants. And honey badgers.

Toddlers and small children specifically shouldn't have pets that have anxious personalities, or species that might carry salmonella, such as reptiles: kids will touch them, then put fingers in their mouths no matter what, and rodents will bite. Don't rely on a pet shop or private breeder to fully inform you of risks.

All children should be taught not to pat animals they are not familiar with, and not to approach or touch wild animals or animals in zoos. 'Petting zoos' are another matter and up to you, but they are not 'no-risk'.

Model kind and gentle behaviour with animals to show your child how to behave. A riled pet or other animal is much more likely to attack. Some kids are wary around 'strange' animals – that's a good thing. Never take a pet owner's word for: 'Oh, he never bites' or 'She's harmless'. Stop your child from patting a strange animal until your own observations about likely safety are satisfied. If a person takes your child's hand and moves it towards their dog (I'm amazed how many dog owners do this), stop them, physically if necessary. Feel free to say firmly, 'We're teaching Hezekiah not to touch new animals unless we do it in a certain way. I'm sure you understand.' If you want your kid to pat a dog safely, follow the suggestions below. And teach your kid that hands must be washed with soap after touching an animal and before eating.

Dogs

This is shocking, but hundreds of children under the age of 5 are treated every year in Australian hospitals for serious injuries caused by dog bites and attacks, and some children die as a result. Most dog bites happen in private homes or backyards. More common biters are German shepherds, rottweilers, blue heelers, Dobermans, bull terriers and kelpies, but any dogs – even small dogs and lifelong docile dogs – can and do bite or attack. The assumed 'safe' breeds of labradors and golden retrievers feature high on the lists of dogs who have savaged or bitten a child, perhaps because of sustained provocation.

No dog and child should be left alone together. A dog has inbred responses: *all dogs will bite in some situations*, even dogs that have never bitten before. Even one bite can severely disfigure or damage a child. Putting a face near a dog is considered a challenge by most dogs. Standing up, a small child's face is right in the face of many dogs, especially when the child does things such as hug them. Most bites to kids under 5 are to the face, with hands and arms the next most likely. A bite or injury to a small child is more serious than one to an adult and more likely to need hospitalisation.

Kids & dog safety rules

Start with telling your toddler the simplest info listed below and adjust as needed or as your child gets older. Tell your toddler:

⭐ Some dogs are friendly. Most dogs are friendly when they wag their tail but they might still bite if they get confused.

⭐ Never go near a dog you don't know.

⭐ Never touch or go near a dog that is eating or sleeping.

⭐ Sometimes when a dog looks like it is smiling, it is really cross. If you can see a dog's teeth and it is not wagging its tail, or it's growling, and its ears are flat down on its head, don't go near. Tell an adult.

⭐ You don't have to pat a dog because someone tells you to: it's okay to be scared and to stay away.

⭐ If an adult is with you and says it's okay, and you want to, slowly go nearer to the dog and stand still with your handheld out flat, palm down, for it to sniff.

⭐ Don't bend down and put your face right in front of the dog's face.

⭐ Pat a dog gently and calmly. Don't talk loudly or squeal or talk in an excited voice, or wriggle about when you're patting a dog. It can make them worried and confused and they might bite you.

⭐ Stand still if a dog approaches and don't look it in the eye or crouch down to its level.

⭐ Never touch dog (or any other animal) poo: it's yucky and has germs in it that can make you sick.

⭐ Always wash your hands after patting a dog.

No dog should be treated as 'part of the human family'. Dogs can't think or behave like humans. They are not 'fur babies'. When a human baby arrives in the family after the dog, the dog will consider the child lower in the pack hierarchy unless you teach it otherwise. This is a recipe for disaster, especially if the child is in the habit of wandering around with food, or gets between the dog and its food, or tries to take something from the dog such as a stick or a bone. Dogs who are allowed to sleep on a family member's bed will also see themselves as higher or equal in the pack.

Trainable animals such as dogs must be taught to recognise all members of the family as superior animals in the pack. If possible have the child first and get the dog as a puppy when your child is old enough to be a 'top dog'. A puppy can be 'socialised' to accept small children and other dogs. But regardless of training or temperament, dogs – and cats, and all other animals – should never be left alone with a child or baby.

Some dogs off leads will attack a child who is running or on a bicycle, or for no apparent reason. Some dogs, even accidentally, can knock down or badly frighten a child. If you take your child to areas where dogs are off the lead, you are relying on every dog being firmly under the voice control of their owner. Yeah, right. There's nothing like being jumped on by a pony-sized animal while an owner uselessly cries from the other side of an oval, 'Come here, Fluffy!'

∿∿∿∿ more info on dogs & kids ∿∿∿

Reputable dog training schools run special courses to help owners and dogs learn how to communicate and make sure who's boss.

rch.org.au/dogsandkids
This page on the Royal Children's Hospital site called 'Dogs and Kids' has lots of info on choosing the right pet, training, behaviour, and dog bites and attacks.

Cats & kids

Cat poo is a known cause of toxoplasmosis, which can cause damage to a foetus when it infects a pregnant woman. Pregnant women, or women who might be pregnant, should be gloved and meticulous when disposing of cat litter, should garden with gloves on, and should keep other people's cats away from their garden.

Children should avoid cat poo because even if the cat's healthy, it can carry diseases and parasites. As with dogs, kids need to be told they must wash their hands after they've touched a cat before eating.

Any cat will scratch and bite if it is under pressure from an unsupervised child.

A child may be born allergic to cats even though its parents are not. Test-run your kid with somebody else's cat before introducing a cat to your place. Be aware of other children with cat allergies if they're at your house.

Rabies & tetanus

If your child is bitten or scratched by a bat – or, overseas, a monkey or dog – immediately wash the wound with soap for five minutes, then douse with antiseptic liquid and get to a doctor. Rabies injections may be given, or a tetanus jab if the kid isn't immunised. Both rare conditions can be fatal.

BLAST FROM THE PAST
'Kissing dogs: it is frequent among children and not
unknown amongst ladies . . . the women may kiss and die . . .
a woman is violating her own fine sense of delicacy in kissing a dog . . .
It is disgusting, not to say something worse . . . and dangerous.'
– Editorial, *The Week*, Brisbane, 1891

33

HEALTH

Kids are supposed to get sick: it's how they build up their immune system. This chapter is about what to do with which kinds of illnesses, such as fever, gastro and other ordinary horrors. Injuries are in Chapter 32, Safety & Injuries; vaccinations and immunisation are in Chapter 34, Immunisation. Right. Latex gloves and shower cap on? Shall we begin?

When to call an ambulance with an illness

Ring the emergency number: 000 (in NZ, 111). Call an ambulance if your child:

* has a convulsion (a fit)
* has difficulty with or stops breathing
* can't be roused or seems severely floppy and miserable
* has fever, repeated vomiting, a stiff neck, a red or purple skin rash that doesn't disappear with gentle pressure on the skin, eyes that seem sensitive to light (these are some of the symptoms of meningococcal disease, which can cause meningitis, a brain inflammation). Some small babies may also have a slight swelling of the soft, top part of their head (fontanelle).

When to go to the doctor with an illness

* Your kid has had any contact with a serious disease that they haven't been fully immunised against yet.
* A fever is accompanied by worrying symptoms such as misery, listlessness, repeated vomiting or a nasty rash, a stiff neck, or struggling to breathe.
* You're worried your child is 'not themselves', too quiet, disinterested or 'floppy'.
* Your child develops wheezing when coughing or breathing.
* There's unexplained crying that isn't helped by the usual methods.
* A toddler keeps telling you something hurts even though they've had a dose of painkiller (see 'Painkillers for babies & kids' coming up.

When to go to a hospital emergency room

If you're very worried about your kid and can't go to your local doctor because it's late at night or the weekend, you may need to go to the emergency department at your nearest hospital (it used to be called 'casualty'). Hate to sound silly, but emergency departments really *are* only for emergencies. Cases are prioritised and you may have to wait many hours in a brightly lit area and then see an overworked doctor or nurse.

choosing a doctor

If you feel concerned about your bub, try to get them to a family doctor during the day. Kids tend to get sick quickly and get better quickly, but if they get worse overnight, your options are more limited for medical help. During your next routine visit, ask your doctor specifically what to do if you need a doctor after hours.

A good GP clinic will have a policy of seeing a baby or child on the day a parent calls. It doesn't matter if there's nothing wrong. It will help get your child used to going to the doctor, and let the doctor know what your kid looks like when they're not sick, which helps in future diagnoses – and a check-up never hurts.

You'll need to find a good local family doctor, usually called a GP (general practitioner). Ideally, choose a doctor who specialises in kids or lives in an area where there are lots of kids – they'll know what's 'going around' and have good contact with specialists. See Chapter 2, Your Help Team, for info on how to choose a GP. Feel free to try another doctor you might like better, or ask for a referral to a specialist. In a shared clinic, see if you can settle on one or two doctors that you like. Many doctors 'bulk bill' Medicare for kids.

If you're not happy with how a doctor speaks to you, or how they pay attention to your baby, go to another doctor – never feel you have to stick with one who doesn't 'feel right'. After all, you'd switch hairdressers if you weren't happy. Now, don't go and look in the mirror. You look fabulous.

'Out of hours' doctors

If at all possible, avoid these. There is a boom in private companies promoting after-hours visits. At the time of writing many of the visiting doctors are inexperienced juniors, GPs in training or doctors who haven't done the ten years' work in Australia needed to join the Royal Australian College of GPs.

'Acknowledge that it does hurt instead of jollying them out of it. Be truthful: "Oh, darling, I know it's really hurting a lot now, but it will start getting better and it will stop soon."' JILL

Nurse on call

The national Pregnancy, Birth and Baby helpline is a daily 24-hour service staffed by qualified midwives and specialist child & family health nurses for the Australian Health Department, on 1800 022 022.

health cover & paperwork

When you gave birth, you should have got a Parent Pack in hospital or from a midwife, with a form to add the baby to both parents' Medicare cards. This makes it easier for either parent to take the child to the doctor and claim the fee. It also means that either card can be used as a form of identification showing the relationship between adults and kids, even if the last names are different. You'll need more paperwork to sort this if you leave it until after your bub is 12 months old. If you have private health insurance, add your baby to that, too.

Ambulance membership

Different rules for ambulance membership apply in different states and territories – in some places it's free for anyone, or only free to people with a health care card or to people with private health insurance. Most private health insurance policies include ambulance membership at a discount for families. If you're not a member it may end up costing thousands of dollars. But call one if you need one – and if you have free ambulance cover, don't call one because you have hiccups. (That really happens.)

more info on medicare

humanservices.gov.au/individuals/medicare
Phone 13 20 11 (24-hour)
The Medicare website and helpline. To find your nearest Medicare service centre, go to findus.**humanservices.gov.au**.

Keeping health records

You might have health info contained in an app (check privacy protection) or on your computer – details about allergies and medicines, appointment reminders, contact numbers for clinics, and pathology results. Make sure it's backed up elsewhere, and/or in 'hard copy' somewhere, in readiness for that time your toddler throws your device down the loo. Doctors can check immunisation records on a national database.

when kids get sick

It's normal for kids to get sick. When a kid gets sick, their immune system works to develop antibodies to provide future protection if that bug arrives again. Kids getting sick is the body doing its job, and building an immune system. When your kid starts day care, or other childcare with more kids, or spends time with cousins or friends' kids on holidays, they will suddenly seem to be getting nearly everything 'going around'. That's because they are. That's why immunisation – vaccinations – is so brilliant. It's a controlled, medical way for your kid's body to recognise a serious, potentially deadly illness and be ready for it, without actually getting the disease. It saves thousands of lives every year. (Chapter 34, Immunisation, covers all that palaver.)

If your kid has a chronic or very serious illness, make sure you get all the medical help you can, and insist on seeing a specialist with the widest possible experience in the area, usually at your nearest major children's hospital. Inquire about any and all services available to you, from accommodation for country visitors to support groups, tax breaks and equipment sharing. Start with your family doctor.

The immune system

The immune system recognises and repels many viruses and bacteria you've had before, preventing you from getting sick again. Having an immune system in good shape helps kids recover more quickly.

Good immune system boosters:

* immunisation
* coming into contact with germs
* breastfeeding
* fresh air and exercise
* enough protein and carbohydrates, fruit and veggies.

What causes illnesses?

Childhood illnesses are not caused by a low immune system, or not being breastfed, or not eating organic food. Childhood illnesses are generally caused by viruses and bacteria, both of which are germs. Viruses are 'bugs' that need to multiply to survive, so they reproduce themselves by being passed on to other people. Bacteria are little organisms that can live and grow independently (such as germs on a loo seat or in raw milk or chicken), with the side effect of infecting people.

When are illnesses contagious?

Illnesses are most contagious when the germs are multiplying the fastest. This often happens after you 'catch a bug' but before any symptoms, and in the first few days of symptoms. Sneezing and diarrhoea are excellent ways of spreading the germs, so while these symptoms continue the bug is probably still contagious. It usually takes three to five days after you receive cold germs for you to show symptoms. It depends on what virus it is. When people say 'It's not contagious any more', they're often just guessing.

Quarantine times

How long should you keep a sick kid isolated to avoid 'passing on' whatever illness they have at childcare or a friend's house? If your kid is unvaccinated and has a suspected infectious disease usually protected by immunisation, such as whooping cough or measles, call your doctor's office to ask for advice. Don't run the risk of infecting other kids in the waiting room. A kid with a fever or a cold doesn't have to be isolated from other kids, but if they feel miserable home's probably the best place to be.

There are various recommended quarantine times to keep a kid home. Here are some:

* Diarrhoea, gastro and worms – 24 hours after last diarrhoea-y poo and vomit.
* Doctor-diagnosed flu – until all symptoms are gone and the kid is well again.
* Conjunctivitis (eye infection) – until yucky stuff has stopped coming out.
* Impetigo ('school sores') – until after the first 24 hours on antibiotics, if all sores are covered with watertight dressings.
* Hand, foot and mouth blisters – until old blisters are dried up and there are no new ones.

Experts and instincts

You're the expert on your kid. You know your child best, so take your own uneasy feelings seriously. All parents have these: some call them 'instincts' and act on them, others mistrust them and are unsure whether they're worrying unnecessarily – but they're the same feelings. The only way to check them out is to take your child to a doctor. Even if nothing is revealed, keep on trusting your instincts.

Sometimes the only symptoms of a kid's illness are listlessness, whingeing and a pressing need to be right next to mum or dad, or at least in the same room. Kids under 5 are not likely to fake being sick unless it's learnt behaviour (they can often suddenly say they have a sore back if you have one, for example, or might talk about a hurty or squirgly tummy when they mean that they're anxious).

～～～～ more info on kids & illnesses ～～～

rch.org.au/kidsinfo
kidshealth.schn.health.nsw.gov.au
The Sydney and Melbourne children's hospitals both have fact sheets and info for parents.

raisingchildren.net.au
Search this trusted site for 'baby health doctors and medicines', 'baby toddler health: what to expect', 'going to hospital' and other relevant keywords.

healthdirect.gov.au
Click on 'Health topics A–Z' for lists of conditions on this government-run site, or you can search via condition or symptom.

cyh.com
Choose 'Parenting and Child Health', then 'Illnesses & Health Problems', or a topic from the alphabetical list, on this South Australian government health site.

Dr Dog
by Babette Cole (Random House, UK)
Oh, what a disgusting family Dr Dog has to treat – farting fun and all.

Peppa Goes to Hospital
(Ladybird, UK)
A board book about Peppa Pig to help prepare your littlie for the experience of going to hospital.

Using 'common sense' with kid health

What one person thinks is 'common sense' could be outdated, or based on anxiety. It might be 'conventional wisdom' that's wrong.

Sometimes, the right thing to do is counterintuitive. When something hurts, for example, it feels like it should be warmed – but an icepack on a bruise will stop it getting worse. People worried about food allergies might ban foods that the child's immune system needs to recognise so they *don't* get an allergy.

It might seem like 'common sense' to give a child raw milk because it's 'natural' if you don't know that thousands of kids used to die every year because of pathogens in raw milk, before pasteurisation became law. It might seem like 'common sense' not to inject stuff into a healthy kid – until you know immunisation is safe, and can save their life (more on this in Chapter 34, Immunisation).

looking after a sick kid

Sick babies can be carried in a sling or wheeled about with you in a pram. With a toddler, you can help the patient camp out in the living room. Make up a comfy, nest-like bed on the couch with special toy friends and settle the patient in for the day so they're not isolated; or move an armchair into their bedroom with something for you to read, or the phone, or work you can do there. If disgusting vomiting or pooing is not a possibility, the parental bed can be a good haven.

Sick kids often sleep a lot as a natural defence or because of the sedative effect of medicines such as painkillers. Don't use painkillers just to sedate: it's not good for kids to have too many painkillers (see 'Painkillers for babies & kids' coming up).

See 'Gastro & "tummy bugs"' coming up for looking after a kid who's vomiting.

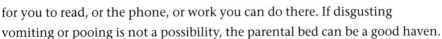

'Take toddlers seriously about their illness. If you are seen to be taking care of it they can worry less themselves, and can recover sooner.'   ROBERTO

Handy hints for sick days

'Forget commitment, housework and cooking – cuddles, cuddles, cuddles.'
ANN

⭐ Show sympathy about feeling sick, and explain that the feelings will go away again soon. Even if a baby doesn't understand the words, they'll understand the sentiment, and a toddler learns that most illnesses are temporary and that you understand how they're feeling and take it seriously. Don't complain about not being able to go to work or get something done.

⭐ Don't insist on games or activities – sometimes kids are too sick to do anything but lie about.

⭐ Read them a favourite book or two, or play favourite sleepytime or relaxing music, or audio for a story.

⭐ The younger the child, the more screens are too much stimulation with no advantage. Try old favourite books (or audio books).

⭐ Offer simple food and healthy favourites. Sore mouths and throats often mean food rejection. Gloopier comfort food such as custard, soup or mashed root vegies can be good, depending on the illness.

⭐ Don't forget to change the sheets after an illness to freshen up, and get some outside air into the 'sick room' during and after an illness.

⭐ Put your kid in a tepid bath if the weather is horribly hot; or a warm one can be relaxing if it's cold. If your child doesn't want a bath, try a wipe-down with a face washer. The patient can practise on teddy first.

⭐ Reality check: you might have to gently re-establish your child's sleeping routine after an illness.

kid medicines

Most children's medicines come as a liquid that can be sucked up into a dropper or syringe (without the needle bit, obviously) and squirted into the child's mouth; or it can be given on a spoon or in a tiny measuring cup. The dropper, spoon or measuring cup often comes with the medicine or you can buy them separately at the pharmacy. Never leave a bottle of medicine where kids can reach it.

Giving medicine

It's always handy to teach your kid how to take medicine from a dropper as soon as possible. Don't pretend it's yummy or lollies. Again, it can help to pretend to give some to a fluffy toy first.

If you're having trouble, you can gently lay the kid across your lap, then put the syringe inside their mouth, aim at the inside of a cheek and fire.

Most will say to aim a syringe at the inside of a cheek, not the throat, to avoid the gag reflex and a sudden vomit. If taking the medicine is imperative and you know your kid will fight it, ask the nurse or doctor at your clinic for advice or, better still, to show you how to medicate a struggler – they're *experts*. If your child is old enough, try full-on bribery – you take your medicine, you get a sticker or a star on a chart.

If you have to disguise medicine in a mouthful of something, use a tiny amount of breastmilk or formula milk for a baby, or a small teaspoon of food such as ice cream for older kids. It's no good putting medicine in a glass of juice or a bowl of cereal, because they'll only drink or eat 56.78 per cent of it and then you'll have no idea how much of it was medicine.

Unfortunately pharmaceutical companies seem to insist on over-flavouring and over-colouring children's medicines, which is guaranteed to make any baby or fussy toddler suspicious. A good pharmacist will know which one most kids like the taste of. A leading name brand of paracetamol is often rejected by kids because it tastes worse to them than another common brand.

It can be bloody hard to see tiny little markings on a measuring syringe or cup in the middle of the night when you're exhausted and can't find your glasses. Feel free to mark the recommended dose with a careful swipe of indelible marker and make sure it's still the same dose the next time you get the bottle out, if it's months later.

> 'Try putting your baby's medicine into an upturned teat and let them suck it like it was on a bottle.' SAMANTHA

～～～～～ more info on giving medicines ～～～～～

gosh.nhs.uk
London's Great Ormond Street children's hospital website has hints on giving or crushing tablets, eye and ear drops, painkillers, a squirty syringe, sprays and suppositories. Click on 'Medical information', then choose 'Giving your child medicines' from the drop-down menu.

Possible overdose
If you do accidentally give too much medicine, stay calm, write down how much you gave, have the bottle/packet with you, and ring the Poisons Information Centre immediately.
Poisons Information Australia: 13 11 26
🥝 **Poisons Information New Zealand: 0800 764 766**

Storing medicines

Make sure any medicines that need to be in the fridge are also safely out of reach, perhaps in a snap-closed plastic container. Strictly observe dosages, use-by dates and doctor's instructions on the label. Recommended medicine doses tend to be calculated by weight, so if your cherub is much smaller or bigger than average for their age, ask your pharmacist or doctor for an adjusted dose.

Painkillers for mums

Don't take ibuprofen or aspirin if you're trying to get pregnant or are pregnant. Aspirin has stuff in it that thins the blood, and that's not a good idea if surgery is a possibility, while ibuprofen and aspirin can interfere with fetal heart development and have other effects. (Under certain circumstances a doctor might prescribe either drug to a pregnant woman, but always check with an obstetrician before taking them.) Also see 'Medication & breastfeeding' in Chapter 4, Breastfeeding.

painkillers for babies & kids

Ask your doctor for advice on paracetamol and ibuprofen for babies and kids, and ask which you should keep in your first-aid kit. Often, the answer is 'both'. Both are dangerous if there's an overdose, so they should be kept out of reach and locked away.

You don't have to buy the most common or advertised brand – ask your pharmacist which other brands are okay that kids tend to like the taste of.

Although safe for most babies and toddlers, both ibuprofen and paracetamol can cause side effects in some kids. Babies and children with asthma may have special needs when it comes to which painkiller to choose. Don't ever exceed the dose or give the medicine too many times in a day – more will not kill pain quicker or more efficiently. The recommended dose should do it within 20–30 minutes. If it doesn't, you'll need more medical advice.

medicine dropper

Paracetamol

Paracetemol (the most popular brand name is Panadol) shouldn't be given to babies younger than 1 month old.

It will bring down a fever as well as stop pain, but see 'Fever & high temperature' coming up for why that might not always be the aim. Paracetamol isn't designed to be used all day every day, for several days in a row, without medical supervision. The packet might say you can give paracetamol every four hours – but that doesn't mean you can give it every four hours for 24 hours – only up to a maximum of four times in 24 hours.

See your doctor for a diagnosis if pain continues. A whacking great paracetamol overdose can cause permanent liver shutdown.

Ibuprofen

Ibuprofen (the most popular brand name is Nurofen) shouldn't be given to babies younger than 6 months.

It's not suitable for long-term use because it can cause tummy upsets and bleeding. The recommended dose should be given a maximum of only three times in 24 hours. See your doctor for a diagnosis if pain continues.

'My kids will take medicine off the "magic spoon" (we got it out of the packet).'
PRUE

> ## Don't give aspirin to babies or kids
>
> Aspirin (the most common brand name is Disprin) must never be given to babies
> or children. In rare cases it can contribute to Reye syndrome, liver failure and brain
> inflammation, which can be fatal.

Gels and drops

Teething gels that provide a local painkilling effect can be used in some cases of ulcers
in the mouth, or on the feet, if a doctor says it's okay. Painkilling drops for earache
could be an option, but you need a doctor's diagnosis and go-ahead each time.

when you get sick too

This is when parents find out who their real friends and actually helpful relatives are.
Many people want to stay away when there is illness in your home. It can be especially
daunting, even frightening, when you're a sole parent and have literally been laid out
by something really serious. Don't be afraid to ask friends and family for help: even if
it's just supplies left at the door or a promise to come and help do washing and folding
in two days' time.

Carer fatigue

When people used to tell me they couldn't come to work because their kid was sick,
I thought that was nice of them to stay home with their kid. I imagined a kid sitting
up in bed in a pair of freshly ironed pyjamas and a button-up cardigan, quietly doing
a jigsaw puzzle on a tray, with a handkerchief and a small posy of pansies in a short,
bulbous vase on the bedside table. (I don't know why I thought it was rural England
in 1956.)

   For some reason I didn't imagine a kid projectile-vomiting over 24 surfaces just
after you'd put new sheets on the bed; the jolt of fear when feeling your child's burning forehead; the effect of three nights of random and broken sleep on a parent trying
to make smart decisions about health care; the listless misery and tears of a child who
doesn't understand why they feel bad and can't yet explain it; the fundamental need

of a sick child to have their parent in sight at all times. I was, quite frankly, not even in the vicinity of a clue.

Most children who are sick wake up a lot, distressed, and even if *they* go straight back to sleep *you* might lie awake until the next 'alarm'. If you have a partner, try to alternate the sleepless nights. One partner can wear earplugs or sleep in the furthest-away room when it's not their turn on shift. (Earplugs are a choking hazard, so they have to go up high in a bathroom cabinet in the morning.)

common childhood conditions

Please roll the dice to select from this unwanted buffet of common childhood conditions.

Fever & high temperature

We're used to the idea that fevers are scary. It's comforting to know that most fevers are your friend with a sensible purpose: they show that the immune system is working to repel a virus or bacteria.

Diagnosing a fever

One of the quickest ways to see if a baby has a fever is to put the back of your hand against their tummy (their forehead and extremities may have been in a cold wind or near a heater, and may not be representative of their core temperature). If it feels very hot, there's probably a fever. You can use a thermometer to measure a temperature.

To be on the safe side:

⭐ **If your baby is under 3 months and has a temperature higher than 38 degrees –** take to your doctor or hospital emergency department as soon as possible, with more urgency if your baby is less than 1 month old.

⭐ **If your kid is older than 3 months, and has a temperature that stays above 38.5 for more than four hours, or has a temperature which fluctuates but hits that high more than once over a four-hour period –** go to the doctor.

⭐ If a baby seems sick at any temperature or you're worried, see your doctor. Tell the staff member when making an appointment it's a baby with a high temperature. A good doctor will want to see your baby straight away just to be able to reassure you, and to rule out a more serious illness or start treatment straight away.

A febrile convulsion

It's rare, but a rapid rise in temperature can trigger a 'febrile convulsion' or fit, which causes the eyes to roll back and the baby or kid to shake and jerk. A fit is scary but usually takes only a few minutes, isn't dangerous and has no lasting effects. (A tendency to have 'fits' sometimes runs in the family.)

If your kid has a convulsion, make sure they're in a safe position and can't fall or thrash into danger. Call an ambulance. It'll probably all be over before they get to your place, with no harm done except to your nerves.

Paramedics or local hospital emergency room staff should always check a baby who has had a convulsion, especially if it's the first one they've had, or it's an unfamiliar type to you.

Fits probably happen because the temperature rises very quickly, rather than because a particular thermometer number is reached. By the time you know your kid has a very high temperature, if they haven't had a fit they're probably not going to.

Painkillers, though many of them reduce fever, won't prevent a convulsion. The vast majority of kids never have a febrile convulsion, and those who do are not harmed by it.

Ways to treat a fever

⭐ If your baby or kid has a convulsion, call an ambulance on 000.

⭐ Don't keep the kid too bundled up, and don't use ice or anything else sudden to 'bring down' a temperature.

⭐ If your darling is in pain or miserable, give them a dose of paracetamol according to the label. If they're jaunty, let their fever fight the illness.

⭐ See a doctor if your kid has other worrying symptoms with a fever, such as being 'not themselves', cranky, listless, confused or off their food, or they have a rash or vomit repeatedly, or their breathing changes.

Gastro & 'tummy bugs'

'Gastro' is short for 'gastrointestinal infection' and means a very upset tummy and the vomiting and diarrhoea associated with a short-term germ rather than a tummy parasite, or one-off vomiting caused by getting something caught in the throat. The throwing-up is often very upsetting for a baby or kid, especially if it wakes them or they don't know what's happening. A toddler will need it explained: their tummy is upset and so the food they ate comes back out and makes them feel sick, but it will stop soon.

Luckily there are far fewer cases of severe gastro dehydration resulting in hospital stays these days. That's because babies and kids are now immunised against one of the common causes, called rotavirus (see Chapter 34, Immunisation, for more).

Babies and toddlers can dehydrate if they're too sick to keep fluids down or keep drinking fluids. This can happen quite quickly to babies: 24 hours of vomiting and diarrhoea can be enough. If you can't rehydrate them, they need to be assessed in a hospital and may be rehydrated, usually with a feeding tube that goes down to their tum through their nose. Scary for you, but standard procedure. Sometimes anti-vomiting medication is prescribed by medical staff.

Gastro is caused by a virus or bacteria and can be picked up anywhere, especially around other kids. Symptoms are usually most full-on for the first 24 hours, and the diarrhoea often lasts longer than the vomiting. There may be only throwing up or only diarrhoea, or – jackpot – both.

Viral gastro usually seems to come on suddenly even though the germ was 'caught' one to three days earlier. A kid complains of feeling nauseated or goes quiet, then suddenly vomits. It may be accompanied by other charming features such as runny poo and tummy-ache. This is the most common, catching kind.

Bacterial gastro such as food poisoning usually comes on within about 12 to 48 hours of contact. The food involved can be anything from a tiny bit of old milk not jooshed out of an otherwise clean formula bottle, to something that touched a surface contaminated by raw chicken. Tummy cramps and explosive poo usually come first, followed by vomiting. It normally lasts two to three days, though poo might only look normal again after a week or so. If you are worried that it seems endless, back to the doctor with you.

Much more rarely, what looks like gastro turns out to be something else: a bladder infection or appendicitis. But it mostly isn't.

Treatment for gastro

See your doctor if the vomiting and diarrhoea last longer than 48 hours, or if your kid still looks sick, or you see the signs of severe dehydration, coming up. Give them reassurance and cuddles. Throwing up and feeling sick are horrible, especially when you don't understand them. You can't give a kid adult medicine for vomiting symptoms.

There's not much in the way of medication you can give for gastro – usually you have to ride it out by doing the following.

babies under 6 months with gastro

Babies under 6 months can become dehydrated very quickly, so babies with gastro need to be seen by a GP. Ask for advice about rehydrating. If they want to weigh your bub, take your baby's clothes off first, then you'll have a baseline measurement for comparing with, later.

If your baby is breastfed, keep offering breastfeeds regularly. If they're a formula-fed baby, ask your doctor whether you should try a special rehydration formula for their age from the chemist in their bottle for a day, before going back to normal formula. Some babies come good suddenly and can probably go straight back on to their formula.

babies 6 months to 1 year with gastro

See your doctor if the the kid refuses water and rehydration fluids, if the vomiting and diarrhoea last longer than 24 hours or if you're worried, or if they're weeing less and look unwell. Your bub should go back on breastmilk or formula milk as soon as possible.

Rehydrating a toddler with gastro

Give rehydration fluids or rehydration ice blocks or popsicles from the chemist. If the gastro isn't too bad, water will do. Keep a drink next to a child who's old enough to help themselves and also offer it to them often, even if it 'comes up again'. Some will still be absorbed by the body, which is useful. Small amounts of fluid taken in often is the key: about 5 millilitres, or one teaspoon, every five minutes. Too much gulped down will trigger more chucking. Avoid sweet drinks like cordial or soft drink or flavoured drinks – the sugar can make dehydration worse. Don't give only plain water for longer than 24 hours: the body needs more nutrients than that.

'When they say they have a tummy-ache and turn a shade of green they ARE going to vomit.' TRACEY

Signs of severe dehydration

Severe dehydration from vomiting or diarrhoea can mean a need for immediate medical help. Here are the signs:

* The baby or kid has repeated runny poos over the course of 24 hours.
* Their skin feels dry and papery or cold and clammy and is paler than usual, with cold hands and feet.
* The skin on a baby's fontanelle (the small, soft part at the top of their head) dips downwards.
* Foul breath.
* A dry mouth, lips and tongue; no tears when crying.

* The eyes seem more sunken into the face.
* Increased breathing rate and/or heart rate.
* Very thirsty.
* A spaced-out, glazed look: tired, floppy, listless, confused.
* Less wee than usual or fewer wet nappies.
* Wee is darker coloured than usual (this is sometimes hard to see if they're wearing a nappy).

General anti-gastro measures

Make everyone wash their hands all the time, thoroughly, with soap – after clean-ups, before eating, after eating, after going to the loo. Antibacterial liquid soap might be good.

Keep cross-infection to a minimum by washing all towels and jarmies on the hot cycle with antibacterial washing powder, and use hot water and detergent, or the dishwasher, to clean utensils and sick bowls.

What to feed a kid with gastro

When a toddler or preschooler with gastro wants to eat again, feed them simple, healthy things that they already like, and don't worry too much – they will be getting a few nutrients even if they throw up everything soon after. This could include little bits of plain cooked rice and pasta, porridge, mashed potato, pureed or mashed frozen berries or fresh fruit, grated apple with yoghurt, banana, mashed vegies, and homemade chicken soup with the chicken bits chopped up.

What not to feed a toddler with gastro

⭐ Water or rehydration fluids are best – avoid lemonade or other sweet drinks. Apple juice can be offered to toddlers aged 2 and over under medical advice if other fluids are refused.

⭐ No bottled electrolyte or sports drinks: they're only for adult athletes.

⭐ No spicy, acidic or rich foods, chocolate, junk food, sweets, cake or other sugary things: these can make the diarrhoea worse.

⭐ No salty things: these can increase dehydration.

⭐ No anti-diarrhoea medicines unless your doctor has prescribed them specifically for this bout of illness (these medicines are rarely given, and hardly ever to babies).

⭐ Many children may become dairy-sensitive after an episode of gastro; this can usually be managed by reducing their dairy intake for three weeks after the infection. Most kids will want their milk back. Ask your doctor or child & family health nurse for individual advice.

Explaining gastro

Never assume a toddler or preschooler knows what's going on. Explain about getting germs: you can't see them and they make you sick, and then you get better again because of medicine and because your clever body learns how to fight the germs off inside. Explain why you're offering different foods and drinks, why you're going to the doctor, why you're staying quietly at home and not going to childcare (because other kids can get the germ while your kid is still feeling sick).

A kid old enough to understand (but who has forgotten what throwing up is) should be reassured that the situation will end soon, that they have a germ that is making their tummy have a tantrum, and that you're trying to fix it as fast as you can but sometimes it might take until tomorrow (anything longer is virtually incomprehensible).

contagious bug

How to look after a vomiting kid

Sick bowl

Protect yourself and bedding from sudden vomits by teaching your child to use a bowl for being sick into as soon as they can understand the point. Long hair? Pop it in a ponytail to keep it out of the way. Give lots of praise for using the bowl, rub their back and make sympathetic faces. Make sure you have a couple of non-metal sick bowls or buckets (who wants to see their reflection at that point?) and plenty of layers of towels to avoid getting vomit on the bed or furniture. (Don't throw out old, thread-bare towels!)

Stripping the bed

When a kid throws up in bed, it's all hands on deck.

Soothe the kid thoroughly first, then completely clean them with a nice warm face washer and a soap substitute, paying special attention to their face, hands and hair. Rinse off the soap substitute, wrap your darling in a clean towel and prop them somewhere they can't fall off, or over. Dress them in loose clothes that you'll be able to get off easily if they're sick again, or if it's warm, just a nappy. Don't assume they won't vomit again or that there's 'nothing left to come up'.

Strip the bed of all the sheets and towels with vomit on, and soak up any extra vomit with kitchen paper or old towels. Clean any vomit-touched hard surfaces with antibacterial spray (or similar) and another towel. Explain that you're taking all the bedding, jarmies, towels and vomity stuffed animals to the laundry, or leave everything in a pile to take away later.

Everything will have to be washed on a hot-water cycle and with an antibacterial washing powder. Sick bowls will have to be swapped and disinfected in the sink with boiling water at intervals, too.

Starting again

Come back, have a cuddle and remake the bed: if you don't have a waterproof mattress protector use a couple of layers of old towels. Give them only toys that are washable. (We've had to have Pinky reupholstered twice, and it's quite undignified.) Explain that the vomiting might happen again but it might not, and their body is working to make them better. Offer them a drink of water.

Back to the laundry, rinse off anything chunky, do a short but adequately cleansing washing-machine load with antibacterial powder in hot water.

If you're unlucky, do it all again.

Of course if there are two adults, divvying up the actions just described will work even better.

~~~~~~~~~~ **more info** on gastro ~~~~~~~~~~

rch.org.au
Click on 'Patients and Families', then 'Kids Health Info', then G for 'gastro'.

Sniffles & colds

Plain saline nasal drops, warm, diluted lemon-and-honey drinks and painkillers can be used if necessary or as recommended, depending on the age group (make sure you read 'Painkillers for babies & kids' earlier in this chapter).

Doctors now recommend against using vapour and other chest rubs on children, which have been shown to have no effect on their symptoms, and in some cases can make breathing more difficult or cause skin irritation. Essential oils including eucalyptus and lavender won't help, can cause a rash, and are a poisons risk.

Electrical steam vaporisers can cause damp in your home, and hot-water scalding if they're tipped over, so avoid them. Sitting together in a steamy bathroom near a shower or bath can sometimes seem to help. (Obviously, never leave a kid unattended there.)

Everyone needs a yearly flu injection

Make sure everyone in your extended family, including all kids over 6 months old, has a flu vaccination every year. Flu (influenza) is not the same as a severe cold. Each 'flu season' kills people, mainly the elderly and the very young. Immunisation will protect them and help doctors diagnose anything else your kid may have.

Coughs & cough medicines

If you are worried, or a cough has been going on for several days or getting worse, see a doctor for a proper diagnosis.

⭐ A wheezy cough can indicate asthma and should always be checked by a doctor.

⭐ A cough that ends in a heaving sound or big intake of breath must be checked by a doctor, as it could be whooping cough, which is very dangerous.

Doctors say no cough and cold medicines or syrups should be given to babies or children under 6 years old. Any cough or cold 'treatments' should only be given to older kids if prescribed by a doctor. Over-the-counter medicines from pharmacies or supermarkets – cough syrups (decongestants and expectorants), medicated nasal sprays, antihistamines, and cold and flu tablets – have no effect on how long a kid has a cold or flu virus. They don't cure coughs. They can also 'mask' symptoms of something more serious, and sometimes cause unwanted side effects, including irritability.

Croup cough

'Croup' is caused by a virus and causes a cough that can sound scary – like a dog or seal barking. It usually starts by looking like a cold, or with a croaky voice. If there's also wheezing or difficulty in breathing, go to the doctor that day. Croup symptoms often disappear during the day and then reappear, possibly worse, the next night. So even if a kid seems fine the next morning, go to the doctor because a diagnosis is important. Some croup-sounding coughs are caused by flu.

Croup inflames the vocal cords and 'windpipe': prescribed medication for croup will help keep a little airway open. Most croup gets better by itself after three or four days, but stay away from childcare and school as it's very contagious. Croup coughs can be scary and make breathing and coughing more distressing. Comfort and reassure the kid, and offer them lots of drinks.

In severe case, signs of difficult breathing can include the sounds your child makes when trying to breathe (doctors call it 'stridor'), and also flared nostrils, a sinking-in of the throat and upper chest as a baby or child tries to breathe in, and reluctance to lie down. As always, if your kid is really struggling to breathe or seems to turn blueish, ring an ambulance on 000 (or in NZ, 111).

Disordered sleep breathing

Odd breathing during sleep can be a sign a kid isn't getting enough restful sleep. This is definitely linked to behaviour and mood, and their ability to concentrate and learn well. It can be part of a sleep problem that disrupts family life and drives parents bonkers. A kid (or a parent) could have disordered breathing during sleep because of sleep apnoea or allergic rhinitis ('hay fever'). Symptoms common to both can include teeth grinding, daytime dozing, irritability, and behaviour and attention problems. See your doctor if you suspect either of these.

Sleep apneoa can cause snoring snonky sounds, loud gasps, and lots of night waking. Treatments include steroid nasal sprays, working on maintaining a healthy weight and, in rare cases, throat surgery.

Rhinitis symptoms can include breathing through the mouth, especially at night; sneezing (especially in the morning); runny, red and itchy eyes; itchy ears, nose, throat or roof of the mouth; and headaches. Rhinitis allergy is most often caused by dust mites, pollen, animal fur and skin particles, mould or cigarette smoke. See your doctor and get help to identify the allergy.

Treatments for rhinitis include steroid nasal sprays, 'snot-sucking' (sorry) tube devices from the pharmacy and baby shops, some immunotherapy medications using allergen extracts (don't try this yourself!), and, in rare cases, surgery.

Snonk

Ears

Lots of babies and small kids get ear trouble, usually after a cold or other virus. Most kids will have at least one ear infection before school starts. The three main types of ear conditions are outer and inner (middle ear) ear infections, and 'glue ear'.

Outer ear infection

This is often caused by 'picking something up at the pool'. You can see the ear is red, perhaps with a discharge; older kids might say it feels blocked or sore. It could go away by itself but should be seen by your doctor and may need antibiotics or steroid ear-drops. Never ignore a sore ear: have it checked out, as it's easiest to treat it early.

Middle ear infection

Inside everyone's ear is a tube that drains any fluid from the middle ear. It's protected from the outside world by the eardrum. Colds can lead to fluid arriving in the 'middle' ear, and if the fluid stays horizontal and doesn't drain out, it can get very infected and painful. The symptoms are usually bad earache and a lack of interest in food (because it hurts to swallow). In a smaller bub early signs may be listlessness, tears, tugging at or touching the ears, runny nose, maybe a fever, and a little temporary deafness that might be obvious or not.

In some cases the build-up of fluid can eventually cause the eardrum to bulge out and tear, causing sudden relief of pain or a sharp pain. Off to the doctor to check it out, if this happens.

The first treatment is pain relief – usually the label dosage of paracetamol for the correct age. If the yuck has burst through the eardrum, the pain of the pressure will be released and the drum will probably heal nicely by itself. It's important that perforated eardrum are checked by a GP. After such a 'rupture', you have to keep your kid's head out of water (shower, bath, pool, waterhole, beach) until your doctor confirms it's okay to do so. Most middle ear infections are caused by viruses, so antibiotics don't help. The problem is likely to recur until (or if) the tube starts draining properly, usually around age 3.

'Glue ear'

The ear may become blocked when fluid can't drain away or doesn't burst through the eardrum – but it's not necessarily infected. There's no pain, but there is some hearing loss while it's there. Kids can get very good at lip-reading and finding other ways around their deafness. Parents often first realise when a child has their back to them and doesn't respond to questions, or keeps asking for the music or TV to be turned up.

In persistent cases or when some (temporary) deafness in one or both ears that would lead to learning and social difficulties, the kid may have to have a quick operation under general anaesthetic to insert 'grommets'. These are little eyelets that hold open holes in the eardrum so the fluid can drain out. While grommets are in, you can't let water get into their ears as it can get through into the eardrum and cause infection. After a few months grommets drop out of the ear naturally and the drum heals itself.

Treating ear problems

As soon as you suspect a deafness or hearing-loss problem in a baby or toddler, ask your doctor about a hearing test. The earlier a problem is detected, the more can be done.

See a doctor if there is ear pain or redness, if your child pulls their ear often, if there is suspected hearing trouble, or there is a discharge from the ear.

If you need to give eardrops, have your child lie down with their head sideways on your lap and let gravity help you. Say it won't hurt (if that's true) but might feel wet or tickly while the drops are draining into the ear. Don't apply non-prescribed eardrops unless your doctor says it's okay.

Don't push anything, even a cotton bud, into a baby's or a kid's ear. Clean the bit you can reach with a face washer.

'Ear candles', sold under various brand names at some health food shops and by alternative practitioners, cannot and do not work – and are dangerous because they involve lit candles near a child's ear and hair. Natural-remedy eardrops should only be used when your doctor is certain the eardrum has not been perforated.

Constipation

Constipation is really common in babies and toddlers. It means doing hard poo, or not doing poo regularly. For babies, ask your child & family health nurse or doctor. For toddlers, try giving them more water to drink, more fresh fruit and vegies, and more fibre (porridge, wholegrain cereals and shredded wheat is good). Don't give laxatives without checking with your doctor. Breastfed babies can poo less than formula-fed babies. It's uncommon, but recurring constipation can cause other health problems. If you're worried, ask your doctor.

~~~~~ **more info** on constipation ~~~~~

rch.org.au
schn.health.nsw.gov.au
Search 'constipation' on these children's hospital sites.

Head lice & nits

Lice is the plural of louse, the little critters that can invade hair, crawl about and lay eggs (called nits), which they 'glue' onto the base of hairs at the scalp with icky, lousy secretions. The first sign of nits or lice is usually your child scratching their head, or an alert from playgroup, childcare or kinder. The itchiness is caused by the lice sucking tiny amounts of blood from the scalp – euwwwww!

A louse can lay several eggs a day. Eggs hatch in about a week, and within a week the babies are laying their own eggs.

You will probably be able to see the tiny, yellowy-white eggs, like tiny dandruff, and maybe some little browny-grey lice skittering about. If an egg is a centimetre or more away from the scalp it's either dead or hatched. The live eggs are down nearer the scalp.

When your kid has lice you might have them too – or you will just feel like you do. I am so itchy just writing this!

Don't be embarrassed or make your kid feel bad. All kids get lice. It's nothing to do with hygiene. Lice can't jump and they can't live on pets. Chemical companies say lice can live for up to a week without their human host; natural treatment advocates say lice rarely survive this for more than a day or so.

Lice won't harm your kid, but a visitation needs to be treated so kids don't feel distracted and itchy and uncomfortable, become isolated from other kids or teachers because they're known to have nits, or spread them to other kids.

Treating lice

Chemical-free lice treatment kit

1 Conditioner – the gloopier the better and the more gaudily coloured the better, so the eggs are visible against it. White conditioner makes it hard.
2 A fine-toothed metal lice comb – the plastic one is a bit bendier and so not as efficient.

Chemical-based lice treatment kit

Get 1 and 2, above, plus:

3 Lice-killing lotion from the pharmacy – depending on your philosophy, either the laboratory-made chemical stuff or the 'natural' poisonous stuff, such as tea-tree oil. 'Natural' chemicals can still cause a rash: follow instructions carefully.

Lice-killing treatments

Almost all lice are now resistant to chemicals in potions that used to kill them. When buying lice treatment, ask the pharmacist for a recommendation based on your kid's age. Some chemicals are not recommended for kids under 4.

Babies and very small children with lice shouldn't be treated with strong chemicals. All the manufacturers say babies under 6 months should not be treated with their product, natural or otherwise.

Poisons that used to slay the evil lice menace are the chemicals malathion and permethrin. Tea-tree oil based products were less effective. This is not a DIY situation: never try making lice-killing stuff from chemicals or oils yourself. Undiluted tea-tree oil can cause blistering and rashes. My nanna used to put her three girls through the sheep dip on the farm in the 1950s (full of now-banned chemicals) and they've survived. Mind you, they're all completely mad. But Mum says their hair was very shiny.

Keep any lice-killing lotion safely out of reach and keep an eye on the use-by date. If it is swallowed, call the Poisons Information Centre immediately, in Australia on **13 11 26** or in New Zealand on **0800 764 766**.

Conditioner combing or 'bug busting'

Chemical methods are not recommended in babies under six months. Some people choose not to use any lotion except the conditioner, preferring to comb out all lice and eggs and squash them rather than use chemical or natural killing agents. Lice covered in conditioner will be immobilised for a short period enabling easier removal. This method could be more reliable than using special lotions, either because of chemical resistance (see above) or because those preparations don't always kill the eggs (despite what they claim), requiring a repeat treatment a week later.

This technique is often called 'bug busting' because it aims to break the life cycle of the lice by ridding the head of them before they are mature enough to start laying eggs. It might need to be done every three days for at least two weeks to be sure of removing all the lice, which can be too much for your child to bear. Because they usually have much less hair, babies are usually pretty easy to inspect for eggs and lice, which you can remove yourself.

Rub conditioner (or, if you're using it, lice-killing lotion) gently but thoroughly through the kid's hair. Sit the child on your lap on a towel, divide their hair into sections, and comb each section of hair meticulously with the metal lice comb.

Get out all the dead lice and drag out all the eggs. This can take a very long time. Older children can be kept amused by pretending you are a family of chimps. (Do not go so far as to eat the lice.) Wash your hands and wash the towel in hot water. Give the child a treat for putting up with the treatment. Now reward yourself and try to stop scratching your head by association. It's crucial to repeat treatment seven days later, when missed eggs (inevitable!) will have hatched.

Washing the lice away

You can wash in hot water all the bedclothes, fluffy toys and clothes the child has been using. But lice expert and researcher Professor Rick Speare from James Cook University found that lice don't stay alive off the head: 'We searched the floors of 118 primary school classroom carpets for head lice while the pupils were out of the classroom. We also checked the children's heads. We found no lice (ZERO!) on the floors and 14 033 lice on the heads of the 2000 or so children using those classrooms. To treat head lice, concentrate on the head!'

The professor added that a few lice might survive on a pillowcase for a while, recommending you 'change the pillowslip when you are treating your child, or heat it up (hot wash, iron, hot dryer) to kill any head lice that could have walked across to the pillowslip. However, focus your main efforts on the head, not on the environment. The head is where the action is!' So it's okay to stop boiling teddy and washing all the towels you've ever seen in your life.

BLAST FROM THE PAST

'Kerosene three parts and olive oil seven parts or kerosene, vinegar and olive oil in equal parts are useful mixtures to remove lice but are not recommended to use on children owing to the danger of the kerosene igniting.'
– *Kiama Independent*, 1951

Hiccups

Hiccups are quite common in babies and nothing to worry about. Painless hiccups that go on for a while in toddlers and children are also not a problem. Don't try to give the kid a fright to stop the hiccups. And don't give them an adult 'medicine' such as an antacid.

Rituals that probably don't cure the hiccups but distract a kid and make them feel like they're doing something include family traditions of holding their breath for a few beats (you can show them how), drinking water while you put your fingers gently in their ears, or getting them to do a little jig: the hiccups dance.

Eczema

Itchy, dry skin can develop a red rash and flaking known as eczema, which can affect babies and kids. Reliable studies suggest that breastfeeding doesn't stop, reduce or prevent eczema. It's more common in kids who have allergies, and sometimes it's made worse by contact with pet fur or a diagnosed food allergen. Most kids grow out of it before they start school. Some babies who have eczema develop asthma, so see a doctor if your baby starts wheezing.

Babies usually get eczema on the face, especially on the cheeks and around the mouth, and behind knees. Factors that make eczema worse include wetness (such as in high-dribble places), heat and dryness.

Risk factors in getting eczema

- ★ Kids with eczema are more likely to have rhinitis or other allergies.
- ★ Dry skin.
- ★ Scratching dry skin.
- ★ Chlorine pools.
- ★ Dust mites or pollen sensitivity.
- ★ Being overheated.
- ★ Being in water a lot, or washing hands often.
- ★ If eczema 'runs in the family'.

Hints to help prevent eczema

- ★ Use a soap substitute for baths and handwashing.
- ★ Washing-machine detergents can be too harsh: try gentler wool or handwashing mixes.

- ⭐ Car and home heaters can be very drying, particularly those that blow hot air. Better to put on more clothes than to turn the heater up. There's not much you can do in a windy, drying, harsh environment or a humid, sticky one, but try to adjust for the weather as much as you can.
- ⭐ Avoid woollen clothes or hats, 'non-breathing' unnatural fabrics, and soap and detergents, which dry the skin.
- ⭐ Keep the car and pram as cool as possible with shade devices. Adults often take off one layer while we're in the car: don't forget to do this for your baby or kid as well.
- ⭐ Doonas can be too hot (and mustn't be used for babies anyway): try using a combination of cotton blankets and woollen ones (away from the skin) or, in the case of babies, a cotton sleeping suit (like a sleeping bag with arms, available at baby clothes retailers).

Treating eczema

- ⭐ If the eczema rash breaks the skin, or the skin is scratched, it can become infected: see your chemist or doctor for info about a therapeutic cream or antibiotics.
- ⭐ Long-term eczema may require extra medication. Some dermatologists recommend safe light exposure.
- ⭐ Check with a pharmacist which moisturising creams will help with red, dry skin and can be used on a baby's or toddler's face and hands (in other words, the bits most likely to be sensitive or that can easily transfer cream to the mouth). See your doctor if the dry skin becomes rashy and doesn't respond.
- ⭐ Baths should be short, and neither hot nor cold. Use a soap substitute. Two to three baths a week is plenty. Otherwise just do a gentle 'wipe-down'.

~~~~~~~~~ more info on eczema ~~~~~~~~~

eczema.org.au
The Eczema Association of Australasia is a non-profit support and info group.

Asthma

Asthma is caused by the little tubes in the lungs being squeezed or inflamed so it's harder to get big, full breaths in and out. The mildest symptom is usually wheezing, and symptoms step up to asthma attacks or 'respiratory distress', which in very severe cases results in the child not being able to breathe at all. Australia has one of the highest childhood asthma rates in the world.

Wheezing can also be caused by bronchitis or other viral illnesses, so it's important to get a proper diagnosis. Other causes of wheezing include the kid having swallowed something that's stuck halfway down, an infection in a baby under 1 year old (bronchiolitis), and an allergy.

It's not known why some people get asthma and others don't, though there is great research going on that will eventually probably solve it. It's known that the incidence is rising, that Australia has one of the highest rates in the world, and that certain kinds of thunderstorms can bring on dangerous attacks. Asthma can 'run in the family' as a genetic risk.

Other known trigger or associated factors include being around cigarette smoke, having allergies, the house dust mite, pollen, mould, and pet fur. It's held that breast-fed babies are statistically more likely to grow up asthma free, but many children who were breastfed for years have asthma and many formula-fed children don't.

Asthma & painkillers

Painkillers containing aspirin, which should never be given to children, or ibuprofen can cause a reaction in some kids who have asthma, so ask your doctor about what to use.

Treating asthma

Asthma is not so much cured as managed so that it has as little effect on someone's life as possible. The main medications used are liquid ones and inhalers – some are preventative and some are used during an asthma attack. Asthma doesn't mean a kid should stop being outdoors or active. Several high-profile sportspeople have asthma.

Asthma plans

Your doctor will help you develop a written plan for managing asthma and 'attacks'. Current medical thinking is that preventative steps and medication are much better ways of managing asthma than intermittently having to use heavier drugs to treat severe attacks. Specialised slow-breathing techniques have helped some people.

Your kid's babysitters and childcare centre need to be told about your kid's asthma status and have a copy of the plan, including any regular or emergency treatment or procedures. The centre's or kinder's fridge can hold a spare inhaler, with instructions.

Spare inhalers should be kept in your toddler bag, in your handbag, at homes you regularly visit, in the holiday first-aid kit, and anywhere else sensible – but not the car glove box (too hot). And check the use-by dates regularly.

Management of asthma usually includes:
- ★ taking asthma medications as directed
- ★ monitoring the asthma symptoms, while staying active
- ★ talking to your doctor about whether to try to avoid allergens entirely, or to occasionally introduce small amounts to 'train' the body to handle reactions
- ★ having your asthma plan regularly reviewed by your doctor.

Asthma 'attacks'

A child who suddenly has an asthma attack should be taken to a doctor or hospital straight away, where they can be treated and you can check your plan for managing any further attacks. Shortness of breath or an obvious asthma episode mustn't be ignored, as a severe attack can cut off breathing entirely.

Part of the scariness of an asthma attack for a kid is any panic that goes on around them. You can let the professionals do their job while you concentrate on keeping your kid calm.

more info on asthma

asthmaaustralia.org.au
1800 278 462 (1800 ASTHMA)
Click on your state or territory. Includes a free 'control pack' of info for families, explanations and info on first aid, info on what schools and childcare centres can do to help, links to pollen counts, thunderstorm triggers, research and more.

Vulvovaginitis

Vulvovaginitis is such a doctor-type freaky-sound term but it's totally common; many girl toddlers get a red, irritated rash on their vulvas (around the vagina) that can make it sting a bit when they wee. It happens because that area has thin skin when the body doesn't make oestrogen (before puberty and after menopause). It's not thrush (thrush likes oestrogen, too). Ask your doctor for a diagnosis to rule anything else out.

It will go away by itself but here are some ideas to help it along. All these things go for anyone at any age managing a cranky vulva:

⭐ Avoid perfumed and exfoliating soap.
⭐ Try a moisturising liquid soap substitute.
⭐ Only pat dry after going to the loo or having a wash – no dragging or rubbing, and always wipe bot from front to back.
⭐ Wear cotton undies.
⭐ Use unscented toilet paper.
⭐ Use a 'sensitive' product in the washing machine.
⭐ Allow good airflow.
⭐ Be vigilant about changing wet nappies.

Vulvovaginitis treatments

⭐ Throw half a cup of white vinegar into a shallow bath and have them squat in it or sit with legs open for 10–15 minutes, or have a bath with a handful of salt thrown in and stirred.
⭐ Apply cold compresses (not icepacks).
⭐ Use a barrier cream such as Vaseline regularly to put a protective layer on the skin.
⭐ Give the whole family a treatment for worms: similar symptoms are also seen with threadworms.

Threadworms

Oh, the joy of inspecting your kid's itchy bot-bot for tiny parasitic worms, or worm eggs. The condition isn't dangerous, just common, easily contagious and fiercely unglamorous. You can get a diagnosis from your doctor, and simple treatment from the pharmacist: anti-parasitic tablets for all in the family, after the diagnosis and again in two to four weeks. When doing the worm treatment, wash all the sheets and towels and undies in hot water.

'natural' therapies

Many people see a herbal or naturopathic practitioner. If you do, you'll need to also have a medical diagnosis and treatment recommendation for your kid before considering whether extra natural treatments are appropriate. Of course, natural therapies are not appropriate for possible serious illnesses or injuries. A herbal practitioner or naturopath is not an appropriate main practitioner option for babies and toddlers.

Herbalists should be told about any medications the child is on, and doctors told of any herbal remedies the kid is taking, as well. Sensible herbalists will not recommend their remedies alone for serious illnesses or injuries, and won't give advice outside their area of expertise.

Avoid any natural therapist who advises against vaccination, and any who claim that homeopathy 'works', and any who recommend exclusion diets or who bad-mouth medical treatment.

Be wary of herbalists and naturopaths who prescribe you long lists of things that are only available from their dispensary. Some entrepreneurial herbalists have been known to prescribe up to 30 different items for the same patient!

Homeopathy

Homeopathic stuff in bottles or pills, also known as Bach flower medicines, 'rescue remedies' and bush flower essences or remedies, cannot and do not work. They may have a suggestible or 'placebo' effect in some cases when people believe in them. They're made by getting a bit of ground-up plant and then diluting it so many thousands of times that eventually there is no trace of the plant. None. At all. It's like chucking a teaspoon of red food colouring into a creek that runs into the Amazon river and then bottling some water where the river runs into the sea, and calling it tincture of food dye. The other thing that homeopathic manufacturers say they do to the liquid is to 'succuss it vigorously' – which means they whack the container during the manufacturing process (I am not making this up).

The 'remedy' will also have a preservative in it, usually alcohol.

Homeopaths believe the water in their products retains a spiritual imprint or memory of the original substance. All reputable scientific studies using double-blind techniques have found that homeopathic substances have no effect on the body. Anybody who tells you that homeopathy is a substitute for immunisation is wrong. Naturopaths and homeopaths often recommend homeopathic stuff as 'safe' for children. It usually is, unless they're allergic to the preservative used. But it won't 'work'. Many products labelled 'homeopathic' have herbs or other properties in them, or contaminants, depending on their source. Because they are unregulated we don't really know what's in them. So something labelled 'homeopathic' is either useless or dangerous.

'Bush flower' and 'bush essences' – cousins to homeopathy – have no effect on the body. The claim that they can be used to treat 'shyness', 'aggression' or 'bedwetting' in a child is disturbing. Bedwetting, for example, is caused by either a medical or a psychological issue; neither can be addressed with a 'bush essence'. Some makers claim it makes 'vibrational medicine', others that it stops emotional blockage. One manufacturer says they are made 'by instinct'.

What they are selling is a form of spell, or ritual. That's okay if you understand that you're paying for rituals and sweet little bottles of things, charms, potions, pretty crystals, the idea of treating yourself kindly, and talismans. There's a witchy spell shop in my home town – they have lovely charms and rituals for 'a new beginning' or 'true purpose'. I appreciate their honesty in calling them 'spells'.

Just because it's in the pharmacy doesn't mean it works: homeopathic stuff is there because government regulators don't think it will do harm, and because pharmacies say they are giving buyers a 'choice'. Profits are good. Pharmaceutical companies now produce homeopathic 'remedies' as a multimillion-dollar industry sideline because a demand has been created.

Aromatherapy

Mindful of the long list of essential oils that are a poisoning risk can cause skin rashes, I should say that small children should probably only be given some drops of lavender oil in their bath (as an association with relaxation). Don't use aromatherapy candles or other heated devices for children, and never leave these (or anything else with an unprotected flame) unattended in a room that a child is in.

Chiropractors, babies & kids

Newborns, babies and kids should not be 'treated' or routinely examined by a chiropractor. A good chiropractor can help some adults with back pain, but spine manipulation or any chiropractic 'treatment' should never be performed on babies or young children. Chiropractic treatment doesn't help crying, sleeping, 'colic', 'reflux' or any other issues in babies or children, and doctors say it can cause serious injury. Some people believe these treatments 'work', but that doesn't make it true. A few chiropractors give parents info and instructions about diet and immunisation – they're not qualified to do this, and the advice can be dangerously wrong.

Not all 'doctors' are doctors

Due to a quirk of history and the law, chiropractors and Chinese medicine practitioners can call themselves 'Dr' without having a medical qualification as most people expect it to mean. Chiropractors have years less training and study than medical doctors. They do a university course and study anatomy, but they don't study physiology, pharmacology, evidence-based research, chemistry or microbiology. They do not have experience in hospitals or in doctors' offices. Some people who are not qualified doctors call themselves 'physicians' or use letters after their name that suggest medical or university-level science training or a medical research background, but may be the result of 'weekend' or online courses. See Chapter 2, Your Help Team, for more.

sun care

Because running around in the fresh air and sunshine is one of the bonuses of living in Australia, we have to find a happy medium between toasting our children and making them move slowly in the shade dressed in head-to-toe beekeeping outfits.

You probably already know that Australia has a very high skin cancer incidence, and that the more times you're exposed to UV and the more times you're sunburnt, the more chance you have of developing cancers.

The main risk factor for later cancers is 'UV damage' – getting burnt a lot when you're a kid, and having a lot of skin changes due to UV exposure (freckles, tans). Babies and kids are at special risk of sunburn.

The UV index

It's ultraviolet radiation (UV rays) that cause a burn. UV rays can't be seen or felt. The World Health Organization has a rating system for UV radiation levels. You can check the UV index on a weather app or an online report: if it's at 3 or above, there's a greater sunburn risk. Australia usually has a rating of 3 or above most days from August to April in the southern states, and it stays higher all year in the north. A lot of UV rays are reflected from below by water, sand or concrete.

Cancer Council Australia says that on a clear January day (for example) it can take as little as fifteen minutes to get sunburnt. It recommends that babies and children stay out of direct sun – in the shade or very well protected – especially between 11 a.m. and 3 p.m. daylight saving time. In the north of Australia these recommendations can apply all year round. Sunscreen is never enough on its own, even when applied following instructions: see 'The 5 ways of sun protection' coming up.

~~~~~~~ **more info** on the UV index ~~~~~~~

You can get the Cancer Council SunSmart app to get a UV alert forecast every day, or check the Bureau of Meteorology website (**bom.gov.au/uv/**).

Sneaky sun

UV rays themselves don't feel hot, so sunburn is very common on days when people don't expect it. Yes, you can be burnt on cloudy days. And on cool days with sun, and on windy days that feel cool. And in the snow, where there's lots of intensifying reflection. Most people get burnt in temperatures between 18 and 27 degrees Celsius. The biggest factors are time of year and time spent outdoors. Even if you're making sure your kid uses the beach only in the early morning and later afternoon, you should still use 'The 5 ways of sun protection' coming up.

Babies & sun protection

Babies lying on a rug in the park or at the beach should be in serious shade. Even so, kids still need to be protected from reflected or 'scattered' UV rays by clothes, hats and maybe sunglasses. You can use sunscreen on a baby older than 6 months, but sunscreen alone should not be relied on to protect a baby, even in the shade. 'Babies can use sunscreen but only on the small bits that can't be protected any other way', says the Cancer Council.

Check any sunscreen bought for babies under 1 year for suitability with your pharmacist or GP. For a baby over 6 months, keep up the application of sunscreen every two hours, or more often if water or wiping off may have affected the coverage. Sunburn for a baby or toddler can be very serious, causing blisters and rapid dehydration.

~~~~~ more info on babies and sun protection ~~~~~

cancer.org.au
Search 'sun protection infants' to find a fact sheet called 'Sun protection and babies'.

Sunburn

Sunburn can happen when a kid is in direct sun or outside on a cloudy day without sunscreen, and UV rays are reflected from water, concrete, sand or snow. Most sunburn happens because a parent thought the kid was protected, but not enough sunscreen was rubbed on, or much of the spray-on sunscreen phouffed into the air or didn't form a thick-enough layer. Photos of kids with terrible sunburn on social media are almost always photos of kids who didn't have enough sunscreen on, as product testing has confirmed.

There is no such thing as 'windburn'. That's sunburn on a day when the wind made you feel a bit cooler so you didn't use enough sunscreen or have a hat or protective clothing on.

The 5 ways of sun protection

For babies and kids, always use the five ways of sun protection all together at the same time: clothes, sunscreen, hat, shade and sunglasses. If the adults in the family do all these sun protection steps they'll set a good example and be far less likely to get skin cancer (and wrinkles caused by sun damage), too.

1 **sun clothes**   When the UV forecast is 3 or above kids should be dressed in loose clothes that cover as much of the body as possible. If you hold a fabric up to the light and the light passes through, UV rays will too. Clothes with tags saying UPF (ultraviolet protection factor) 50+ have the most sun protection. Lycra-elastane mixes tend to have 50+, and plastic, nylon and polyester are all much better than thin cotton, which tends to be only 5 to 20+. All fabrics have less UV protection when they're wet.

Surf shops and kid departments now sell 'rashies' (originally designed to protect against surfboard friction): high-protection quick-dry tops with short or long sleeves, as well as shorts. Check the labels, and make sure tops are long enough or attach to the bottom half so they don't ride up and risk midriff and back sunburn.

2 **sunscreen**   This should be Australian-made, broad spectrum (which means it absorbs both kinds of relevant UV rays), at least sun protection factor (SPF) 30 or above (usually labelled SPF 30+), and water resistant. No sunscreen gives total protection. A higher SPF factor is more of a marketing gimmick than anything, as it misleads people into thinking they and their kids are much more protected and can go longer between applications: not true.

You can test a little bit of sunscreen on the back of your kid's hand to see if it causes a rash. If it does, talk to your pharmacist about a replacement: rashes are usually a reaction to perfumes or preservatives rather than the sun protection part. Remember that a thick layer of sunscreen lotion is what you need, and that layer will make a kid hotter, so it's better (and cheaper) to cover large areas of skin with loose protective clothing.

Keep sunscreen at home under 30 degrees Celsius – the fridge is fine. Don't leave it in the boot or glove box.

Sunscreen should always be used with clothes and hats as the main line of defence, not on its own, says the Cancer Council.

Sunscreen should be applied about twenty minutes before going outdoors (there's a complicated chemical reason that will put you to sleep). Use a big dollop: an adult needs one heaped teaspoon of sunscreen for each arm, each leg, their face, neck and ears, and again one for their front torso and one for the back.

A small child needs *at least* half a teaspoon to each body part. Spray sunscreens, some of which tend to phouff off into the air, are responsible for many cases of sunburn in children. Avoid them.

Reapply the same amounts of sunscreen at least every two hours. Some people burn within that time even with sunscreen on. And it should be applied more often than that if it is likely to have been wiped, washed or sweated off.

Sunscreen ingredients cost about the same so if you pay more, it's usually for perfume, moisturiser or a brand name. Check the use-by date and chuck it out if you haven't used it.

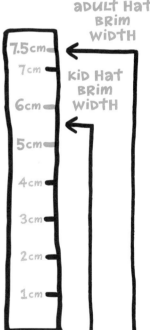

3 **sunhats**   They should not be mesh or have holes in them that let sun through. They should be legionnaire-style (like a baseball cap with a flap at the back and sides), or upside-down bucket-style with a brim that sticks out 5 to 6 cm on a little kid and 7.5 cm on an adult. I doubt you'll have a ruler with you while shopping, so have a look at this one and measure it against one of your fingers, which you probably *do* take shopping with you. An adult brim is the length of my index finger and a kid brim is about the length of my little finger.

4 **shade**   Shade means proper shadow: dark and sharp-edged, cast by trees, shade cloth or an awning, an umbrella, or those pop-up tenty things (as long as they're not too hot inside). UV rays get through mesh netting and light-weave fabrics and flyscreens. Most baby and car shops sell suction or stick-on shade shapes for car windows. There are also retractable rollerblind-style ones, or try an old towel with one end trapped in the top of the rolled-up car window. Prams and strollers should have a shade roof for when you're on the move, but park them in the shade. Drape a solid cloth over the pram or

stroller to get complete protection if you can't get into the shade, but make sure the baby is cool and well ventilated. Wetting the cloth might help lower the temperature.

5 sunglasses   Intense sunlight can make babies and toddlers squint or get cranky, and in the long term can lead to the development of cataracts as the eyes try to protect themselves. Shade your baby's eyes by not having them in the direct sun. Look for sunnies for your toddler with an Australian Standard tag (this only relates to the lenses) and that block out all UV rays (check the labelling). Cool-looking toy sunglasses have no protection. Wrap-around styles will protect the eyes from sun coming in at the sides. Some toddlers and preschoolers won't have a bar of them but others, when told they look cool, or who see older kids or adults wearing them, might wear them proudly. A hat with the right brim (see 'Sunhats', previous page) will also help protect eyes.

See the light

Kids need light to develop their best sight. Ideally they should get up to three hours outside every day; but being in the shade and with sun protection on will expose them to enough light.

more info on sun protection

cancer.org.au/preventing-cancer/sun-protection
Helpline: 13 11 20
Note the hyphens in the Cancer Council website title. All the sun protection advice and statistics you'd expect, plus lots of practical hints.

Skin type & sun care

Fair-skinned blondies and dear freckly gingernuts are most in danger from sunburn. A tan or freckles are evidence of sun damage – of the skin trying to protect itself. A tan does not protect kids against further damage or cancer.

Vitamin D & sunlight

All kids need some exposure to sunlight at safe times of the day, to 'convert' it into vitamin D. Some foods have vitamin D (egg yolks, canned fish, fortified milks, plain oat porridge) but the body 'makes' it more efficiently from sunlight. Kids with very dark skin could need minimal sun care in order to make enough vitamin D (pale folk can convert sunlight each day to enough vitamin D in minutes, but darker-skinned folk can take hours). Sun protection authorities say kids with very dark skin can get sunburnt, and need their eyes protected. All babies and toddlers, regardless of skin colour, need protection.

The amount of sunlight needed to make enough vitamin D in relation to skin colour is not an exact science, so use your own judgement in consultation with your doctor: some kids might need a supplement, especially those who get very little sun exposure at all due to covering clothes, or who are most often indoors because of another health condition. A real vitamin D deficiency can lead to serious health problems. A few years ago, after more research, US authorities doubled the recommended amount of vitamin D that kids need.

immunisation

Immunisation is one of the top five inventions ever
(the others are electricity, contraception, hot water bottles,
and drinking tea through a biscuit). Parents used to have
to worry about their baby dying of measles and ten other
things, or being paralysed with polio. Now because
of fanatical fringe campaigners with wrong information,
some parents worry about vaccines.

This chapter explains why you can relax about doing the
right thing. When you've read it all, you can have a sticker.

the best present you'll ever give your kid

Your baby and toddler, if they get booster jabs as recommended on the national immunisation schedule, can now have lifelong protection against lots of scary diseases and various miserable illnesses that used to kill and damage millions of kids a year, before the vaccines were invented.

⭐ **A vaccination** is the injection of a tiny amount of medical vaccine.

⭐ **Immunisation** is the effect that vaccination has.

Your baby, if they get booster jabs as recommended on the national immunisation schedule, will be immunised against so many scary diseases and various miserable illnesses which used to kill millions of children a year before.

It is some kind of miracle, really: a quick jab containing three vaccines adds no more challenge to your kid's immune system than licking the floor, or spending a day playing. It gives you peace of mind and your kid lifelong health advantages that are truly miraculous. And by the way, they now use distraction and pain-relief tactics and tiny needles: nothing like the big ones you see in stock photos on websites.

Our great-grandmothers would be thrilled for us: they lost so many babies and children to these diseases, which are active in some countries and an imminent threat to areas where not enough children are immunised.

Vaccine combos

Although the list of vaccines at each scheduled age looks daunting, they'll be combined in 'cocktails' so there probably won't be more than two jabs at any appointment, except at 12 months when there'll probably be three. The combination vaccines have undergone years of rigorous trials and testing and they don't busy your kid's immune system much more than a big lick from a dog. Babies happily deal with billions of germs a day. Actual billions!

BLAST FROM THE PAST
'There were 214 cases of diphtheria in January 1934 in NSW.
— *Sydney Morning Herald*, 1934

how does a vaccine work?

Vaccines work by introducing into the body a bit of deactivated (no longer dangerous) disease virus or bacteria. And then the body's immune system says, 'Oh, no you don't! You look like a dodgy intruder!' and starts producing antibodies – defences to the disease – without being threatened by the disease itself. When your kid's body encounters the germ again later in life, their immune system is able to say 'Oh, ho! Not you again! I already know how to keep you out.'

Other bits inside vaccines include a preservative (no mercury or mercury-like substance is used for this in any Australian childhood vaccines), a sugar 'stabiliser', sterile water, the relevant germ, and the relevant compound to make sure the germ isn't 'active'. Vaccines are not 'full of toxins'.

A new vaccine is first tested on laboratory animals, then larger animals, then finally on human adult volunteers first. This process takes many, many years. Results are then reported, published and checked by government licensors before a vaccine is released for medical use in kids.

> **BLAST FROM THE PAST**
> 'Of the 200 children in the Queensland Blind, Deaf and Dumb [sic]
> Institution, 60 are the victims of [rubella: German measles] . . .
> their mothers had it before they were born.'
> – *The Worker*, Brisbane, 1949

stuff to know about immunisation

Australia has a list of recommended vaccinations for all babies and kids called the National Immunisation Program. With a few strategically spaced injections and some liquid vaccine, by the age of 5 your kid will be protected from measles, mumps, rubella, diphtheria, tetanus, whooping cough, polio, hepatitis B, pneumococcus, rotavirus, meningococcal bacteria, chicken pox and a bacterium called Hib (*Haemophilus influenzae* type b) that used to be the most common cause of meningitis, among other things. Other vaccines will go into the mix in the future. Doctors also recommend all kids over 6 months old have a flu injection each year (see flu info coming up in details on diseases).

The immunisation program protects individual children from these 'old-fashioned' diseases; and creates a safer community for those who can't have immunisations: this includes some kids who are already dealing with serious health problems or disadvantages.

A public health campaign of immunisations eradicated smallpox, and we got close with polio until anti-vaccination extremists made it harder again. There's also what is known as 'herd immunity' (moo). When enough people in a population have been immunised, even the unimmunised people are protected, because the disease can't spread. This whole-community protection is called 'herd immunity' and if it drops below a certain level, diseases can infiltrate again. This has already happened with deadly whooping cough in hotspots for vaccine refusal.

Before worldwide immunisation programs, millions of children died of vaccine-preventable diseases every year. In Australia the number of deaths from diphtheria, whooping cough, tetanus, polio and measles has plummeted dramatically since immunisation began. Each year around the world tens of thousands of children die of measles – it used to be millions each year. It's hard to get your head around those sorts of statistics.

Where do you get immunisations?

Kids are given an injection or swallow a little bit of liquid (oral vaccine) by their family doctor, or at a community clinic, or by specially accredited nurses on a particular day arranged by the local council or other health department. It's free, covered by Medicare. Flu vaccinations and a vaccine that protects against extra strains of meningococcal may cost extra. Vaccines needed for overseas travel must also be paid for.

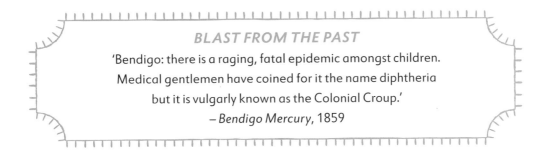

BLAST FROM THE PAST
'Bendigo: there is a raging, fatal epidemic amongst children.
Medical gentlemen have coined for it the name diphtheria
but it is vulgarly known as the Colonial Croup.'
– *Bendigo Mercury*, 1859

australian immunisation schedule

Vaccines are 'bundled' in combinations of double or triple vaccine injections, which means that even though a baby is being protected against many dangerous diseases, there won't be more than two injections at their appointment. 'Booster' shots after the first vaccination, in later years, make sure a child is eventually fully protected against a disease.

This is the standard schedule:

in the days after birth	hepatitis B
2-month-old baby	pneumococcal disease; rotavirus (liquid); one-shot diphtheria, tetanus, whooping cough and polio (DTP); Hib bacteria and hepatitis B
4-month-old baby	pneumococcal disease; rotavirus (liquid); diphtheria, tetanus, whooping cough and polio (DTP); Hib bacteria and hepatitis B
6-month-old baby	pneumococcal disease; rotavirus (liquid); diphtheria, tetanus, whooping cough and polio (DTP); Hib bacteria and hepatitis B
1-year-old baby	meningococcal A, C, W and Y and Hib bacteria; measles, mumps, rubella (MMR)
18-month-old baby	measles, mumps, rubella and chicken pox; diphtheria, tetanus, whooping cough and polio (DTP); pneumococcal disease; rotavirus
4-year-old preschooler	boosters for diphtheria, tetanus, whooping cough and polio (DTP).

As babies under 2 months are unvaccinated and need further boosters after that, everyone else in contact with your family should be fully immunised. Adults may well need boosters for whooping cough. Kids should be up to date with the schedule.

Newborn immunisation

If a mum tested positive for hep B in pregnancy, then her baby should have their first hep B immunisation at birth. Otherwise you can wait until the first scheduled as part of the vaccines given at 2 months.

Babies have injections in their thigh up to age 1, and then into the arm for older kids because the muscle is bigger then.

The vitamin K injection is not an immunisation or vaccination but must be given at birth to make sure babies don't develop a haemorrhage condition. See 'vitamin K' in the index to find out more.

more info on the immunisation schedule

The Australian Immunisation Register (AIR) keeps your child's immunisation record throughout their life. This avoids getting unnecessary extra immunisations when you can't remember who's had what. Doctors should be able to access it online when you ask them. On request, the register will send you an up-to-date certificate free, by post. Many childcare centres, kindergartens and schools require a copy of this to enrol a kid.

humanservices.gov.au
1800 653 809
Search 'immunisation register' on this government site for more info.

immunise.health.gov.au
Official site of the Immunise Australia Program, with current schedules and lots of explanations for any parent worries.

BLAST FROM THE PAST
'The oldest inhabitants recollected no period at all at which measles had been so prevalent, or so fatal to infant existence; and many were the mournful [funeral] processions . . .'
– Charles Dickens, *Oliver Twist*, 1837

Diseases & their vaccinations

Disease	Symptoms and effects	How it can be spread
Hepatitis B	Virus that causes fever; nausea; tiredness; dark wee; yellow skin; eventual liver damage or cancer in midlife (babies usually don't show symptoms when they are infected but have liver damage).	Bloodborne; in children, being born to or breastfed by a carrier, or (very rarely) stepping on a syringe or wound-to-wound contact.
Meningococcal A, C, W, Y	Different strains of bacteria in many healthy carriers that causes flu-like symptoms in some people, with rapid decline. Symptoms may include muscle pain; fever; stiff neck; aversion to bright lights; a serious red or purple rash (which doesn't disappear with gentle pressure on the skin). Can be quickly fatal.	Droplets being transported from the throat, often by sneeze.
***Haemophilus influenzae* type b (Hib)**	Bacterium that can cause meningitis, blood poisoning; hearing loss; swelling in the throat that can suffocate; pneumonia; infections; and death. A severe problem for under-5s.	Coughs, sneezes and close contact.
Diphtheria	Sore throat, fever, hoarse voice and cough. In severe cases, swelling causes a throat blockage, possible suffocation, rarely paralysis, death in up to 10 per cent of cases.	Sneezes, coughs, contact with bacteria on hand or hanky.
Rotavirus	The most common cause of the most severely dehydrating form of 'gastro', which used to cause many deaths in babies and toddlers. It can recur.	Contact with poo, sneezes, coughs; kids putting fingers in their mouth.
Tetanus	Muscle spasms; stiff jaw and neck; breathing problems; convulsions; the nervous system shuts down; can lead to death.	A common bacterium in dirt, manure and some animals, which produces a toxin if it gets into a deep wound.

Possible side effects of the vaccine	Why we need the vaccine	Alternative to the vaccine that would guarantee safety from infection
Rarely, low-grade fever, sore arm at injection site.	Some children born to hep B carriers will become infected and have a 1 in 3 chance of later serious liver disease.	None.
Injection site inflammation, temporary crankiness in babies, temporary headache in adults.	This combination vaccine protects against 4 of the most dangerous meningoccocal strains known to have damaged or killed Australian children. Meningoccocal B is not covered under the schedule.	None. An unimmunised person exposed can take antibiotics that can reduce chances of getting it. See a doctor immediately.
Low-grade fever, sore injection site, nausea, joint pain.	Before routine vaccination (1993), there were 10–15 deaths a year and many more cases of deafness and brain damage. By 1998 there had been a 90 per cent drop in cases.	None.
See 'Whooping cough' jab side effects, coming up.	The most deadly infectious disease in Australia in 1900; now virtually eradicated in many countries.	None.
Small chance of slight tummy upset. Very rare side effect of a bowel blockage that needs early treatment; be aware in the 3 weeks after the first and second doses.	Fiercely contagious. Most kids get it before age 5. Talk to your doctor if worried. Pre-vaccine, each year 10 000 Aussie kids (mostly under 2) were hospitalised and 100 000 went to doctor or emergency room.	None.
See 'Whooping cough' jab side effects, coming up.	Tetanus is very rare in Australia now and almost exclusively strikes under-vaccinated people. The death rate of patients is about 10 per cent. The tetanus bacteria will always exist so we'll always need the vaccine.	None. Unimmunised people need a tetanus immunoglobulin jab (has side effects) and vaccine after a puncture or similar wound.

Diseases & their vaccinations (continued)

Disease	Symptoms and effects	How it can be spread
Whooping cough (pertussis)	Cough and sniffles; cold-like symptoms usually develop into distressing coughing fits and inability to draw breath after coughing spasms with distinctive 'whooping' sound, or paused breathing episodes; the coughing may go on for 2–3 months; sometimes vomiting; more rarely, permanent lung or brain damage, convulsions and coma; death more likely in babies under 6 months.	Coughs, sneezes, contact with the bacteria on hands, tissues, etc. Highly contagious: 3 vaccine doses by the age of 6 months are needed to give high protection to a baby.
Polio (infantile paralysis)	Most children don't show symptoms, but some have nausea, diarrhoea, fever, vomiting, nerve damage; less than 1 per cent will become paralysed or have muscle stiffness; up to 5 per cent will die from their breathing muscles being paralysed; and half of the survivors will have permanent paralysis of the legs.	Virus spread by saliva and poo.
Pneumococcal disease	Fever; fussiness or listlessness, especially in septicaemia or blood poisoning; neck stiffness; sensitivity to bright light; headache in babies or children with meningitis; pneumonia with rapid breathing and cough; ear infections, bacterial meningitis.	Sneezes, coughs, dribble. From contact with the bacteria to symptoms may be less than 24 hours.
measles	Fever; cough; conjunctivitis; feeling miserable; irritability; exhaustion; usually in children aged 1 to 4; 10–14 days after contact cold-like symptoms appear, followed after 3–7 days by tiny red spots on inside of cheeks, then fine blotchy rash, usually starting on the face; spreads to rest of body; symptoms last 2 weeks. It's harder to see the spots on dark skin. Complications include ear infections, pneumonia, diarrhoea and, rarely, inflammation of the brain, causing death in 10–15 per cent. More rarely, it can cause progressive brain damage up to 7 years later, which is always fatal.	Sneezes, coughs or other contact. Hugely contagious virus, active for 4 days before and after the first appearance of the rash.

Possible side effects of the vaccine

Why we need the vaccine

Alternative to the vaccine that would guarantee safety from infection

Possible sore arm from jab and, rarely, low-grade fever, irritability, redness at jab site, or *very* rarely (1 in more than 30,000 doses) a pale, floppy episode in the 48 hours after the vaccine, but this is brief with no long-term effects.

Unvaccinated babies have died of whooping cough in recent years. Adult booster shots may be needed to help protect everyone.

Treatment with antibiotics doesn't cure it but may shorten duration of symptoms and prevent infection of others.

See 'Whooping cough' jab side effects above.

Polio was a major health crisis, causing public panic and paralysed children in Australia. In 1938 nearly 40 people in every 100 000 had it. An import is always possible from somewhere else in the world. There was a PNG outbreak in 2018.

None.

Rarely, fever, redness at the jab site. Extremely rarely, vomiting or diarrhoea.

Pneumococcal disease results in serious infections and is a major cause of meningitis in kids (mostly under 2). The vaccine stops 13 types of bacteria that cause most cases here. In 2003, before the scheduled vaccine, 7 babies died.

None.

Sore arm; in 10 per cent of children a mild fever and non-contagious rash 6–11 days after the injection. Up to 1 in a million children may experience a seizure. A case of measles itself is much more likely to cause a seizure.

Before the vaccine, measles was a common childhood disease in Australia and contributed to millions of deaths worldwide a year. In 1873 a ship carrying measles docked in Fiji, and within 3 months a quarter of the 30 000 Fijians had died from the disease. In 2006 the Jarawa tribe of the Andaman Islands was almost wiped out by measles.

None. The MMR (measles, mumps, rubella) vaccine given within 72 hours of contact (if patient is aged over 9 months), or an immunoglobulin injection given within 7 days, may help or have no effect.

Diseases & their vaccinations (continued)

Disease	Symptoms and effects	How it can be spread
Mumps	Fever; headache; big puffed-out cheeks caused by infection of salivary glands; trouble or pain when swallowing; shivering; avoiding light (it 'hurts' the eyes); 'floppy' tiredness. Rarer side effects include deafness; swollen testicles in teen boys or men, which can cause infertility; brain inflammation in 1 out of 5000 kids.	Airborne drops in sneezes, coughs; caused by a virus.
Rubella (German measles)	Swollen glands around the neck, in the groin and/or in the armpits; a pinky-to-red rash on the head and neck behind the ears for 2–3 days; slight fever; joint pain in adults. Symptoms can last for 2–3 weeks. Varies in its effects, but can be devastating. If caught by a woman up to about her 20th week of pregnancy, is most likely to cause birth defects such as blindness, deafness and brain damage.	Very contagious: coughs and sneezes. A person with rubella is contagious for a week before the rash appears and until 5 days after it first appears. If you have rubella you must try to avoid passing it on to a pregnant woman at risk.
Chicken pox (varicella)	Usually starts with a fever, listlessness, loss of appetite and a rash, followed by the telltale spots, usually 10 days to 3 weeks after catching the virus; the spots keep appearing for a few days and then go through the process of becoming blistered, then itch, before finally drying up; scratching them may cause a scar.	Usually sneaky virus droplets: damp kid contact (infected clothes and bedding), sneezes. It's very contagious for 2 days before rash appears; stays contagious until last spot disappears.
Flu (seasonal influenza)	Flu is more common April to October in Australia. Each year a flu vaccine is formulated for the most likley strains around. The immunisation lasts for the 'flu season'.	Coughs, sneezes, germs on hands. The flu vaccine cannot cause flu.

Possible side effects of the vaccine

Why we need the vaccine

Alternative to the vaccine that would guarantee safety from infection

Low-grade fever, which is related to the measles component, and in about 1 per cent of cases, slight facial swelling.

Nearly all people in Australia had mumps during childhood before the vaccine made it very rare.

None.

Slight fever and sore arm are the most common; some women develop temporary joint pain.

Before immunisation it was a common cause of lasting damage to babies. Now, pregnant women are far less likely to catch it. Rubella has made some comebacks, including in the Pacific region, where MMR immunisation rates have fallen below a herd immunity.

None. Women need to be immunised up to 1 month before getting pregnant.

Possibly sore arm, fever and rash.

Before vaccine schedules, 1500 Australian kids were hospitalised a year, with 5 or so deaths. Not usually life threatening but miserable for most kids. Rare complications include skin infections, pneumonia and brain inflammation. Possible recurring painful shingles throughout life.

None. Kids get the vaccine with MMR at 18 months, which is up to 85 per cent effective, so some kids may get a milder case of chicken pox than they would have otherwise.

Possible sore arm, fever, headache, muscle aches.

You need a new jab each year. Antibiotics don't stop the flu. Flu can be fatal, especially in children and the elderly.

None.

~~~~~ more info on any immunisation worries ~~~~~

immunise.health.gov.au
Advice line: 1800 671 811
Australian Health Department hub with lots of useful info and fact sheets. Choose 'About immunisation', then 'Safety of vaccines' or Myths about immunisation'.

ncirs.edu.au/consumer-resources
Top immunisation and vaccination experts and researchers have joined to honestly and respectfully address the concerns parents can have. The program is called SKAI, Sharing Knowledge About Immunisation. On this National Centre for Immunisation Research and Surveillance site, choose any of the options under SKAI.

Search 'flu vaccine protects healthy children RCH' on YouTube to see a Royal Children's Hospital Melbourne video about how serious the flu can be for small children. It is not just a severe cold but a potentially deadly virus.

BLASTS FROM THE PAST

'Infantile paralysis (polio) . . . It was tragic, how many kids would just disappear from school. Sometimes they would return after months, pale, thin and wasted. More often they would just fade from life. They died, from pneumonia, scarlet fever, diphtheria, whooping cough, polio . . . adults died too, from diseases that today are curable.'
— *Australian Women's Weekly*, 1963

'News has been received here that an epidemic of measles caused 500 deaths in the Tonga Islands.' — *Express and Telegraph*, SA, 1893

'Thirty-eight more deaths from pneumonic influenza were officially reported . . . in the metropolitan area in the 24 hours ended at 8 p.m. yesterday. The new cases reported in the same period totalled 189.'
— *Daily Telegraph*, NSW, 1919

~~~~~ more info on the immunisation debate ~~~~~

Autism's False Prophets: Bad Science, Risky Medicine, and the Search for a Cure by Paul Offit (Columbia University Press, USA)
A world-renowned vaccine specialist and child health expert explains why the anti-vaxxers are getting in the way of real research and understanding of autism spectrum disorder.

briandeer.com
A British journalist's definitive round-up on the scandalous 'research' that lied about a link between the MMR vaccine and autism, and how the hoax was exposed. Click on 'Investigating the MMR fraud' at the very top of the page.

badscience.net
British website that tracks the misbehaviour of both the pharmaceutical industry and anti-vaxxers, and new-age nonsense.

polioeradication.org
The Global Polio Eradication Initiative.

~~~~~~~~~~~~~~~~~~~~~~~~~~~~~~~~~

getting immunised

If you have a lot of questions you'd like answered, it's probably best to go to your doctor or child & family health nurse. They'll be able to answer any questions about why the vaccines are safe for your child and your family. They'll check that there are no previous illnesses or allergic conditions that mean your child should see an immunisation specialist at your local children's hospital.

If you buy a vaccine from the chemist on prescription and take it to the doctor for the injection, make sure you keep it at the right temperature to maintain its usefulness – usually refrigerated but not frozen. All parents are asked to hang around with their baby or toddler after the injection for fifteen minutes to ensure observation of any allergic reaction, such as anaphylactic shock (this is very rare).

If your kid is quite sick and has a fever, it's probably best to postpone the immunisation in case it's harder to spot any side effects of the vaccination. If your kid has sneezes, sniffles or an ordinary old cold or is on antibiotics, it's almost always fine to go ahead with the immunisation, but ask your doctor if you're worried.

Making injection day okay

For babies, you just have to soothe and cuddle them because they won't understand. Distraction might still work with them, too.

Babies usually just look momentarily horrified and accusing when they get their injections in their chubby wee thighs, and cry briefly until they're cuddled and distracted, perhaps by a breastfeed or bottle-feed. Some doctors and nurses give a little dose of sugar to soothe a baby just before the injection, which helps dull their perception of the needle.

Toddlers can be more stoic or cry a little, and they too forget the pain moments later, especially when cunningly distracted. You might be surprised to see how slender the disposable needle is these days and how brief the injection is.

Have on hand tissues for tears, a distraction device or toy, a special 'reward' for an older baby or small child, and a comforting toy or other item. The following things should help with toddlers and preschoolers.

⭐ Be guided by your toddler: do they need a lot of preparation? Immunisation nurse Jennifer Irwin told me: 'Sometimes it is good to have a story or two a day or so before, or perhaps some play with a toy medical kit to prepare.' You can ask your playgroup or childcare centre to have a group chat about it.

⭐ Don't give a toddler the option of saying no to a jab. This is one of the times as a parent that you need to gently tell them what's going to happen, not ask them if it's okay with them, or wait until they think it might be a good idea to have a jab.

⭐ Be matter-of-fact about having an injection: don't build it up to be important or scary.

⭐ Never say 'Don't cry'. Crying's okay.

⭐ Explain (even if it's been explained before) that the nurse or doctor is going to put some very special medicine inside them to stop them from getting bad sicknesses, and that the nurse or doctor is going to use a needle and it will only take a second.

⭐ If asked, don't pretend that it won't hurt. Say it might sting for a short time but you'll have a special surprise treat ready for them straight afterwards.

⭐ You'll be asked to hold the kid firmly to help them be very still. Try to make this feel cuddly rather than restraining.

choccy frog reward

⭐ Straight after, ask the kid to choose between, say, a sticker and a jelly bean, or a cartoon bandaid over the injection spot. The 'choosing' makes their brain switch to something new.

⭐ Praise them afterwards for sitting still during the injection and for having it. Make a fuss of them.

⭐ You can press on the injection site afterwards to dull the stinging, but don't massage it.

STICKING PLASTERS

⭐ If the injection site is red and sore afterwards, a covered cool pack can be held gently on it and a usual dose of paracetamol can be given: check with your doctor.

⭐ Many toddlers and preschoolers appreciate a 'debriefing', so answer any questions again about why they had the injection and how they're protected against special sicknesses now.

⭐ The site of the injection can be sore to the touch for a few days. This is because injection into soft tissues can cause low-level bruising.

⭐ Ask your doctor or nurse for any side effects you should keep an eye out for and what to do if they appear.

← sticker rewards

How to distract a kid during an injection

Most kids prefer to look away, but some like to watch: either is fine. A parent blowing bubbles, a new and exciting toy, making a favourite toy 'talk', or singing a silly happy song are all good. If your kid is really anxious, ask your doctor to refer you to a specialist immunisation clinic, often at a hospital, where nurses have many tricks, and sometimes a fancy distraction like a buzzy bee toy from the fridge strapped onto the kid's arm above the injection site, with tickly wings: with those the kid usually doesn't even feel the injection.

Reactions to vaccines

In extremely exceptional cases, about one in a million kids, a vaccination can cause anaphylactic shock: an immediate, severe allergic reaction. Usually it starts with raised welts or hives, or an itchy rash, swelling around the eyes or mouth, or perhaps a vomit, but then progresses to difficulty breathing, a hoarse voice and even collapse. If it's going to happen, it will probably be within five minutes of the injection or a little later, in the vast majority of cases within half an hour; in all cases within two hours. (A nurse giving 100 immunisations a week for 52 weeks a year would see one of these reactions once every 200 years. And she'd be very wrinkly by then too.)

Treatment is usually a swift adrenaline injection, possibly extra oxygen, and always a trip to hospital for observation.

If a fever develops, a trip to your doctor is a good idea: it may not be the immunisation that is causing the high temperature. (Young children pick up new infections often but usually fight them off.) A sudden high fever can cause a brief fit called a febrile convulsion (see 'A febrile convulsion' in the Index). If your kid has a convulsion for the first time, call an ambulance on 000 (in NZ, 111) immediately.

Teddy's had 27 injections

Or after it has stopped go straight to your doctor's office or hospital emergency department to have your child checked.

In very rare cases your child's fever might go up very quickly due to the vaccine, but it's far more likely there's another cause that needs to be treated. Fever does not cause brain damage and there are no long-term problems from a febrile convulsion, but they can be scary for you to see.

Because thousands of kids in Australia have vaccinations every day, coincidence says some of them will get a cold or have a fever afterwards, or even a febrile convulsion, that's unrelated to the injection.

If your child has had a reaction to an injection that worries you, talk about it with your doctor, and if you're still concerned, ask for a referral to the specialist immunisation clinic at your local children's hospital. If needed, they'll have a chat with you and maybe schedule your next injections at their clinic, where they can keep watch and reassure you.

Anti-vaxxers

The anti-vaccination movement in Australia is run by a small but very active group of extremists online who lie and mislead about the effects of vaccines, using social media, social pressure and videos or films. Members of the group regularly harass parents of babies who have died of vaccine-preventable diseases such as whooping cough who have taken part in awareness campaigns.

They continue to post misleading info such as 'vaccines cause autism' (disproved) and claims such as 'rubella is a relatively mild illness' (wrong: if contracted by a pregnant woman, rubella can make the baby blind and deaf.)

Since vaccines were invented there have been protest activists. First they were usually religious, and now it's a strange coalition of 'natural' or 'no chemical' advocates, conspiracy theorists, parents who get wrong information online, and organised activists with links to ultra-right-wing groups in the USA.

myths about immunisation

If you follow certain organisations online or join a parent or friendship group that's a vortex of anti-vaxxers, you will be in an echo chamber of disproven extremist theories presented as fact. Let's bust some myths.

MYTH 'Children who were breastfed and eat natural foods are protected.'

Not true. A breastfed, fully organic-eating unvaccinated child has the same vulnerability to an infectious disease such as measles as an unvaccinated bottle-fed kid who eats junk food.

MYTH 'The doctors and nurses are in league with pharmaceutical companies to make more money. They make more money by making kids sick.'

Aside from being a monstrously bizarre conspiracy theory that covers all doctors and nurses in the world, this can't be true. Doctors and nurses don't make more money by giving vaccines. The vaccine part of a pharmaceutical company's profits is very small compared to the rest of it. Vaccines don't cause illnesses, they prevent them, and thousands of repeated studies have proved it.

MYTH 'Vaccines cause autism.'

This has been totally disproven. It was suggested by one study in the 1990s by a gastroenterologist called Andrew Wakefield, whose 'research' was shown to be a fraud, and who is banned from being a doctor in Britain. He was then paid to be an anti-vaccine spokesman by an anti-vaccine organisation in the USA. He is not a vaccine or immunisation expert. At the time he was saying the MMR triple vaccination shot caused autism, he had filed patents on single-shot vaccines that would have made him a fortune had parents been persuaded to switch from the triple shot. Repeated huge-scale studies around the world have proven over and over that vaccines don't cause autism.

'Paediatrician here . . . I've seen measles in action. The clinical description and photo given [by you] are NOTHING LIKE measles. You might as well seek medical advice from a potato.'
ONLINE COMMENT ON ANTI-VAX SITE

MYTH   'It's the mercury or "thiomersal" in vaccines that damages kids or gives them autism.'

That isn't true, but anyway there is no mercury or thiomersal in any Australian childhood schedule vaccine.

MYTH   'Autism symptoms happen after the MMR vaccine.'

The MMR vaccine jabs are given at 1 year and at 18 months. This is around the same age that many parents notice a regression or developmental delay in communication skills. It makes sense to suspect the jab, but only if you don't have enough information. There is no cause and effect. Vaccines do not cause autism. See 'Autism spectrum disorder (ASD)' in Chapter 35, Special Needs, for more.

MYTH   'It isn't natural.'

Neither are hospitals, tampons, anaesthetics, aeroplanes, treatments for broken legs, men without beards, or salted caramel. But I like them.

MYTH   'The diseases don't exist any more.'

Yes, they do. Whooping cough cases are in most children's hospitals in Australia right now; any disease can be brought in by a returning traveller; and more cases of infectious diseases and deadly tetanus are happening in Australia, and also elsewhere in the world where immunisation rates aren't high enough for 'herd immunity'. Thousands of kids around the world have measles right now.

> 'In Australia on any given day there are hundreds of babies having their MMR jab or preschoolers having the booster. That means any cold, cough, fever or dribble could be mistakenly blamed on the MMR even though it is probably not associated at all. One child in the queue here . . . had a fit just before his injection. If it had been five minutes after, it would have been blamed on the injection.'
> DR NIGEL CURTIS, immunology specialist

MYTH   'Vaccines don't work. It was improved hygiene that stopped diseases.'

Absolute piffle. Hygiene improved health, but didn't stop infectious disease. Anti-vaxxers often use fake or deceptive 'charts' and 'graphs' to seem scientific about this.

MYTH   'It's too much of a challenge to the child's immune system to have multiple vaccines in one jab.'

Single and combination vaccines cannot overwhelm a baby's or toddler's immune system. As a world expert in vaccines told me, 'Compared with a vaccination, a child probably gets more of an immune-system challenge by licking the floor or kissing the dog. Babies could make antibodies to tens of thousands of vaccines if they needed to: thankfully, they won't have to!' Another doctor put it this way: giving eleven vaccines at a time would use a tenth of 1 per cent of the immune system's capability. You're not overwhelming your kid's immune system: you're training it, safely.

MYTH   'Babies and toddlers are too vulnerable to have this stuff injected into them. Wait until they are older.'

They are too vulnerable to the diseases while they're little to delay immunisation. A baby's immune system is one of the things that starts working well as soon as they've come out of their mum. From that moment, babies are colonised by trillions of bacteria (the mind boggles, truly – mine is boggling away totally bogglingly) and immediately start making antibodies, the clever little treasures. Each of those bacteria can have between 2000 and 6000 immunological components. Early vaccines, decades ago, had up to 3000 immunological components. Baby and toddler vaccines now only have about 150 components in them, and together protect against fourteen diseases. Kids' immune systems are challenged more by a day of normal playing than getting a vaccine.

MYTH   'We don't know that the mixed vaccines are safe.'

Yep, we do. Combination vaccines and booster jabs have been being given to millions of kids for many years, and all the evidence shows this is safe. It has taken decades of research and testing, covered by stringent ethics rules and scientific proof, to come up with multiple protection vaccines in one injection.

MYTH   'But the anti-vaxxers seem so sure.'

Yep, that's how extremists work. They're sure.But they're wrong. There's also a genuine Flat Earth Society.

MYTH   'You can use homeopathic vaccines.'

They don't work: even the peak bodies of homeopath organisations agree on this.

MYTH   'Childhood diseases are mostly trivial, just requiring a couple of days in bed.'

This is a lie for many babies and children. They are potentially life-threatening to all kids, and especially vulnerable children – premmie babies, kids who are already sick, and Aboriginal kids in remote areas.

BLASTS FROM THE PAST

'Doctors fear an epidemic of measles which has broken out in Victoria will affect between 20,000 and 30,000 children and cause up to 200 deaths, mostly among children aged 2 to 3 years . . . About 200 cases and a few deaths already in North Melbourne.' – *Sydney Morning Herald*, 1939

NSW Government Statistics for March 1913: 'Infant mortality was 81 per 1000 births. The rate is satisfactory, being equal to the average for the past five years . . . whooping cough caused 18 deaths, diphtheria 13, typhoid fever 7 and influenza 1.' – *Guyra Argus*, NSW, 1913

'Two more positive cases of polio were notified yesterday bringing the State total to 13 . . . 12 new cases of poliomyelitis which were reported to the Health Department today brought the total of victims to 607. Thirty-eight people have died since the outbreak.' – *The Advocate, Burnie*, 1949

35

LUCKY DIP

SPECIAL NEEDS

Who's normal? We're all variations of normal, and so are our kids. We all have differences, from an especially long toe or a psychological quirk to a learning difficulty, a surprising skill, a developmental delay or a physical disability. Nobody, in other words, is 'perfect'. There is no 'perfect'. And yet each child is loved and cherished, and families do their best to embrace what is needed when it comes to their child's special needs.

disabilities in kids

A special challenge or disability in a baby or child can be one they are born with that's obvious, such as Down syndrome or spina bifida, or one that only becomes recognised over time, such as autism or an attention deficit disorder. A disability might be due to random chance, a genetically inherited trait, a medical condition or an accident. Some can be easily incorporated into life with some strategies or corrective surgery. Others are conditions that will remain into adulthood and require constant management.

Some families will need to make minor adjustments to cope with a temporary problem; in other cases, families have to make major, long-term adjustments – to their expectations and perhaps even to their homes – to deal with 'the new normal'.

Some disabilities are noticed when a baby or child misses developmental milestones, such as crawling, talking or walking, or learning social behaviours.

Because we're so used to our own kid's quirks, something out of the ordinary might be pointed out by a relative, friend, carer or teacher. Don't freak out or be angry about this. It may just be that your kid is at the lower edge of the development range (Einstein famously didn't speak until he was 4). But if someone has raised a red flag, it's worth checking with your family doctor, because early intervention is a precious advantage to any child that will allow them an easier life at home, at school and with friends. And if everything is okay, you have peace of mind.

But, oh dear, be prepared to get confused. For many parents, the search for an accurate diagnosis can be frustrating and confusing, as different doctors in different specialties or even in the same medical team can disagree or use different terms. The opinions can be especially different when the disability is in the brain, which can't be easily examined and so the condition can't be easily named.

Diagnosis

While some parents resent the idea of 'labelling' their child, fearing that it will lead to discrimination or hold them back, others are relieved to have a diagnosis so that they can accept it and focus on treatment and help.

As soon as you suspect there is a problem, or just to set your mind at rest if someone else has mentioned a concern, arrange an appointment with your child & family health nurse or family doctor. In most cases, they will refer you to a specialist, to identify or rule out a certain condition. A diagnosis is usually made by a paediatrician who specialises in the area. It might include extra expert testing and evaluation. Take notes or feel free to bring a friend to see specialists and other relevant consultants – it can be a time when shock causes everything to go in one ear and out the other.

It's comforting that Australia has some of the best-trained and most dedicated hospital midwives, doctors, paediatricians, specialist surgeons, hospital social workers, counsellors, researchers, support groups and educators in the world. Consult widely and find doctors and other professionals you trust. This is where being stubborn comes in handy: keep asking questions and asking for more referrals, or stay with one doctor or group of specialists who treats your child well and who you understand and respect. Keep pushing until you feel satisfied that everything that needs to be done is being done.

You will want to do your 'own' research, but don't feel you have to become an instant expert on a condition and know all the answers.

You are already the expert on your kid, and that's the most important thing.

When searching info online, remember that large international sites are often good sources of information but local sites may have links and resources that are more relevant to you. Beware of single-issue sites and others that may push unproven theories and extreme or unhelpful ideas.

Whole family needs

As well as looking after your child, you will need to attend to your own wellbeing. In the early days a diagnosis of a serious disability or a confronting diagnosis may leave you feeling shocked, grief-stricken, disorientated and fiercely protective. You'll probably go through the 'Why me?' stage and 'I can't cope' moments. There's no fault attached to you as a parent. This stuff is random, or hidden in a combination of genes you can't anticipate. Be assured, it wasn't caused by eating or doing the wrong thing in pregnancy, or by immunisations. You don't have to know exactly what to do next or what will happen in the future. Take it one step and, if necessary, one hour at a time.

If you have a partner, keep an eye on your relationship. The stress of having a special-needs child can take its toll on the happiest couple. Be honest with each other and recognise that you might end up 'taking it in turns' to be the optimistic or strong one, and the pessimistic, worried and weepy one. Talk together to try and be on the same page, respect each other's different ways of grieving or searching for answers, and make time, if you possibly can, to do things together to 'escape' and bond, even if it's just slipping away to see a movie.

Be aware of the feelings and needs of your other kids. Special-needs support groups often have resources to help with this.

Getting help when your kid has special needs

It's okay to feel sad, confused, angry, guilty. Start thinking about support systems of family and friends, and ways you can have a break now and then. Give yourself time to work out new priorities and strategies. Make time to talk to your partner (if any) about what's going on. Siblings and relatives need to be involved and to be given space to express their concerns – but you are the boss of your family, and make the decisions.

Be truthful about the condition but don't forget to talk about all the positive things – about how much love there is to go around and how there are lots of people to help.

Many disability services are available in Australia, but access is not always straightforward. Start with your doctor, and then add other medical specialists, or local children's hospital visits. Support, info and advocacy groups tend to be well organised and offer detailed and accessible information.

Talking to other parents who have a kid with a similar disorder can be reassuring and give you lots of options to consider. Parent support groups for specific conditions usually have contacts for parents who've been through, or are going through, what you're experiencing. This can be invaluable in terms of support and suggestions. Ask your doctor, or find peak bodies online.

Quality control

Talk to your doctor and specialist about extra help you might need, and ask them to refer you to practitioners they approve.

Many people have businesses selling services, devices, apps or products for 'special needs', and it can be easy to think you need to do or buy everything on offer or advertised to help your kid. Just because it's available, or for sale, or is well-meaning advice from people, doesn't make it useful. They might sincerely believe what they are saying but that doesn't make it true, or true for you and your family.

~~~~~~ **more info** on kids with special needs ~~~~~~

www.ndis.gov.au
1800 800 110
The Australian government's National Disability Insurance Scheme (NDIS) is required to connect you to services and can provide funding to help with a plan for a disability or a developmental delay. Click on 'Our Locations', find your state or territory, then click on 'Early childhood intervention services' to find your closest one.

specific special needs conditions
healthinsite.gov.au
This federal government health site has a useful A–Z topic list on its home page, usually with good up-to-date info on various conditions.

kidshealth.org.nz
On the home page of this government Health Department website, search 'special needs' for useful links and info on support groups, specific conditions and financial entitlements.

~~~~~~~~~~~~~~~~~~~~~~~~~~~~~~

autism spectrum disorder (ASD)

This is a term used to describe variations on developmental conditions, including Asperger's syndrome through to autism and what is sometimes called, would you believe, 'pervasive disorder not otherwise specified'.

The autism spectrum covers a wide range of symptoms and different developmental difficulties and mental disabilities. Kids on the spectrum can have a range of intelligence levels, just like any kids. A kid with Asperger's syndrome or autism could be much better at some tasks and ways of thinking than other kids. Everyone with autism isn't a 'mathematical genius' despite the stereotype.

'Pervasive disorder' diagnoses tend to cover symptoms that still allow a person to be 'high functioning'. So 'high functioning' or Asperger's or 'Aspie' might be terms you hear to indicate a kid whose intelligence isn't affected but who has difficulty with social interactions.

'Autism' on its own as a word tends to extend to the more intense versions of spectrum characteristics, as well as other difficulties, such as in some cases being non-verbal and entirely dependent on others. A kid can be anywhere along that spectrum from mild to severe, and have their own unique mix of symptoms.

Most people on the spectrum don't have severe autism, and find hobbies, jobs and families that suit their quirks, skills and difficulties in negotiating the 'normal' social world.

Some people on the spectrum find that they are very good at tasks and pursuits that involve intense concentration and focus or obsession, patterns, systems or collection and categories. Many 'high-functioning' kids on the spectrum go to mainstream schools with help; others are home-schooled. Kids with more challenges who perhaps cannot communicate with words or who have a lot of actions, such as rocking, making noises, screaming or becoming agitated, can attend a 'special school', though there are not enough of these schools.

Kids with recognisable characteristics can get along without any intervention if their symptoms don't get in the way of a normal life for them. It is usually difficulties at school and the need for extra support that lead to a clinician and parent realising that the child could benefit from a diagnosis. Their 'traits' might just be seen as quirks, special skills or something they need extra help with now and then, like having somebody else's feelings explained to them.

IQ & aptitude tests

Beware of these. They can't tell us much about a person. A kid might be given a 5 per cent result on one test and a 95 per cent result on another. What's most important is your love, and knowing your individual kid and their potential, and that you can find kind specialists who will treat you as a person, not a score that could change in a few minutes.

It doesn't matter what a 'label' is, or where exactly somebody is on the spectrum (impossible to say). The important thing is to get tailored help for the special needs of your child. It's basically what all parents do, but some get dealt a more complicated hand to play. 'Developmental delay' can be confusing because it implies that the development will happen eventually. In many kids, it won't. Other kids can learn many new skills with special help.

Shared characteristics of the spectrum

People 'on the spectrum' tend to share variations of behaviour in these areas: difficulty in social understanding and communication; difficulty with the idea of imagination; and a focus on repeated or restricted interests or behaviours, sometimes seen as 'obsession'. A few have a very overactive imagination.

Someone on the spectrum might speak later and less than other kids; not like having eye contact; and have trouble identifying the meaning of gestures, body language, facial expressions, sarcasm, irony and other jokes. Kids like this can always seem to be 'the odd one out'. They could be more comfortable with 'telling' than having a conversation.

Kids may not 'make up' games or play 'pretend' things, or be much interested in interacting with others during a game. You know where you are with a kid on the spectrum because they'll give you the straight version. They might put their toys in lines or categories rather than pretend they're talking to each other. Up on the autism end of the spectrum this can mean no verbal communication.

Most kids on the spectrum are soothed by routine and repetition, and become upset at schedule and other changes. They may also like repetitive movements or sounds, made by themselves, or in repeated playing of music or stories. They often have a kind of super-sensitive response to sensory changes, including lights, noise and textures, and enjoy feeling firmly confined. They might fixate on a toy or object for a while and then forget about it.

Many social, coping and responsive skills can be taught to kids on the spectrum so it's easier for them to feel okay around other people and have friends and show affection to family, or acknowledge the bonds they feel.

Some kids on the spectrum are prone to anxiety, tears, rages or all three when they can't make themselves understood, or when things don't go to a predictable pattern or

'I love working with kids with high-functioning autism as a lot of the things they struggle with can be taught – emotions, how to deal with emotions, social etiquette, how to read body language and facial expressions. If you teach these kids this stuff, they do end up doing well! (Just look at me!)'   AUSSIE DOCTOR

schedule, or they feel some sort of sensory overload. There are helpful strategies that can help them manage their feelings. Outsiders can see these as tantrums or the result of being overindulged, which doesn't help.

Of course, many of these behaviours can feel indistinguishable from normal, toddler-like carry-on, which is why outside professional assessment is a good idea.

Remember, though, that kids are individuals, and your kid, more importantly than having a 'condition', will have their own quirks – they may like a squeezy hug or get a twinkle of delight in their eye about certain things . . . you'll get to know your kid.

The cause of autism spectrum disorder

We know it isn't caused by vaccinations, or mercury poisoning, or a simple vitamin D deficiency, or the behaviour of parents. It's almost certainly to do with a combination of genes from both parents, with or without other factors. Boys are more likely to be diagnosed with autism, and so is the twin of a child with autism. Research continues.

Kids diagnosed these days as 'on the spectrum', in the past would have been diagnosed with something else. Depending on where on the spectrum, it might have been 'mentally retarded', or 'not right', or not diagnosed with anything at all and just thought to be 'a hermit', 'odd' or 'his own person'. Others would be labelled 'loner' or 'genius'. Girls were more likely to be called shy, or 'weird'. Such labels are still unhelpful now.

Diagnosis of autism spectrum disorders

This must be done by a specialist paediatrician or psychiatrist. Symptoms of ASD can be seen in some kids from 18 months old onwards if you are an expert trained to know what you're looking for. It's only looking back, given more information, that parents can sometimes see there were signs earlier.

Sometimes suspicions and concerns of relatives, friends and childcare workers or teachers are dismissed due to parents wanting to protect their child from 'labelling', or because they don't want to believe there's something 'wrong', or because they see such talk as hurtful criticism or non-acceptance.

Others in the family could say 'Oh, he's just like Uncle Ferdinand was' or 'You were just like that and you turned out fine' – but your child is not exactly like anyone else, and that sort of talk can be unproductive. It's important to have your suspicions checked, though, for your own peace of mind, starting with a visit to your family doctor. They see lots of kids with all sorts of different developmental times and spurts and delays. All experts and parents with experience agree that the earlier you know there's a special need, the earlier you can get help.

It can be hard to get a firm diagnosis before the age of 3, and you might be given a kind of 'holding diagnosis', something to get on with until your baby is older and things become clearer – because there are developmental differences in all kids, and some will catch up or fall behind a bit in different areas. There can be long waiting lists for medical services and special programs in preschools and primary schools and during holidays, and there is not enough government funding in this area, so the sooner you have some idea of what you're dealing with, the sooner you can do the best by your child in terms of finding the best help you can.

Asperger's syndrome

Kids who used to be diagnosed with Asperger's syndrome are now diagnosed with ASD (Autism Spectrum Disorder), because symptoms can vary. But it's still a useful category for some parents, and many doctors still use the name.

The child's difficulties can be seen as anxiety or depression, or bad temper, when they are trying to fit in and mask their social difficulties. Because they can't 'read faces' to interpret emotions, and can find it a challenge to join a conversation and express interest in other people, and don't understand jokes or non-literal conversation, it can make it difficult for them to keep friends.

'Aim for the moon and see where you end up. He may not be able to live independently or he might end up being an astronaut.' MUM OF A BOY DIAGNOSED ON THE AUTISM SPECTRUM

Girls on the spectrum

Girls tend to be better in general at social skills and dealing with emotions, so their place on the spectrum can go unnoticed. Many find a sense of relief in their teens or adulthood to have a diagnosis of high-functioning autism or Asperger's, to explain some of their feelings and challenges. Identifying a need early can lead to a specialised psychologist explaining social cues and helping to teach social skills, which can be transformative.

Absorbing the shock

Learning that your child has autism, especially if it's 'severe', can be a big shock or perhaps an intense disappointment. But that doesn't mean you don't love your child just as much, or that you won't accept them for who they are. It means you need to reconfigure your life, just more so than most other parents. But it's also true that families do adjust, turn up the dial on their sense of humour and practical sense, muster all the support they can and get on with it. In many ways these families are like everyone else's – hard times, good times, different needs of different siblings, and everybody getting through it the best way they can. For those in that zone, ask for help when you need it. For those outside the zone, don't wait to be asked: ask what you can do to help.

Managing autism spectrum disorder

There is no cure for autism spectrum disorder, in spite of what you might read online. But an early diagnosis and access to special programs can help improve the happiness, behaviour and responsiveness of many kids over time. Special programs can include treatment by psychologists, speech therapists, occupational therapists, early intervention teachers, physiotherapists and music therapists; and dance and music activities, respite workers, and help with transport or education costs.

Start with your doctor, and see 'More info on kids with special needs' earlier in this chapter for educational and other services you could have access to. As more and more is known about autism therapies, better and more individually tailored programs should become available. Make sure your trusted doctor refers you personally to any extra physical therapists or speech pathologists, so you know you are being sent to the right place. This way, there is always a central coordinator of continuing care.

'Cures' for autism spectrum disorders

There are many ways to improve the quality of life and maximise the potential of a person on the spectrum. There's no known cure for autism. This doesn't stop some people claiming they sell 'cures'.

Chelation 'therapy' is based on the idea that autism is the result of heavy metal poisoning. The theory is wrong and the 'treatment' is expensive, dangerous and frightening. Giving bleach to children by any means has no effect on autism and can be agonising and cause death.

Stem-cell therapy has not shown any promising scientifically backed results in this field. Giving an autistic child large doses of vitamins or other nutritional supplements is also unlikely to help, although digestive treatments may help the symptoms of tummy and bowel problems that many autistic kids have.

So far the medical consensus is that the 'cures' cause nothing but unsettled children, and parents having their hopes raised and dashed.

Enlisting friends, their kids & the community

If you have a kid who has some of the social symptoms of autism spectrum disorder, or Asperger's, ask your friends, relatives and your kids' teachers to understand the

'Autism is diagnosed medically, but the "treatment" is educational. It can be so confusing. When our boy was diagnosed and they said there was no cure I cried and cried. He wasn't talking so we sent him to a speech therapist (so expensive), and then found he needed an occupational therapist more, so that came first, then we went back to "language". Now, at 12 he has about ten words, and because we know him so well we can guess right a lot of the time about other stuff. There's a special system at his school, which we use at home so he can show us a picture on his tablet device when he wants something, and he understands when we ask him to do something (and does it, better than some "normal" kids!).'　GRETA

situation, be kind themselves, and enlist other children to be kind and understand the differences. You might want to explain to them that your Eloise finds it hard to understand people's facial expressions, so if they are sad or happy or cross, they will have to use words to tell Eloise. Or, that Jack doesn't like to look at people's eyes all the time, and might find it hard to talk about what other people like doing.

Other kids can be told that changing the rules, or doing something unexpected, can be confusing and difficult for a kid who's on the spectrum. Find things they can do 'together' that all the kids will enjoy, including the one who has some spectrum symptoms.

As awareness of ASD increases, many airports and shopping centres and some entertainment venuesare providing a quiet space for families with kids who have spectrum-related sensitivities. The rooms have adjustable lighting and adjusted audio volumes.

~~~~~ more info on autism spectrum disorder ~~~~~

autismspectrum.org.au
1800 ASPECT
Autism Spectrum Australia has a great website with info and support.

raisingchildren.net.au
On the home page search 'Asperger's', 'autism' or 'autism spectrum disorder'.

tonyattwood.com.au
This website by an Asperger's specialist author and psychologist has many resources parents find helpful. He has written several books about kids with high-functioning autism or Asperger's and how to improve their lives, abilities and understanding. There are links to other info and support on the site.

yellowladybugs.com.au
A non-profit organisation that links girls on the autistic spectrum to social events, such as birthday parties for girls who are not invited to parties. They also have a birthday-card club to make sure girls get to send and receive cards. Some people are just completely ace, aren't they?

attention deficit disorders (ADD & ADHD)

Being an energetic, livewire kid with an active mind who forgets things is a normal part of childhood. Kids diagnosed with attention deficit disorder (ADD) or attention deficit hyperactivity disorder (ADHD) have a medical brain problem that means it's much harder for them than other kids their age to pay attention, stay still and calm, control impulses, or behave in a predictable way.

★ Kids with ADHD are the classic 'livewires' who can't sit still.

★ Kids with ADD without the physical hyperactivity still have a problem with being attentive, which can look more like a child being a daydreamer or 'in their own world'. ADD is more commonly diagnosed in boys, but some girls miss out on a proper diagnosis because they're more likely to be an ADD 'daydreamer' and not hyperactive, so not such a 'problem' for others.

Diagnosis of ADD & ADHD

ADD and ADHD need to be investigated and diagnosed by a paediatric specialist. Your doctor can refer you. You don't 'cause' your child's ADD or ADHD because of bad parenting or discipline problems. The behaviours seem similar to a sleep-deprived kid, or shown by a child in a stressful home or school situation. (A child with both a genetic inheritance and an unsettled life will be dealing with a double whammy.) Because true ADD and ADHD remain into adulthood and throughout life, it's important to know it's not a stage and a child won't 'grow out of it'.

Treatment of ADD & ADHD

There is a definite link between sleep problems and ADD and ADHD symptoms, so try to institute a sleep routine (see Chapter 20, Toddler Sleep, for more). We don't know whether bad sleep patterns can trigger the problem, or the problem causes sleep difficulties, but either way, try some of the suggested strategies for better sleep habits.

Kids and their families can be greatly helped with some coping and learning strategies and, in some (not all) cases, medication. As with most conditions, early diagnosis and intervention with expert treatment give the best chance of a happier child who can do better at school and in social situations.

more info on attention deficit disorders

adhdaustralia.org.au
National info and advocacy group ADHD Australia.

cyh.com
On the home page of this reliable government health site, choose 'Parenting and Child Health' to find the A–Z list of topics, then A for 'ADD and ADHD'.

healthinsite.gov.au
This Australian Health Department site has fact sheets. On the home page choose 'Health topics A–Z' and go from there.

36

teeth

Let's chew over a few teeth facts.
And then suck on some info about
dummies and thumbs.

which teeth arrive, when

Some kids are born with weeny teeth, but the majority have their first couple start to come through between the age of 4 and 10 months, usually more in the middle of that range. They usually get the teeth at the front first, often at the bottom, and then the rest are 'filled in' over the following months. These first ones are sometimes called 'milk teeth'.

Between the age of 1 year and 18 months your kid should have enough teeth for a good chew. Eventually your little gummer will have a mouth full of about twenty teeth by the age of 2 or 3.

Later on, starting at age 6 or 7, they'll start losing baby teeth and replacing them with adult ones and pretending they believe in the tooth fairy for years. By the time they're 12, or in their teens if you're counting 'wisdom teeth', they should have their full set of 32 adult teeth. (Allow for tooth fairy inflation.)

what are the symptoms of teething?

Sometimes a baby rubs their gum, cries or is cranky from the pain of the teeth slowly 'coming through' the gums. These symptoms are not always recognised as teething-related by baby experts but many parents disagree: drooling, red cheeks, a runny nose, fever, nappy rash, sleep disturbance. The gum will often look red and swollen, then you'll see a bit of white poking through and suddenly there's a whole tooth. Each tooth that comes through may cause the baby to be cross and feel pain – or they might hardly notice.

What can you do?

Explain soothingly to your baby what's happening: even if they can't grasp everything they will feel reassured. Give them lots of cuddles and perhaps rub their gum gently with your finger. Mostly kids want to chew on something, which is why rusks (like tiny, hard breadsticks) are popular: check that any you buy are sugar and salt free.

Give babies teething rings from the chemist that can be refrigerated (but don't freeze them). Giving babies frozen things or ice to bite on can be too harsh and can freeze the tissues in the mouth.

The teething stage can be a good time to start your baby learning to sip from a spouty cup, because babies find biting on the spout gives them some relief. Make sure babies aren't biting off bits of things that then become choking hazards.

Teething gel, which is supposed to numb the gum, is not recommended by a lot of doctors because it gets sucked off quickly. You can give a baby painkiller if the pain seems really bad (see 'Painkillers for babies & toddlers' in Chapter 33, Health).

Babies can find it hard to resettle themselves on the nights when a tooth is about to appear.

Teeth on the move

Some teeth naturally grow in odd spaces or at different angles: check with a paediatric dentist if you're concerned. Little teeth can be gradually moved and displaced by dummy or thumb sucking. In some cases this makes a difference to chewing or speech. The teeth will often travel back slowly to the right position if the habit is broken (do this gently: see 'Dummies & thumbs' coming up).

looking after kids' teeth

The main thing is not to give any sweetened drinks (fizzy drinks and cordial) or fruit juice, or to let babies or older kids suck on bottles of milk or juice for ages, particularly at night. All these things almost guarantee decay and, in the worst-case scenario, the unhappy prospect of a general anaesthetic and the pulling-out of some or all of their teeth.

It's best to give a bottle of milk before bed, then clean their teeth. Any daytime drag-around drinks or night-time sips should be water. Breastfed babies can also have their teeth wiped or brushed after the last feed of the day. Make dessert and treats a 'sometimes' thing, not an everyday or always-after-dinner thing. Lollies should be very rare.

Some kids genetically have 'strong teeth' or ones that are shaped better to avoid decay, but they will still need to take care of them; others have to work harder to get the same protection with cleaning.

Going to the dentist

Take the kid to the dentist for a check-up about six months after the eruption of their first tooth, at about 1 year old, and after that take them once or twice a year. Also, get along to the dentist pronto if there is any sign of toothache, bleeding gums, crowding, or anything else that concerns you. Regular trips to the dentist are important. It gets the kid happy with the idea, and helps avoid wayward teeth and orthodontic problems down the track and the huge price tag that comes with them (Medicare and most private health insurers don't cover most kinds of corrective dentistry).

Explaining the dentist

Tell your child why we need to visit the dentist (because they help us look after our teeth, not so we can enjoy the blindingly painful razzle-dazzle of root canal work). Make a game of practising at home or at childcare, especially opening the mouth and letting someone look inside, being on a big chair that goes up and down (pretend or visit someone with one of those TV-watching recliners the size of an aircraft carrier, and shine a light into the kid's mouth).

Don't ever use the dentist as a threat ('You can't have any lollies because you'll get holes in your teeth and the dentist will have to drill your teeth and it hurts'). If your kid is apprehensive, find a paediatric dentist (one who specialises in children) who has a drawcard such as a fish tank in the waiting room or special things to look at in the surgery. Your dentist will probably have all manner of perfectly thrilling pamphlets, free toothbrushes and other paraphernalia tucked away in the cupboard.

~~~~~~~ more info on the dentist ~~~~~~~

Harry and the Dinosaurs Say 'Raahh!'
by Ian Whybrow and Adrian Reynolds (Koala Books, Australia)
A boy and his dinosaurs go to the dentist and open wide.

Cleaning little teeth

Baby teeth can be cleaned gently with your index finger covered by a face washer. From 18 months you can introduce a toddler-sized (weeny) toothbrush and toothpaste. Kids are supposed to have their teeth brushed twice a day – it's most convenient after brekkie and after dinner. Very sugary or acidic drinks, including fresh citrus juices and slices or quarters of citrus fruit can create an acidic environment in the mouth that makes tooth enamel very vulnerable to wear and tear. So keep these to a minimum and wait an hour after they've been eating or drinking them before brushing your kid's teeth.

At first you can do the teeth cleaning, making sure you get to every surface. When your child is a toddler, and if you can afford it, introduce a battery-operated toothbrush – the kid can do more themselves and get more surfaces done properly before you give a final once-over. Put a mirror where the kid can see it: it will guarantee more time spent cleaning the teeth. Kids aren't able to clean their own teeth thoroughly until they're 6 to 10.

Fluoride & toothpaste

Babies and kids should only have a tiny amount of toothpaste for each cleaning. Until they're much older the recommended amount is no more than the size of a pea (the ones under my mattress are huge). Toddlers who put their own toothpaste on will squeeze an entire tube out in seconds.

Fluoride helps protect teeth against decay. Some dental associations say only use water to clean baby teeth until they're 18 months old; others say you can use a tiny smear of fluoride toothpaste the size of a grain of rice from the time the first tooth comes in, then when the kid is about 3, move to a 'pea-sized' amount of toothpaste. This is to avoid a kid swallowing too much fluoride, which can result in mottled stains on the teeth. Fluoride added to the water supply does not pose a health risk, or cause staining.

~~~~~~ **more info** on looking after kids' teeth ~~~~~~

raisingchildren.net.au
For fact sheets, search 'dental care for babies' to find a chart of the teeth and their names, and 'dental care for children' or 'toddler teeth issues', on this federal government–funded parenting supersite.

dummies

Some people are very sternly against dummies (and some of the sternest end up using them). Some want to use a dummy but the baby spits it every time. Others never feel the need. Some parents prefer their kids to suck their thumb and then realise that, too, can be a problem. Other people say Praise Be the Dummy and the Thumb for Yea, Verily, a parent gets a better night's sleep. Others say noooo the baby yells every time it falls out in the night. Dummies and thumbs (or fingers) are certainly not newfangled ideas: both have been used for generations, and both are acceptable for a relatively short time.

Good points about dummies

★ Most babies love them.
★ They will usually soothe an upset baby.
★ They can help solve a sleep problem.

The trouble with dummies

★ Using them in the first month or so can confuse a baby learning to suck from the nipple in the right way.
★ They cost money, deteriorate and get lost, and you need spares.
★ If a baby can't replace their own dummy, they'll cry until you come and do it about 94 times in the night. (This is a very good moment to give it up: one or two nights of fussing and it's over.)
★ Dummies are addictive.
★ When the kid has a cold and they want to suck on their dummy, they can't breathe.
★ They can 'buck' and misalign teeth, especially the longer they're used.
★ They need to be sterilised.

'No 18-year-old is going to be sucking a dummy – don't stress. They'll not want it when they go to school.'
SUSIE

When not to use a dummy:
- ⭐ To shut a child up instead of trying to find out what's wrong.
- ⭐ If they're going to sleep.
- ⭐ If the child always spits it out.

Dummies need to be:
- ⭐ labelled with the Australia/New Zealand Safety Standard
- ⭐ sterilised regularly (after your kid gets bigger and you see what else goes into their mouth you probably won't be quite as rigorous with sterilising – but still, sticking it in your own mouth is amazingly NOT, technically, sterilising)
- ⭐ checked regularly for damage – throw out damaged ones
- ⭐ without liquid of any sort in the handle or teat
- ⭐ given to your child without honey.

Dummies are called pacifiers in the USA because they calm children, and dummies in England and Australia because kids don't speak with them in. If they're still being used after the age of 18 months they can have an effect on children's speech (they can't get much practice while they've got a dummy in!), and teeth problems caused by dummies are common after the age of 2.

Getting rid of the dummy

Here's some advice from parents. You'll need to match a suggestion to the personality and sensitivity of your kid, or gently experiment.
- ⭐ Give the dummy up when the baby is young enough to not be able to put it in themselves, or wait until the child can participate in the decision to stop, so it's not traumatic.
- ⭐ Don't try to do it when a new baby comes along and needs a dummy.
- ⭐ Leave it out for Santa, the Easter bunny or the dummy fairy to take. A present will be left in its place.

> 'We thought we'd just let her decide when to stop the dummy. Cost us $8000 in orthodontist bills a few years later.' JEFF

⭐ Post it to 'a newer little baby who needs a dummy' (send it to your least favourite politician).

⭐ Older siblings, cousins or friends can help by saying they don't use one now, but they mustn't ridicule the littlie: get them to just set a non-critical, matter-of-fact example, maybe even saying they missed theirs for a few minutes on the first night they didn't have it, but then they forgot about it.

⭐ Say 'You're a big girl now' or 'You're such a big boy', and have a discussion about getting older, then ask them if they're ready to give the dummy up themselves.

⭐ Pretend you've left the dummy at home, at the holiday place or at a friend's, or that it's lost. Be very sympathetic but positive about not having a dummy any more.

⭐ Safety-pin the dummy to a teddy or dolly who needs it more than they do that night and the next, and then teddy or dolly can lose their dummy.

⭐ Introduce another aspect to the sleep ritual (such as a special sleep toy) before you take the dummy away.

⭐ Let the child choose when to swap their dummy for a new toy they really want.

⭐ Get up early together and give the dummy to the garbage crew: you can watch them go away in the big truck and then have a special breakfast to celebrate getting older.

⭐ Plant the dummy in the garden to see if a dummy tree grows.

BLAST FROM THE PAST

'(The dummy) is the invention of the devil . . . the mouth is the gateway to the body and if people will not keep it clean they will be forced to do so.'
– The rather overwrought superintendent of the Perth Dental Hospital, Mr Graham Poock, reported in *The West Australian*, 1929

I have to say a lot of kids will see through any ruses. For the sort of child who's likely to say, 'Well, why don't we buy one with your credit card on the internet?', the direct bribery approach is best.

Here's the worst suggestion I've EVER heard: 'The Dummy Monster took it away.' It almost made *me* cry.

thumb sucking

Thumb (or, less commonly, finger) sucking is certainly cheaper than buying dummies, but you can't throw away a thumb and know the habit has stopped, and thumb sucking is more likely than dummies to cause 'buck' or misaligned teeth. Most parents use a gradual, conscious cutting-down and rewards system for stopping the thumb sucking. Daytime stopping is largely a matter of keeping the hands busy, and night-time will need some new comfort rituals or objects.

Apart from gently taking the thumb out if it creeps in when the kid's asleep, many people suggest something bitter tasting on it to break the habit before adult teeth come in. It's probably best to give that a miss and skip straight to help, reassurance and a bribe, and embarking on it together rather than as adversaries.

> **BLASTS FROM THE PAST**
> 'A wide piece of cardboard bound securely round the elbow joint with a bandage will prevent the child from flexing his arm and reaching his mouth . . . painting the thumb with some harmless but unpleasant tasting concoction may also break the habit.'
> – NSW Chief Superintendent of Public Health's top tips on deterring thumb sucking, *Grenfell Record and Lachlan District Advertiser*, NSW, 1936

> 'Don't make it a confrontation, or shameful. Wait till the kid's 3 or so and can understand why it's good to stop, and then be their cheer squad, rather than the thumb police.' SHANNON

raggies, blankies & other comfort items

Kids who suck their thumb, and some who don't, often have a little bit of fabric (velvet, sheepskin or a silky material are favourites) or a soft toy to stroke while they're sucking – part of the comfort ritual. It's always a good idea to rotate a few pieces so they don't get too filthy and there's one on the go while another's in the wash. And keep a spare in the baby bag in case one is flung out the window of the car.

It's usually tough for everyone to give up a comfort object and a dummy or thumb sucking at the same time. You will probably need to have a program of cutting down and then eliminating the comfort object, to be replaced with a teddy of some sort, following some of the suggestions for getting rid of a dummy (see 'Getting rid of the dummy' above), before you can start tackling the thumb sucking. (I know a grown woman who still sucks her thumb and rubs a piece of fabric – but not when she's on a first date.)

BLAST FROM THE PAST

'Glasgow Airport has created special tags for kids' soft toys. they include contact information so that any wandering toys can be reunited with their owners. Staff said they introduced the tags because they know children can be left "distraught" by losing a cuddly friend.
– *Stuff*, online NZ magazine 2017

BiRTHDays

Parties! Presents! Invitations! Gift bags! A magician flown
in from Las Vegas! Stop right there! A bit of colour and
movement, some streamers and balloons, a cake and
lots of fuss on the morning of the birthday make for a
2- or 3-year-old's great day. A 1-year-old is quite happy
with an empty cardboard box, thank you very much.

planning a party

If you're the sort of insane person who wants a petting zoo, industrial-music circus and modern mime performance for your baby's first birthday, I suggest you have a good lie-down. The kid won't remember any of it.

If you're not sure what's a good present to take to a party, see the lists coming up. It's best to steer clear of anything that might create a blood feud between you and other parents, such as a live animal, a toy gun or 'little girl' make-up and high heels. Or a nice bottle of riesling.

Try to start planning early to minimise stress: before 2008 would have been a good time. And rope in as many people to help as you can – this is a great event for special uncles, aunties, friends and babysitters, especially ones who don't have their own children, to help with. 'Bring a plate' is a good maxim, as is 'You know you're staying to help clean up, right?'

Toddlers under the age of 4 can choose what kind of cake they fancy, but not how many guests or what sort of party it is. Keep it short, and if in a park, somewhere away from roads or in a fenced play area. Ask other parents before posting images of their kids on social media, and make sure they know if you don't want pictures of your kid in their posts.

Brief your toddler about the behaviour expected of them as host (but don't expect them to necessarily get it together). Sometimes the birthday child behaves very badly at their party or gets hysterical. A brief time out may help – as a breather, not a punishment. The birthday is more likely to be relaxed if you keep your child (and yourself) calm the day before and perhaps only remind your little person it's their birthday on the actual morning rather than creating a '33 more sleeps to go' hysteria.

The under-3s aren't really big on coordinated games: somebody is more likely to try to eat the package during 'pass the parcel' than unwrap it. Just being there and having a bit of a dance, a go on the swings if you're at the park, a bemused stare at the cake and blowing out the candles, followed by, well, cake, will do. If you want to do a special theme cake, go for it. But I release you from this obligation by saying: nobody remembers what cake they had for a toddler birthday. You can totes get away with 'bought cake'.

A baby or toddler party longer than one-and-a-half or two hours is asking for trouble; staying at one for less time is fine (it's considered bad form not to attend one that you're hosting). If the party's at your house and you're expecting a horde of toddlers, get a pal to mind your pets elsewhere for the duration. Cats will probably go off in a huff by themselves.

Here are some 'take 'em or leave 'em' suggestions for party themes.

Party ideas for 1-year-olds

A giant party for a 1-year-old is a ludicrous proposition likely to result in maximum stress for minimum impact on your kid. The most common suggestion from a parent survey I did was: keep the first birthday to family only or extended family. But if you're keen, suggestions include bubble-blowing, a picnic afternoon tea, lots of crunching of wrapping paper, playing with cardboard boxes.

Party ideas for 2-year-olds

Plan your party venue to avoid stress: not unfenced near roads or a pool. Suggestions included a family day, a teddy bears' picnic (everyone brings their teddy – don't let them go home without them!), an indoor picnic (always a good option in winter), playing in the sandpit, a local playground, bubbles again.

Party ideas for 3-year-olds

Themes based on a favourite book, or story character; butterfly designs on paper plates and cups; Winnie-the-Pooh; a single colour (for example, purple costumes and decorations); the local playground; a music or dance party; face painting (you'll need the special non-poisonous paints from a craft or toyshop).

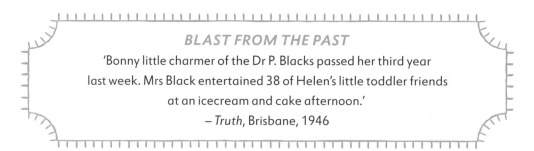

BLAST FROM THE PAST
'Bonny little charmer of the Dr P. Blacks passed her third year
last week. Mrs Black entertained 38 of Helen's little toddler friends
at an icecream and cake afternoon.'
– *Truth*, Brisbane, 1946

'Keep a party short, otherwise it's too overwhelming.' CAROLYN

Party themes

Many commercial or sponsored websites have ideas for kids' party themes: some of them are sexist and even a bit creepy, including make-up parties for little girls. There's no reason why karaoke and a movie red carpet should only be appropriate for girls, and outer space and sports themes be restricted to boys. Don't forget to look at 'girls' and 'boys' list of suggestions for party themes for your little individual.

To save yourself worrying about safety, avoid a party involving anything with wheels, pools or unrestrained animals.

> 'Don't try to organise them – just let them be together.'
> LISA

Party decorations

A few balloons and streamers should do the trick. A bunch of balloons tied to the front gate on the day will announce the party venue. If the party is in a park or other outdoorsy place, signs or balloons will help people find you. Kids can swallow whole, deflated balloons and bits of burst balloon. Clean up all the bits when a balloon bursts, as well as comforting everyone who's crying.

Alcohol at kids' parties

Some people combine adult and extended family with alcohol at a children's party, so several people need to be Designated Kidwranglers (sober and alert). Even a small amount of alcohol can result in liver and brain damage in a small child: kids this young should never, ever be given even a 'sip' of a drink with any alcohol in it. So if you're all having a droi whoite whoine, put it up somewhere hoi. Better still, make it a droi party.

Games & activities without winners

⭐ Statues: play bursts of music and when the music stops everyone has to freeze.

⭐ Bubble-blowing: give everyone a wand to dip in a bowl with bubble mixture.

⭐ Create a banner or a tablecloth: provide an old sheet or a huge length of paper, and some premixed paints, felt-tip pens, crayons. No glitter glue for kids this young: they eat it when you're not looking. Perhaps kids can take their shoes and socks off and make hand- and footprints (make sure an art-party invitation says to wear old clothes and why). Three-year-olds can make their own poster/hat/tablecloth using craft supplies – but only if you have lots of adult helpers and 23 mops.

⭐ Storytime: have a good storyteller or actor (every family should have one) read a book to the kids. It could be one that matches the theme of your party.

⭐ 'Simon Says', follow the leader, or very simple charades ('What's this animal? Baaa'). No penalties for getting it 'wrong'.

Party food

Personally I think only lunatics try to serve tofu cake and bran granola at a kids' party (unless a child has allergies: see 'Food allergies & intolerances' in Chapter 30, Family Food), but another class of bonkersness is serving masses of sugar, caffeine drinks, chocolate (which also contains caffeine) and sugary drinks at a children's party.

Parents should let you know in advance if their child is allergic to common party-food ingredients. Don't use that food, and make sure the child's parent comes to supervise: tell them which foods contain the substance that causes the allergy. Parents of kids with allergies will have suggestions of what party foods the kid can eat (for example, no dairy in the cake) and in extreme cases can BYO.

Mainly, at this age, avoid choking hazards: no popcorn, no marshmallows, no whole nuts, no hard lollies.

Keep food simple:

- ⭐ a fruit platter
- ⭐ cheese sangas
- ⭐ fairy bread
- ⭐ little cupcakes
- ⭐ pikelets.

'We didn't try any games with the 4-year-olds. (I've given that up; it's like herding cats.)'
MUM

Kids under 5 don't always eat a lot of the party food. Kids over 5 generally do. Don't take it personally.

The birthday cake

Individual cupcakes can be easier for littlies to handle than a large slice of birthday cake, and easier for you to distribute. The birthday kid's cupcake is the one with the candle in it. Sparklers can cause fright and small burns and pointy bits in eyes. (I once went to a party where a novelty candle kept reigniting itself. It was terrifying for all concerned.)

Birthday presents & cards

Some people will give inappropriate presents, especially well-meaning relatives. If a toy is too fragile for your child or not right for their age group, explain this to the kid in a kindly way later, in private. Discourage expensive presents because it sets a difficult precedent. A kid will be just as happy with a packet of crayons or some brightly coloured discount plastic bath toy.

If you're not sure about your idea for a present, check with the birthday kid's parent or caregiver.

As cards these days can be nearly as pricey as a cheap present, start a fun tradition of your kid making their own cards for their little friends or for relatives. Even littlies can make a handprint or do a splendid scribble you can caption. Don't give, or hang on to, musical or audio cards: they are powered by dangerous button batteries and should be nowhere near a kid (see 'Button batteries' in Chapter 33, Health).

Good presents for 1-year-olds

★ a book ★ a balloon (make sure when it bursts or deflates you bin all the bits) ★ clothes ★ something to ride on such as a trike with a pole for parents to push it along ★ plastic bath toys ★ toys that encourage hand-eye coordination such as hammering sets (a plastic hammer on its own will do – anything can be whacked, really) ★ activity toys such as push-down pop-up things ★ shape sorters ★ toys that make a noise (but will the adults like the noise quite as much?) ★ stackable rings, cups or blocks ★ soft, squeaky toys ★ simple, safe musical instruments (clap sticks, not a tuba) ★ balls with different sounds and textures ★ mobiles and wind chimes ★ a baby pram or mower to push ★ a large cardboard box ★ a tree that you can plant together and then take a photo of with your child in front, every birthday afterwards ★ touchy-feely textured cloth books ★ anything bright or musical that the child can have an effect on (It opens! It squeaks!).

See also Chapter 17, Baby Toys & Games.

Good presents for 2-year-olds

★ a book ★ large plastic click-together blocks ★ simple musical instruments ★ a plastic clamshell sandpit ★ an easel ★ big crayons ★ playdough and plastic biscuit cutters ★ a wee umbrella and gumboots ★ a soccer-type ball ★ a bubble-blowing kit ★ a toy tip truck ★ something that squirts in the bath ★ a tea set ★ pull-along toys ★ toddler crockery and cutlery ★ a plastic tool set ★ simple large jigsaw puzzles ★ a bucket and spade set.

See also Chapter 26, Toddler Toys & Games.

'Don't stress about baby's first Christmas present. Wrap up a box of tissues – it will keep them happy for hours.'
PETRATCH'S BOOKSHOP, TASMANIA

Good presents for 3-year-olds

★ a book ★ big snap-together blocks ★ dress-up outfits ★ crayons ★ trikes or ride-on wheeled things ★ an age-appropriate jigsaw puzzle ★ lovely fat coloured chalks ★ a plastic tool set ★ playdough ★ a rolling pin and plastic biscuit cutters ★ stickers ★ a personal audio player with earphones and music or stories ★ little cars ★ a beach ball ★ a backpack ★ a tea set ★ a ball.

See also Chapter 26, Toddler Toys & Games.

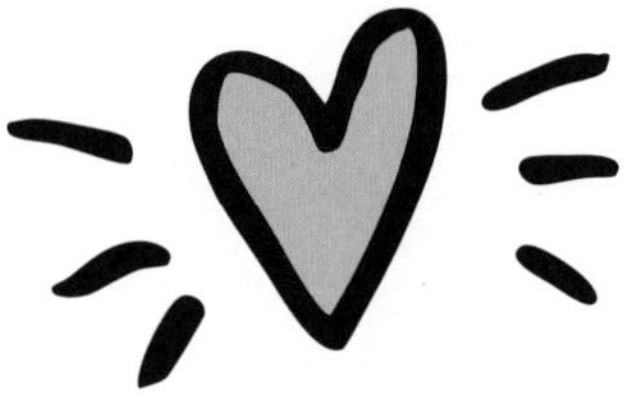

MORE BOOKS FROM KAZ

PICTURE BOOKS FOR LITTLE KIDS:

GIRL STUFF FOR TWEENS & TEENS:

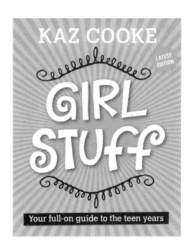

acknowledgements

This book is dedicated to Ben Ball, gentleman publisher.

A book like **BABIES & TODDLERS** is 17.6 times more complex to produce than a normal book due to its tricky design and the need for research, accuracy and updating. It's a much better book because of the superior skills, dedication, and hours of care brought to bear on its editing by Rachel Scully, and to its design by Adam Laszczuk. I thank them for their collaboration and great patience. Other significant allies include production controller Tracey Jarrett, copyeditor Katie Purvis, editorial assistant Rosie Pearce, proofreader Hilary Reynolds, and indexer Fay Donlevy. For being the control group, thanks to TLG and Vi.

A world-class group of doctors and other experts, including tip-top professor types, leading researchers, public-health specialists and family doctors with a wide knowledge of babies and family issues volunteered to read whole chapters, answer follow-up questions and amaze me with their generosity. Their willingness to help with a book for parents, their devotion to patients, and their up-to-date knowledge of public-health issues makes me feel a bit emotional. I am immensely grateful to them.

Special thanks to the Royal Australian College of General Practitioners for helping me to find so many specialised and helpful family doctors, many of whom read several chapters each and made practical suggestions and answered queries, and to the experts at the Murdoch Children's Research Institute, which knows everything about babies and kids or is doing research to try to find it out.

These wonderful family doctors brought great empathy, interest, consideration and extraordinary training and breadth of experience as doctors, and in some cases also as parents: Dr Melita Cullen in Queensland; Dr Laura Wood in Tasmania; Dr Michaela Baulderstone in South Australia; Dr Marita Long in Tasmania; Dr Penny Need in South Australia; Dr Penelope Burns in New South Wales; Dr David Sutherland in New South Wales and Dr Scott Parsons in Victoria. Thanks to GP registrars Dr Dheeshana Sayakkarage in Victoria, Dr Michael Tran in New South Wales and Dr Nadia Shamsuddin in Western Australia.

I am grateful for the specialist help of Professor Louise Newman, Director of the Centre for Women's Mental Health at the Royal Women's Hospital in Melbourne and paediatric psychiatry specialist; Dr Fiona Thompson, the Paediatric and Emergency Physician and Clinical Director of the Emergency Department of Lady Cilento Hospital in Brisbane; Professor Mark Umstad, Director of Maternity Services at the Royal Women's Hospital, Melbourne; Dr Joel Sadowsky, paediatrician and premmie baby specialist; and Len Kliman, obstetrician and surgeon.

Thanks also to Professor Harriet Hiscock, paediatrician and researcher at the Royal Children's Hospital and the Centre for Community Child Health, Murdoch Children's Research Institute, sleep and maternal depression specialist and Director of the Unsettled Babies Clinic at the Royal Children's Hospital, Melbourne.

Hats off and waving to Dr Margie Danchin, Senior Research Fellow, Vaccine and Immunisation and Rotavirus Research Group, Murdoch Children's Research Institute, vaccine and immunisation specialist and paediatrician at the Royal Children's Hospital, Melbourne.

For being full bottle on food, thanks to Professor Katie Allen, paediatric gastroenterologist and allergist, Theme Director, Population Health, Murdoch Children's Research Institute Professor, Department of Paediatrics, University of Melbourne Paediatric Gastroenterologist/Allergist, Department of Allergy; and Kate DiPrima, dietitian, adult and infant nutritionist, expert in fussy and picky eating (I do hope that's on her business card) and spokeswoman for the Dietitians Association of Australia.

Much obliged to Kim Howland, Policy Advisor Maternal & Child Health, Municipal Association of Victoria, and Erika Matthews, working maternal and child (aka family & child) health nurse. I also want to thank Bridie Phillips and the team at Red Nose organisation (formerly SIDS and Kids) for info on safer sleeping, safer equipment and more; David Sutherland and the team at PANDA, the Perinatal Anxiety and Depression Australia, for all their help with the blues, tough times, anxiety and depression; Christine Erskine and the team at Kidsafe NSW for all the info on equipment and safety; Alice Campbell from Baby in Mind infant massage organisation; Justine Osborne from SunSmart Schools, the Early Childhood Program Coordinator Prevention Division and her team at the Cancer Council; Pamela Douglas, GP at the Possums Clinic in Queensland and author of *The Discontented Little Baby Book*.

Thanks, too, to Chloe Hanna, Clinical Coordinator, Endocrinology and Gynaecology Department, the Royal Children's Hospital, for info for parents on differences of sex development. Clinical psychologist and cognitive behavioural therapist Dr Jane Gregory generously shared thoughts on naming and dealing with toddler emotions.

I'm indebted to dental consultants Dr Michael Koller, general consulting dentist and clinical supervisor at the School of Dental Science, at the medical faculty of the University of Melbourne, and orthodontist Dr Martin Poon.

Hooray for everyone who sent me quotes and suggestions for fellow parents on social media, the original survey respondents, others who responded to requests on social media; the redoubtable Neil Branch at the Department of Health in Canberra; Paula Ferrari from No FGM Australia; the raisingchildren.net website; Misha Ketchell, the editor of *The Conversation*; lactation consultant Lisa Amir; and Melissa Bradley from the South Australian Child and Family Health Service. Most of the 'Blasts from the past' were found in newspaper records on trove.nla.gov.au, the archive site of the National Library of Australia, and from old books and books on microfiche at the State Library of Victoria.

Ye olde acknowledgements:

This book was first researched and written almost eighteen years ago and has been constantly updated ever since with medical and other info. The current book is built on the foundations of help from 800 parents who filled in the original *Kidwrangling* survey, and many researchers, editors and consultants over that time. Here are some. *Kidwrangling*'s godmother: Julie Gibbs. Former editors and researchers: Lesley Dunt, Nicola Young, Ingrid Ohlssen, Jane Morrow, Bethan Waterhouse, Felicity Costigan, Charlotte Bachali. Production controller Tracey Jarrett. Former consultants included below in the positions they held at the time of their assistance. Experts who helped included but are not restricted to: obstetrician Mr Len Kliman; midwifery and maternal/child health nurse Cathryn Curtin; paramedic Susan Spence; Kidsafe; SIDs and Kids; Associate Professor Mimi Tang, Director Allergy and Immunology at the Royal Children's Hospital, Melbourne (RCH); Dr Harriet Hiscock, paediatrician at the RCH Centre for Community Child Health; Angela Serong, Senior Physiotherapist at the RCH; and Dr Pamela Douglas, GP. I also consulted papers co-written by Dr Peter Hill, Dr Wendy Brodribb and Dr Harriet Hiscock on unsettled babies; the NSW Association for Children with a Disability; Dr Natalie Silove, paediatrician, the Children's Hospital at Westmead, Sydney; Dr Raina MacIntyre, Professor of Infectious Diseases Epidemiology, University of New South Wales, Sydney; Dr Nigel Curtis at the RCH in Melbourne; Dr Jane Bowen, CSIRO Human Nutrition; Dr Simon Young, Director of Emergency Medicine, RCH (Health); Dr Teresa Lazaro, paediatrician, RCH; and Dr Lochana Ramalingam, paediatric dentist and Director of Clinical Services, RCH.

more info sections index

The more info sections throughout Babies & Toddlers carry extra suggestions for contacts or further help on specific subjects. Here's a list of where to find them:

iNDeX

VIKING

UK | USA | Canada | Ireland | Australia
India | New Zealand | South Africa | China

Penguin Books is part of the Penguin Random House group of companies whose addresses can be found at global.penguinrandomhouse.com.

Penguin
Random House
Australia

First published by Penguin Random House Australia Pty Ltd, 2018

Cover design by Kaz Cooke and Adam Laszczuk © Penguin Random House Australia Pty Ltd
Text design by Adam Laszczuk © Penguin Random House Australia Pty Ltd
Illustrations by Kaz Cooke
Typeset in ITC Stone Serif by Penguin Random House Australia
Printed and bound in China by 1010 Printing International Ltd.

 A catalogue record for this
book is available from the
National Library of Australia

ISBN 978 0 14378 860 7

penguin.com.au

Kaz Cooke is a bestselling author and cartoonist whose books have informed and tickled Australians and New Zealanders for more than twenty years. Her books include *Up the Duff: The Real Guide to Pregnancy*, *Babies & Toddlers: The Sequel to Up the Duff*, *Girl Stuff 8–12*, *Girl Stuff: Your Full-on Guide to the Teen Years* – all updated each year; *Women's Stuff*, the children's picture books *Wanda Linda Goes Berserk* and *The Terrible Underpants*, and the novel, *Ada*. With a background in journalism, she's a mum who enjoys research, toast and having a good lie down.

kazcooke.com.au